P9-DFB-451

Imprints

Imprints 11

Dom Saliani
Jeff Siamon
Janet Hannaford
Lori Farren
Cam MacPherson
David Friend

CONSULTANT
Marg Frederickson

GAGE EDITORIAL TEAM
Joe Banel
Diane Robitaille
Cathy Zerbst

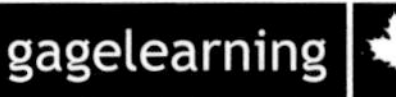

Permissions Editor: Elizabeth Long
Photo Research: Karen Taylor
Design, Art Direction, & Electronic Assembly: Wycliffe Smith Design Inc.
Cover Image: Dave Robertson/Masterfile

IMPRINTS REVIEWERS
Patricia Ames, Rainbow DB, ON
Gerry Bartlett, School District #2, NB
Mike Budd, Greater Essex County DSB, ON
Michelle Coleman, Cape Breton Victoria Regional SB, NS
Kathy Coles, Langley SB, BC
Jennifer Connell, Eastern School District, PEI
Maria DeBerardinis, Dufferin-Peel Roman Catholic DSB, ON
Bryan Ellefson, Palliser Regional Schools, AB
Pat Kover, Calgary B of E, AB
Karen Montgomery-Jones, Algoma DSB, ON
Jane Prosser, Saskatoon B of E, SK
Catherine Reid, Avalon East SB, NF
Robert Riel, Winnipeg School Division #1, MN
Shelley Robinson, Rocky View School Div. #41, AB
Georgina Barbosa Tousignant, Dufferin-Peel RCSSB, ON
Harry Wagner, Parkland School Div. #70, AB

National Library of Canada cataloguing in publication data
Main entry under title:
Imprints 11 : short stories, poetry, essays and media

For use in grade 11.
Issued also in 2 vols.
ISBN 0-7715-0940-5
1. Readers (Secondary). I. Farren, Lori.
PE1121.I536 2001 428'.6 C2001-930048-4

We acknowledge the financial support of the Government of Canada through the Book Publishing Industry Development Program for our publishing activities.

The selections collected in *Imprints* are drawn from a wide variety of sources. To respect the integrity of these sources, Gage has preserved the original spelling, grammar, and punctuation used by each author. Gage editorial style, however, is used throughout for activities and other text generated by Gage writers.

ISBN 0-7715-0940-5
4 5 6 7 8 FP 09 08 07 06 05
Printed and bound in Canada

Table of Contents

Short Stories

Poetry

Essays

Media

✦ indicates Canadian content

Alternate Table of Contents

Ethics

Humour and Satire

Identity

Justice

Media

Relationships

Science and Technology

Scripts, Speeches, and Interviews

Survival

Suspense

War

World Views

Short Stories

Fiction is the truth inside the lie.

Stephen King

Mirror Image

By Lena Coakley

The following story is divided into seven different sections. Identify the time periods dealt with in each. Does the story unfold in a linear or non-linear manner?

If only there were no mirrors, Alice sometimes thought, although she carried one in her backpack wherever she went. It was a silver-plated mirror her father had given her with the initials ACS on the back. Just you, Alice, she would say to herself, looking the way you've always looked. Then she'd pull out the mirror. The surprise and disbelief at seeing the reflection was a joke she played on herself over and over.

It was disquieting, however, to come upon a mirror without warning. She would say "excuse me" to her own reflection in shop windows. Mirrors in unexpected places would make her start and lose her nerve. She avoided the girls' bathroom altogether. Alice took to wearing sunglasses all the time, to remind herself, to keep something constantly in front of her eyes that would remind her that she looked different. Her teachers let her wear them. Maybe the word had come down from the top that she wasn't to be hassled for a while, but Alice thought it was more than that. She thought they were all a little afraid of her.

Of course her mind learned to ignore the glasses. The human mind is incredibly adaptable. Her mother was always telling her that.

"Do you think I move differently?" she asked her twin, Jenny, once identical. "Look how my feet kind of roll when I walk. And my hips, my hips feel totally different." Alice walked across the bedroom like a fashion model, wearing nothing but black bikini underwear. "Actually, as bodies go, this one is a lot better. I mean, check it out," Alice grabbed a chunk of her thigh, "no cellulite."

Jenny watched from inside her own body. "You looked okay before."

"Sorry, I didn't mean … You're pretty. I can see that now. But I never used to think that I was. You know, my old body used to weigh much less than this body weighs but I still wouldn't have been able to walk around naked in it. No one has ever told me that this body is ugly. For all I know it's never had zits. I haven't had one yet. I feel like I could do anything in this body. Hey, did I show you, I can almost touch my foot to the back of my head."

———

Alice had to re-learn how to move in the hospital, and to speak. At first the world was nothing but a mush of dark images, disconnected voices and prickly feelings all over her skin. If someone touched her arm she wasn't sure from which part of her body the sensation came. Colours seemed different. People's voices were pitched a tone higher. When she tried to speak she bit her tongue, which seemed enormous in her mouth and tasted funny. When she finally learned, the tone was different, but the inflections and the slight Maritime accent were the same. She'd had an accident, they said. But long before the psychiatrist told her, she knew. These weren't her hands. This wasn't her breath.

———

"Let me read your diary."

Alice and Jenny lay on top of their beds supposedly doing homework. Above each bed hung a charcoal portrait their father had drawn. He had finished them just before he died. Now, only Jenny's was a good likeness.

"Not now," said Jenny, closing the book and capping her ball point pen.

"You can read mine."

"I know what your diary says—Ooh, I found a new mole today on my new body. Ooh, don't my new armpits smell divine?"

"Come on. What do you have, some big secret in there? We've always read each other's diaries."

"I have to get to know you better." Jenny slipped her diary between her mattress and box spring.

"Yeah, right," Alice laughed. Then she realized her sister wasn't joking. "What, fourteen years wasn't enough?"

"You were in the hospital a long time, that's all I mean."

Alice swung her legs over the side of her bed and looked at Jenny. At one time looking at her was like looking in the mirror, and Alice still found her sister's coppery red hair and masses of freckles more familiar than her own reflection. "Jenny, we're still twins. I have the same memories: Camp Wasaga, moving to Toronto ... Dad. You know, when I draw I can still make the shadows, just the way he showed us. Isn't that amazing? Even though I have a different hand. And my signature is the same too. This is me in here, Jenny. My brain is me."

Jenny rolled over on her bed. "Whatever. You still can't read it."

———

Alice was in the hospital for months. She saw doctors, interns, psychiatrists, physical therapists, speech therapists. Once a reporter, who had actually scaled the building, poked his head through the window to ask, "Hey, Alice, how do you feel?" and snapped a few photos.

All the mirrors had been removed, of course, from her room and bathroom, but Jenny and her mother brought the hand mirror with her initials when the doctors thought Alice was ready.

"They couldn't have saved your old body," her mother said. "This was the only way to keep you alive."

"No one knows what it will be like," said Jenny. "You're the only one who's ever survived before."

"I know all that," Alice slurred. The doctors had taken the precaution of giving her a mild sedative. It made her feel like everything was happening to someone else, far away. She held the silver mirror in one hand. With the other, she pulled at her face, squeezed it as if it were clay. Alice was mesmerized by the unfamiliar eyes, big and brown and dark. Whenever her father painted her he'd spend most of his time on the eyes. The eyes are the mirror of the soul, he used to say. Whose soul is that? Alice wondered. For a moment she considered screaming, but it was too much trouble. Besides, it wouldn't be her scream.

"It's okay, Mom," she said. "Maybe I'll start looking like myself again. If I try hard enough. If I concentrate hard enough. Very slowly, over the course of years, my eyes will change colour … my face. It might … "

Alice's mother stroked her hair. "We'll get through this," she said, "the human mind is incredibly adaptable."

"Mrs. Jarred's on TV again," Alice called.

"Turn it off," her mother said, "it's time for birthday cake," but Alice and Jenny kept watching. Above the television, the faces of the family portrait Alice's father had painted smiled out into the room.

"A new development in the story of Girl X," said the newscaster, "first surviving recipient of a brain transplant … "

Alice's mother stood in the doorway wiping her hands on a tea towel. She had fewer freckles than Jenny, and the long braid which hung down her back wasn't quite so bright a red, but the family resemblance was unmistakable. "I don't want you to worry about the Jarreds, girls. My lawyer says they don't have a legal leg to stand on."

Mrs. Jarred, a middle-aged woman in a red checked coat, stood on a suburban lawn. She had dark hair just beginning to gray and Alice's large, dark eyes. A short man with a pot belly smiled self-consciously beside her.

"Is that your family?" Jenny asked.

"I don't even know them."

"Mrs. Jarred," said a female reporter with a microphone, "has science gone too far?"

"She's our daughter," the woman replied with emotion. "When we signed the release form donating her body, we didn't know they were going to bring her back to life with some new brain. Our Gail is alive and living somewhere in Toronto and I'm not even allowed to see her." Mrs. Jarred began to cry and the camera cut away to Alice and her mother leaving the hospital amid crowds of journalists. Since she was under eighteen, Alice's face was covered with a round, black dot. The girls had both seen this footage many times before.

"Gail. Wow. That's so weird."

"That's not my name."

The TV flashed pictures of the Jarreds before the accident. A girl with a dog. A smiling teenager wearing a party dress.

"Ooh, nice outfit, Gail."

"Darn those TV people," said Alice's mother. "They protect our privacy by not showing what you look like, and then they show pictures of your body before the accident. That makes a lot of sense."

"The Jarreds probably gave permission," said Alice. "Anyway, it doesn't matter. Everyone at school knows. The whole world knows."

Alice's mother continued as if she was talking to herself. "Those Jarreds ... If we start having reporters all over the lawn again ... " She twisted her face in disgust, strode across the room, and turned off the television with a sharp flick of her wrist.

"Hey."

"Come on, cake time. I made it from scratch. Alice's favourite, chocolate with mocha cream."

In the dining room a huge and elaborate cake was waiting on the table. Rich, white chocolate piping swirled over dark mocha. Ornate candy violets decorated the cake's tall sides.

"Awesome, Mom," said Alice. She couldn't remember her mother ever making a home-made cake before. "You blow first," she said to Jenny as she sat down. "You're the oldest."

"By two minutes," said Jenny, "and anyway, maybe I'm not the oldest anymore."

"What do you mean?"

"You might be older than me now with your new body. You might be old enough to drive for all we know."

Alice's brown eyes widened. "Mom, if my body is sixteen, does that mean I can get my license?"

"Forget it," her mother said as she lit the cake. "You could barely walk six months ago." She switched out the lights.

In the yellow glow of the candles Alice and Jenny followed a tradition that their father had started long ago. First Alice and her mother sang Happy Birthday to Jenny. Then, after Jenny had blown them out, the candles were lit again for Alice, and the song was sung a second time.

Alice blinked and squinted when the lights came on again. "I forgot to make a wish," she said.

Her mother smiled and handed a slice of the beautiful cake to each of the girls. "I guess you have to share your wish with Jenny."

Alice and Jenny laughed. One year, when they were little girls, the suggestion that they would have to share a wish sent them into fits of crying which their parents could only resolve by fitting the cake slices back into the cake and lighting the candles for a third and fourth time.

Alice cut the cake with the edge of her fork, happy that the tension brought on by the newscast had begun to melt away. She put a large bite into her mouth. Bitter. Alice tried hard to swallow, tried hard not to let her face show any reaction to the cake, but the taste of the mocha forced her mouth into a grimace. Jenny didn't miss it.

"I guess Gail doesn't like chocolate with mocha cream."

"No, it's good," said Alice, forcing it down.

Jenny pushed her own piece away. "I'm not hungry."

"Jeez, Jenny, why are you angry at me for not liking a piece of cake? I can't help it."

"Who's angry?"

"I have different taste buds now, and they're sending different messages to my brain. They're saying, this cake tastes gross. Sorry Mom."

"Okay," said Jenny. "You're always saying that you are still you because you have the same brain, but who is to say that your whole personality is in your head?"

"Where else would it be?"

"I don't know; maybe there was some other part of your body where part of your self lived. Maybe it was your big toe."

Alice's mother set down her fork. "Jenny, people have their big toes cut off and they're still themselves. People have heart transplants and they're still themselves."

"Right," said Alice. She smiled at her mother, but her mother looked away.

"Maybe not," Jenny said, "maybe they're a little bit different but they just don't notice. You're a lot different. You're a morning person.

You never see your old friends. You hang out with Imogen Smith and those snobs. Now you're going out for cheerleading, for goodness sake. And what is with those sunglasses? Sometimes … I don't know … Sometimes I think my sister is dead." Jenny pushed her chair back and ran out of the room.

Alice sat where she was, poking at her cake with her fork, trying not to cry.

Her mother got up and began to gather the plates. "I think," she began, her voice wavering, "I think cheerleading would be very good for your coordination."

Alice stared at her mother, but again her mother avoided her eyes. Suddenly Alice thought she understood the elaborate cake. She made it because she felt guilty, Alice thought, guilty for thinking, way down deep, that I'm not really the same daughter she knew before.

The first thing Alice saw when her eyes could focus was the white hospital ceiling, but the white had a slightly unnatural blueness to it, the way white looks on TV. Sometimes things were exquisitely clear and sharp, although she wasn't wearing her contacts, and she hadn't yet learned to ignore her eyelashes which seemed longer and darker than they had been before. When Alice saw her mother for the first time she cried and cried. Her skin had a different texture. Her hair hardly seemed red at all. She even had a different smell. And Jenny. Why was everyone she knew so different? Why wasn't her father there? Would he be different too?

When Alice met Mr. Jarred, it was in the middle of the street. A new sidewalk had just been poured on Bedford Avenue, so Alice had to walk in the street to go around the construction on the way home from school. A light rain was falling, preventing the concrete from setting. Mr. Jarred held an oversized umbrella, striped red and yellow, above his head. He might have walked right by her, but Alice was staring hard at him trying to remember something—anything—about him besides the newscast.

"Gail," he said in a soft mumble and then, "I'm sorry … I mean Alice … Do you know me?"

"I saw you on TV."

"Ah, yes." The two stood in silence for a moment.

"You should have an umbrella," he said. "This one's a ridiculous thing, my wife's. Here."

"No, no, it's just sprinkling, really," but Alice took the umbrella Mr. Jarred offered her, holding it upside down, its point in the road.

"This is very strange for me, very strange," he said, staring at her. "We knew you were in Toronto, but, well, to be honest, it was my wife who wanted to contact you. I ... I thought it would be better not to see you. It's very strange," he repeated, then added, "You look so different."

"I do?"

"Your hair. The way you stand, even. Our Gail, she was an early bloomer, always slouched. Your accent is different too." He paused. "I understand, you know. My wife, she thinks our daughter is still alive, but I ... I know." A car turned onto the street and honked at them. "I'd better go."

On impulse, Alice grabbed Mr. Jarred's hand. It was warm and big and rough and Alice knew she had never felt it before. "I knew I wouldn't remember you," she said, "but I was hoping, when you walked by, that I'd know you somehow."

Mr. Jarred took his hand away. "But you don't."

"No." Alice slid her dark glasses to the top of her head. "My dad—I guess you know he died in the accident."

"Yes."

"Sometimes I think if he were alive, he would just look into my eyes and know who was in here." The two stood in silence. Then Alice said, "What will you tell your wife?"

"I'll tell her," Mr. Jarred's voice began to falter, but he looked at her straight on, "I'll tell her I looked into your eyes and that I didn't see my daughter."

"I'm sorry," said Alice. She didn't ask the question that immediately came to her, but the words rang in her mind: who did you see?

Alice gripped the umbrella as she watched Mr. Jarred hurry around the corner. She stepped up to the curb and pressed her waist to the wooden barrier that protected the sidewalk. Then she folded the umbrella and secured the strap. In a small corner of the sidewalk she wrote her initials, ACS, with the tip of the umbrella.

Alice was here, she thought. And then she walked towards home.

Lena Coakley has published a number of other stories. Her short story "Mouse" placed second in *The Toronto Star's* Short Story Contest in 1999. She is currently working on a fantasy novel.

1. ***Response***
   a. The beginning of the story is deliberately written to create suspense. What questions are raised in the reader's mind by the end of the first two paragraphs? What are some possible answers for these questions?
   b. Why does Jenny not allow her sister to read her diary? Do you agree with her reasoning? Explain.
   c. Name some science fiction movies and/or stories you have previously encountered. Do you usually enjoy science fiction? Why or why not?

2. ***Writing*** *Diary Entry* At the end of the birthday party, Jenny says that she sometimes feels that her sister is dead. Imagine you are Jenny. Write a diary entry in which you explore why you feel this way.

3. ***Media*** *TV News Item* Alice says that a reporter scaled the hospital walls to get a picture and quotation from her. Why would a reporter go to such extremes to gain access to Alice? Why would Alice and her family want to avoid the media?

   With a partner, develop a 60-second TV news item that tells Alice's story. You could include an interview with Alice, her mother or sister, a doctor, or one of the Jarreds. Decide whether your item is going to be exploitative or respectful.

4. ***Making Connections*** In Lewis Carroll's classic book, *Alice's Adventures in Wonderland,* Alice undergoes a bewildering number of transformations—one moment she's the size of a mouse, the next she's a giant. During her adventures, she encounters a Caterpillar who raises a question often dealt with in literature:

> "Who are you?" said the Caterpillar.
>
> This was not an encouraging opening for a conversation. Alice replied, rather shyly, "I—I hardly know, Sir, just at present—at least I know who I was when I got up this morning, but I think I must have been changed several times since then."
>
> "What do you mean by that?" said the Caterpillar, sternly. "Explain yourself."

"I can't explain myself, I'm afraid, Sir," said Alice, "because I'm not myself, you see."

"I don't see," said the Caterpillar.

"I'm afraid I can't put it more clearly," Alice replied, very politely, "for I can't understand it myself, to begin with; and being so many different sizes in a day is very confusing."

"It isn't," said the Caterpillar.

"Well, perhaps you haven't found it so yet," said Alice; "but when you have to turn into a chrysalis—you will some day, you know—and then after that into a butterfly, I should think you'll feel it a little queer, won't you?"

"Not a bit," said the Caterpillar.

"Well, perhaps your feelings may be different," said Alice: "all I know is, it would feel very queer to me."

"You!" said the Caterpillar contemptuously. "Who are you?"

Which brought them back again to the beginning of the conversation.

Do you think it is helpful to draw a connection between Alice in "Mirror Image" and Alice in *Alice's Adventures in Wonderland*? Why or why not?

In a group, discuss the meaning of the term **allusion**. What do you think an author might gain by making an allusion to another story, especially one that is well known? Share your ideas with the class.

In a literary work, an **allusion** is a reference to another literary work, or a person, place, event, or object from history, literature, or mythology.

The Prospector's Trail

By Cathy Jewison

"It's the old story. People been comin' to Yellowknife since the thirties, hoping to strike gold. Some make it, some don't."

"Noise! Traffic! Filth! Can't stand the commotion of the city, that's why I come out here," said the grizzled old guy. He leaned back in his lawn chair and stared at the campfire reflectively, taking a long pull of tea from a tin cup. The light from the flames glittered off his creased face and greying beard. The old-timer stared upwards. Norman and Jennifer followed his eyes, examining the dome of the northern night sky, which was still blue at nine-thirty p.m. They could hear a loon call from the nearby lake and the lap of the waves on the shore.

A grumble emanated from the far-off heavens. Thunder? No—the grumble grew into a growl and then into a roar, which gained intensity until it filled the air. Their eyes searched for the source of the clamour. Jennifer covered her ears. Then they saw it. A jetliner, glowing gold with the reflected light of the night sun, made an elegant curve over the city dump and moved in over Long Lake. It lined up with a runway and continued its descent, swooping across Highway 3 for a perfect landing at the Yellowknife airport.

"Flight 592 from Edmonton, right on schedule," Roy announced. He took another drink of tea. He winced.

"You know, when I invited you over for 'tea,' I actually meant we'd be drinking something stronger—you must be thirsty after your long drive. But all the beer's disappeared. Elsie must have had one of her damned card parties this afternoon, while I was out in the bush. And now all the peanuts are gone," he said, shaking the empty bag. "Elsie! *Elsie!*" he screamed towards an immense camper a few feet away. A tall, skinny woman came to the door. It was hard to see her features because an electric light was burning behind her.

"What?"

"We're out of peanuts."

"So go get some more. And get some beer while you're at it."

"You know I hate going into that damned city."

"I'm missing my show," she announced, slamming the door.

"Damned TV," he muttered towards the fire. "Supposed to be enjoying the beauties of nature. Get away from all that city stuff ..."

He continued on, but the rest of what he said was drowned out by the whine of a semitrailer zooming past on the highway a couple hundred yards behind them. He finished his diatribe about the same time the noise of the semi faded into the distance. He rooted in his tin cup with a grubby finger, then flicked something onto the ground.

"Skeeter," he stated. He turned to Norman.

"What kind of work you looking for?"

"Anything," Norman replied. "For now, anyway. I want to start a tourist operation. An interpretive centre—old buildings, dogsled rides in the winter, that sort of thing."

Roy nodded sagely.

"It's the old story. People been comin' to Yellowknife since the thirties, hoping to strike gold. Some did. Giant Mine's that way, Con's over there," he said, waving vaguely in opposite directions. "Then there's the others. Business tycoons. Government people. All want a piece of it. Some make it, some don't."

"Can't be any worse than southern Canada," Norman said.

Roy snorted.

"Bet you think differently when you're still living in a tent at forty below," he said.

Jennifer shuddered.

"Well, Yellowknife is the end of the road for me—and I don't mean just because the highway ends here," Norman said with a touch of bravado. "If I can't make it here, I can't make it anywhere."

"It's the end of the road for all true Yellowknifers. Place pulls a lot of people to it. The right ones stay."

"Any chance you could dig up something for us, Roy?" Jennifer asked.

"What do you mean?" the old-timer snapped. "What have you heard?"

"Nothing," Norman replied, jumping to his feet in alarm. His half-finished cup of tea, which had been balanced on his thigh, catapulted across the fire and hit Roy in the chest. The old man leaned forward and pulled the wet plaid flannel away from his skin.

"Good thing that wasn't hot," he observed. Jennifer stood up and strode away.

"Little missus gets a bit testy at times, eh? Know what that's like," Roy said, with a wink and a nod toward the camper. "I'd better pack it in—gotta rise and shine tomorrow," he added as he started to collect the tin cups.

Norman said goodnight and started off. Moments later, the old man heard a thud and turned to find Norman splayed on the ground.

"Tree root," he explained, hoisting himself upright and limping away.

"Watch your step, son," Roy said with a shake of his head.

Norman found Jennifer standing next to their tent, an artifact he'd bought at a garage sale in Winnipeg a couple of weeks earlier. It consisted of mildew and, to a lesser extent, of beige canvas.

"Get in," she commanded.

The tent came with an odd assortment of poles and guys that more or less kept everything in place. One of the poles was a bit too short, however, and if someone brushed against it, the tent collapsed. Since it was currently in its flattened state, Norman had to dive amongst the loose canvas and restore the poles. Jennifer then went around the outside, refastening guys. She gingerly crawled in. Norman was lying on top of his sleeping bag. Jennifer sat down on top of hers and shook her finger at him.

"Don't move for the rest of the night. Got it?"

"Got it."

Jennifer began to change into her pyjamas. The top was partway over her head when she was seized by convulsions. She gasped. She panted. Her shoulders jerked.

"Achoo!"

The tent rocked ominously. Jennifer sat perfectly still. As soon as she was certain the tent would remain upright, she popped her head through her pyjama top. She glared at Norman through the dim light.

"You realize I'm allergic to this damned thing."

"It's all we can afford."

"No kidding," she muttered.

"You shouldn't be so hard on people."

"It's not my fault I'm allergic," she replied, blowing her nose.

"I meant Roy. I think he can help us."

"I know he can—that camper's brand new."

"Don't push too hard, or you'll scare him away."

Jennifer finished pulling on her pyjama bottoms, then carefully tossed her clothes towards the few inches of floor at the foot of her sleeping bag.

"You'll never get ahead by pussyfooting around," she said.

"We'll just have to give it some time."

Jennifer sneezed again. She wiped her nose. She turned to her husband.

"I'll give it six weeks," she said. "Until Labour Day."

"That's not much time to start a new life."

"Norman. We're living in a tent. This is not a life."

"We've only been here a few hours and we're already accumulating authentic northern experience."

"That's what you call drinking tea with that old guy? Authentic northern experience?"

"He's a character. Local colour. It'll be important when I set up the interpretive centre. Maybe I can get him to work there."

"If you can get something useful out of him, fine. But keep your distance while you're doing it. I don't want you playing the role of hillbilly—trying to out-northern the northerners for the sake of your 'interpretive centre.' You're going to be the owner, so you'll have to show some decorum. Besides, you're lucky you didn't scald him. Like before."

"That was an accident."

"It's always an accident."

Norman sighed.

"Six weeks!" Jennifer snapped. "Unless I catch you wearing a red plaid flannel shirt, in which case I'll leave you on the spot."

She climbed into her sleeping bag and turned her back on her husband. Norman heard her sniffling well into the night. He wasn't sure if she was crying, or just needed an antihistamine. It could be hard to tell with Jennifer.

Norman and Jennifer had arrived at Fred Henne Territorial Park, located on the outskirts of Yellowknife, about suppertime that day. It was, indeed, the end of a long road for them. A year earlier, they had received their tourism studies certificates at a college in Winnipeg, then promptly got married. Norman still couldn't believe it—Jennifer had been a star student throughout the program, and he'd been flattered when she consented to date him because she liked his sense of whimsy.

With a sharp mind and an eye for the big picture, Jennifer was a whiz at developing tourism marketing programs. Norman's first love was interpretation—dressing up and acting like historical personages for the entertainment and edification of tourists. Jennifer's appreciation of his sense of whimsy had evaporated, however. She'd decided interpretation was undignified and convinced him to get into the corporate side of the industry. Norman found a decent job shortly after graduation, but was unnerved by the formality and high expectations of the office. Plagued by insomnia, he had become clumsy. His boss had laughed when Norman tripped on the carpet in the waiting room and landed face first in the fish tank. He had been less amused when Norman spilled a glass of Beaujolais on a client's silk dress. He was livid when Norman gave another client second-degree burns by dumping a pot of coffee on him. Norman's reputation spread and he could no longer get work. Jennifer became the sole breadwinner, but as a recent graduate, she couldn't earn enough to support them both. Jennifer half-heartedly agreed to let Norman pursue his dream of opening an interpretive centre, on the condition that he did it far away from anyone they knew. They scraped together a few hundred dollars, loaded their sparse belongings into Norman's battered Chevy van, and headed north.

The morning after their arrival, Norman walked by Roy's camping spot, where he found the old man seated at a concrete picnic table. He was wearing tattered work pants and a murky T-shirt, his omnipresent red plaid flannel shirt draped over the ensemble. The tea stain from the previous night was lost in a patchwork of grease and dirt. Norman smoothed his own spotless rugby shirt, and adjusted his collar.

"Come have breakfast," Roy called. "Can't get Elsie out here. We're supposed to be enjoying nature and all she does is complain about the bugs. The simple life! That's what it's all about! Wanna Pop-Tart?"

"It's okay—I have some granola back at the tent," Norman replied, but he sat down anyway.

"Suit yourself," Roy conceded as he ripped open a package and took a big bite out of one of the pastries. "You're supposed to toast them, but we're roughing it, after all," he mumbled around the glob in his mouth. "Where's the little lady?"

"Gone into town to look for work."

"Why ain't you with her?"

"She said she wasn't ready to unleash me upon an unsuspecting population."

"I see her point."

Norman noticed a dark rock flecked with gold lying in the dirt. He kicked at it, but missed and jammed his toe into one of the table's concrete supports. He gasped. Roy leaned over and scooped up the rock. He examined it closely.

"Fool's gold," he announced, tossing it away.

"Are you a miner, Roy?"

"You bet. A little prospecting. A little mining."

"Mining pays well, doesn't it?"

"Well enough," he said. He cast a self-conscious look towards the shiny new camper. "Thought you were a big tourism entrepreneur."

"I need to build up a nest egg. I also need to get to know the place. Develop some authentic northern experience," Norman said. "I was hoping you could help me. I'd like to follow you around. To observe."

Roy looked grim.

"What are you going to do today?" Norman coaxed.

"Prospector's Trail, I suppose," Roy replied with some reluctance.

"Prospecting? Excellent! Can I come?"

"Son! You don't ask a lady her age, and you don't ask a prospector to show you where he's working," the old man said firmly.

"It's just that I wanted to use you as the role model for the interpretive centre," Norman said.

"Oh?"

"If you don't mind being famous, that is."

"Well, maybe I could help a bit. You can come with me this morning. But this morning only, hear? Better take some provisions with you," he said, tossing a foil pack of Pop-Tarts at Norman. "Just don't try to walk and chew at the same time."

Roy set out across the campground at a rapid pace, with Norman close behind. They soon reached a huge, uneven field of pre-Cambrian rock. Roy didn't slow down. Norman teetered after him, but managed to stay upright.

"What are those little footprints painted on the rock?" he asked when he finally caught up with the sure-footed Roy.

"Directions."

"This is a walking trail?"

"Of course. Didn't think I'd really show you where I prospect, do you?"

Norman looked as deflated as his mildewed tent.

"I'm willing to share general knowledge, though. See that pillow of grey rock over there?"

Norman walked to the spot.

"Run your fingers over the surface. Feel the bumps?"

Norman nodded.

"What do you see?"

"Brownish-red granules."

"Good. They're garnets."

"Wow," Norman observed quietly, bending closer to the rock to examine them.

They continued on in silence for some time, until they reached the tumbledown remains of a cabin. The skeleton of a bed frame, a rusted-out woodstove and a few pieces of decaying cutlery were scattered around.

"Reminds me of the shack I lived in when I moved up in the forties. Made of plywood and packing crates." Roy sighed wistfully.

"Elsie didn't mind?"

"Living in a shack? Of course she did. But she saw the potential of the place—and of me."

They later found a vein of white quartz that prospectors had blasted.

"Quartz is the key," Roy explained. "Find it, and you just might find gold. Time for a rest."

The old man sat cross-legged beside the mutilated rock and closed his eyes. The sky clouded over, and a breeze came up. Roy's red plaid shirt fluttered around him. He swayed with the wind. His breathing became slower and deeper. Norman cautiously ripped open his pouch of Pop-Tarts and nibbled a corner. Finding that it hit the spot, he gobbled both pastries in the packet. Then, exhausted after another sleepless night, Norman closed his eyes. He, too, swayed with the wind. He drifted off, but jerked himself awake just as his head started to topple towards the ancient and very hard rock. He started to worry about the old man.

"Roy," he whispered. There was no reaction, so he said it louder. "Roy!"

"What?"

"I thought you'd fallen asleep."

"Asleep! Ain't you ever seen anyone meditating, son?"

"Meditating?"

"I thought you were educated. You know—meditating. Getting into the zone. Becoming one with the earth. The earth don't give up her secrets too easily. You gotta get to know her on a personal level."

"Oh."

"Time to go," Roy blurted as he jumped to his feet. He completed the circuit of the trail, which led them back to the campground. "Nice spending the morning with you," he said. "Now I have to get on with business."

Norman wiped a couple of drops of moisture from his arm. Roy had been generous towards him, but Norman would prefer if he didn't spit while he talked. Roy turned away. A large drop hit Norman's face. Rain.

Norman sprinted towards his tent as the deluge began. Moments later, Roy heard a stomach-turning shriek. The old-timer found Norman staring at the sodden puddle of his so-called shelter.

"You can stay in your van," he suggested.

"It's full of boxes and furniture," Norman replied as he began to pace. "What was I thinking? This is never going to work. Jen's going to leave me. I have no money. I can't earn any. It's over." He stopped moving and stared at Roy. "It's all over," he repeated in disbelief.

"You're packing it in? Just like that?" Roy demanded. "No interpretive centre?"

"I'm sorry, Roy. No interpretive centre."

"Don't panic. I'll help you. Get in your van. We're going prospecting."

They stopped by the camper to pick up some gumboots. Roy instructed Norman to drive away from Yellowknife, but they hadn't travelled for more than a minute before the old man told him to turn down a wide, well-maintained road that led past an industrial building. They were heading for the city dump.

"What now?" Norman muttered.

"Right over there," Roy said.

Norman pulled up next to a row of a half-dozen vehicles. Roy climbed out of the van and slowly rambled amongst the hills of debris, his eyes locked on the ground. Every now and then he would bounce on an abandoned couch to test the springs, or lift up a piece of plywood to see what was underneath. Other people were wandering in a similar fashion, but Roy ignored them. He motioned to Norman to join him, but Norman couldn't bring himself to leave the van. He fidgeted with the knobs on the radio. Then he realized someone was peering through the back window. Norman got out.

"You going to dump that stuff, buddy?" asked a young man in ragged jeans and a grimy windbreaker.

"That's my furniture. Back off."

"Settle down. I can find better out here, anyway," he said as he stalked off.

Norman carefully locked the van, put on Roy's extra pair of gumboots and set out after his mentor, stepping cautiously so as not to do a face-plant in the mud. He found Roy digging in a pile of garbage, a battered television and some lengths of two-by-four stacked neatly beside him.

"I thought you hated the noise and traffic and filth of the city," Norman observed.

"This ain't the city," the old man replied, surprised Norman hadn't noticed. He paused to wipe the drizzle from his forehead with a grimy hanky, then continued to root in the mud. "Eureka!" he shouted, as he extracted a dirty orange tarpaulin with a long rip in it. "Can I read 'em, or what?"

"What's it for?"

"It's for you. A fly for your tent. We'll wash it in the lake. Patch it with a little duct tape. Good as new!" he said gleefully. He examined Norman's face. "What's with you, boy? I thought you wanted to accumulate authentic northern experiences, and here you've been missin' one of the most authentic of them all."

"Can we go prospecting now?" Norman asked with as much patience as he could muster.

Roy beamed at him.

"Oh, no! This is how you made your money?" Norman demanded. "Prospecting and mining. At the dump?"

"After the first few years there was so much competition in the bush that I decided to use my skills here. You'd be amazed what you find. Take it home, clean it up, sell it. Got so much now, I'm having trouble shifting it."

Norman's eyes misted over and his throat constricted, but the cause was neither the rain in his eyes nor the stench in his nose. The rubble he saw before him was more than just the detritus of the Yellowknife dump—it was the rubble of his future. Wifeless. Homeless. Hopeless. Suddenly, he bent over. He wasn't sure why, since he could see little through the blur of tears. He ran his fingers over a pile of mud. He felt a bump. He wiped his eyes on the back of his sleeve and examined the mound more closely. A point of brownish-red was poking through. He flicked at it with his finger. A little more red showed. He dug deeper. It was cloth. He grabbed it and pulled out a red plaid flannel shirt, much like Roy's. The old-timer whistled.

"Impressive," he said as he examined it. "One little rip, but otherwise, good as new." He held it close to Norman's chest. "It'll fit you perfectly. Let's see what else you can do. Try over there."

Roy pointed him towards the back of the dump and gave him a little push. Norman meandered through the piles. He saw a strip of white gleaming through the mud. He wiped at it with the shirt he had unearthed. Not quartz this time, but porcelain. It was an old bathtub, the kind with feet.

"Excellent," Roy said. "That'll get you a couple hundred dollars. If you refinish it, you can get more. I'll find some packing crates—we can use them as skids to drag it out of here. Good thing I took you on that walk. Sure got you into the zone."

Norman slumped on the side of the bathtub.

"Don't knock it, son. You have a gift. You're in your element. Do you realize you haven't fallen once since you been out here?"

It was true. Norman felt himself relaxing. He took a deep breath and promptly choked.

"You'll get used to it," Roy assured him.

Norman surveyed the terrain through the mist. He instinctively headed towards the edge of the landfill. He came around a hill of debris and found some freshly dumped computers.

"You've hit the mother lode!" Roy squealed.

Norman examined them. "Fool's gold," he announced.

"I thought computers were worth a fortune."

"Nope. Too old. Got a screwdriver?"

Roy searched the pockets of his work pants and produced a rather nice multitool. "Found it here last week," he explained.

Norman used his sleeve to wipe the rain from one of the computers, then removed the case and looked inside.

"You know about these things?" Roy asked him.

"A bit. I think this one's a 486. Might work if it hasn't taken on too much dirt and rain. Not high powered, but we can use them for parts, if nothing else."

"You know how to set up one of those web site things?"

"Yah. It's not so hard."

"A little e-commerce might move my inventory."

"Who's your market?" Norman asked skeptically.

"People who can't come to visit, but want authentic northern artifacts just the same. You can make a planter out of anything," he said with a wink.

Norman smiled.

"Your little lady's not going to like it. She's more upscale than my Elsie."

"You're right. She won't see the potential. But like I said—this is the end of the road for me."

The sun was shining again when Jennifer returned to the campground with news that she'd landed a job. She found Norman outside Roy's camper. He was seated at the concrete picnic table, surrounded by computer parts. Roy was peering eagerly over Norman's shoulder, which was clad in a red plaid flannel shirt. Jennifer gasped.

"I found it at the dump. Elsie washed it for me," Norman explained as he monkeyed with a partially assembled computer.

"Me and your boy are going into business together," Roy proclaimed. "First e-commerce, then the interpretive centre."

"I think I've got it," Norman announced, as he connected the computer to an extension cord that stretched from the camper. A puff of smoke rose into the air. The two men looked at each other.

"Planter," they sang in unison.

"Grab me another," Norman instructed Roy. Jennifer's eyes shifted to the computers stacked beside the table.

"Found them at the dump," Norman repeated, but this time he looked her straight in the eye. "You wouldn't believe the business potential out there."

It was midnight when Norman wandered over to the tent, now protected with the freshly patched orange tarp. His van was gone, and several boxes of his possessions were sitting outside the tent. She hadn't left a note. Norman sighed and crawled into the rickety tent. It swayed slightly but remained upright. He slept soundly for the first time in months.

Cathy Jewison is a short story writer from Yellowknife, Northwest Territories, whose work has appeared in the Canadian short fiction magazine, *Storyteller.*

1. ***Response***

a. What did you do to avoid confusion and to differentiate among the characters in the opening paragraphs of the story? What other effective strategies could you have used?

b. Write a brief description of Roy's personality. Do the same for Norman and Jennifer. In each case, include specific lines from the story that illustrate the character traits you've described.

c. In your view, do the characters in "The Prospector's Trail" seem like real people? Did you detect any stereotypes? Explain.

d. There are two red plaid shirts in the story. What is their symbolic significance?

2. ***Literature Studies*** *Character* Characters in stories can be dynamic or static. A *dynamic* character changes in some important way as a result of his or her experience, while a *static* character stays the same. In "The Prospector's Trail," which characters are dynamic and which are static? Give reasons for your conclusions.

3. ***Language Conventions*** *Unconventional Grammar* Reread the dialogue in the story, searching for examples of flawed grammar in Roy's speech—things such as sentence fragments and unconventional verb forms. Why do you think the author has Roy speak in this way? Look at the dialogue in one of your own stories. Do your characters speak in a way that is appropriate for them?

4. ***Oral Language*** *Group Discussion* Norman says, "Yellowknife is the end of the road for me.... If I can't make it here, I can't make it anywhere." In a group, discuss whether Norman is likely to "make it" in Yellowknife. Did Norman make a good decision when he chose to stay in the north? What is your evaluation of the decision Jennifer made? Have one group member present a summary of your discussion to the class.

It's not easy being a hero—as Walter Mitty discovers again, and again, and again.

The Secret Life of Walter Mitty

By James Thurber

"We're going through!" The Commander's voice was like thin ice breaking. He wore his full-dress uniform, with the heavily braided white cap pulled down rakishly over one cold gray eye. "We can't make it, sir. It's spoiling for a hurricane, if you ask me." "I'm not asking you, Lieutenant Berg," said the Commander. "Throw on the power lights! Rev her up to 8,500! We're going through!" The pounding of the cylinders increased: ta-pocketa-pocketa-pocketa-*pocketa-pocketa*. The Commander stared at the ice forming on the pilot window. He walked over and twisted a row of complicated dials. "Switch on No. 8 auxiliary!" he shouted. "Switch on No. 8 auxiliary!" repeated Lieutenant Berg. "Full strength in No. 3 turret!" shouted the Commander. "Full strength in No. 3 turret!" The crew, bending to their various tasks in the huge, hurtling eight-engined Navy hydroplane, looked at each other and grinned.

"The Old Man'll get us through," they said to one another. "The Old Man ain't afraid of Hell!"—

"Not so fast! You're driving too fast!" said Mrs. Mitty. "What are you driving so fast for?"

"Hmm?" said Walter Mitty. He looked at his wife, in the seat beside him, with shocked astonishment. She seemed grossly unfamiliar, like a strange woman who had yelled at him in a crowd. "You were up to fifty-five," she said. "You know I don't like to go more than forty. You were up to fifty-five." Walter Mitty drove on toward Waterbury in silence, the roaring of the SN202 through the worst storm in twenty years of Navy flying fading in the remote, intimate airways of his mind. "You're tensed up again," said Mrs. Mitty. "It's one of your days. I wish you'd let Dr. Renshaw look you over."

Walter Mitty stopped the car in front of the building where his wife went to have her hair done. "Remember to get those overshoes while I'm having my hair done," she said. "I don't need overshoes," said Mitty. She put her mirror back into her bag. "We've been all through that," she said, getting out of the car. "You're not a young man any longer." He raced the engine a little. "Why don't you wear gloves? Have you lost your gloves?" Walter Mitty reached in a pocket and brought out the gloves. He put them on, but after she had turned and gone into the building and he had driven on to a red light, he took them off again. "Pick it up, brother!" snapped a cop as the light changed, and Mitty hastily pulled on his gloves and lurched ahead. He drove around the streets aimlessly for a time, and then he drove past the hospital on his way to the parking lot.

—"It's the millionaire banker, Wellington McMillan," said the pretty nurse. "Yes?" said Walter Mitty, removing his gloves slowly. "Who has the case?" "Dr. Renshaw and Dr. Benbow, but there are two specialists here, Dr. Remington from New York and Mr. Pritchard-Mitford from London. He flew over." A door opened down a long, cool corridor and Dr. Renshaw came out. He looked distraught and haggard. "Hello, Mitty," he said. "We're having the devil's own time with McMillan, the millionaire banker and close personal friend of Roosevelt. Obstreosis of the ductal tract. Tertiary. Wish you'd take a look at him." "Glad to," said Mitty.

In the operating room there were whispered introductions: "Dr. Remington, Dr. Mitty, Mr. Pritchard-Mitford, Dr. Mitty." "I've read your book on streptothricosis," said Pritchard-Mitford, shaking hands. "A brilliant performance, sir." "Thank you," said Walter Mitty. "Didn't know you were in the States, Mitty," grumbled Remington. "Coals to Newcastle, bringing Mitford and me up here for a tertiary." "You are very kind," said Mitty. A huge, complicated machine, connected to the operating table, with many tubes and wires, began at this moment to go pocketa-pocketa-pocketa. "The new anaesthetizer is giving way!" shouted an interne. "There is no one in the East who knows how to fix it!" "Quiet, man!" said Mitty, in a low, cool voice. He sprang to the machine, which was now going pocketa-pocketa-queep-pocketa-queep. He began fingering delicately a row of glistening dials. "Give me a fountain pen!" he snapped. Someone handed him a fountain pen.

> Imagination and fiction make up more than three quarters of our real life.
>
> Simone Weil

He pulled a faulty piston out of the machine and inserted the pen in its place. "That will hold for ten minutes," he said. "Get on with the operation." A nurse hurried over and whispered to Renshaw, and Mitty saw the man turn pale. "Coreopsis has set in," said Renshaw nervously. "If you would take over, Mitty?" Mitty looked at him and at the craven figure of Benbow, who drank, and at the grave, uncertain faces of the two great specialists. "If you wish," he said. They slipped a white gown on him; he adjusted a mask and drew on thin gloves; nurses handed him shining—

"Back it up, Mac! Look out for that Buick!" Walter Mitty jammed on the brakes. "Wrong lane, Mac," said the parking-lot attendant, looking at Mitty closely. "Gee. Yeh," muttered Mitty. He began cautiously to back out of the lane marked "Exit Only." "Leave her sit there," said the attendant. "I'll put her away." Mitty got out of the car. "Hey, better leave the key." "Oh," said Mitty, handing the man the ignition key. The attendant vaulted into the car, backed it up with insolent skill, and put it where it belonged.

They're so damn cocky, thought Mitty, walking along Main Street; they think they know everything. Once he had tried to take his chains off, outside New Milford, and he had got them wound around the axles. A man had had to come out in a wrecking car and unwind them, a young, grinning garageman. Since then Mrs. Mitty always made him drive to a garage to have the chains taken off. The next time, he thought, I'll wear my right arm in a sling; they won't grin at me then. I'll have my right arm in a sling and they'll see I couldn't possibly take the chains off myself. He kicked at the slush on the sidewalk. "Overshoes," he said to himself, and he began looking for a shoe store.

When he came out into the street again, with the overshoes in a box under his arm, Walter Mitty began to wonder what the other thing was his wife had told him to get. She had told him twice, before they set out from their house for Waterbury. In a way he hated these weekly trips to town—he was always getting something wrong. Kleenex, he thought, Squibb's, razor blades? No, toothpaste, toothbrush, bicarbonate, carborundum, initiative and referendum? He gave it up. But she would remember it. "Where's the what's-its-name?" she would ask. "Don't tell me you forgot the what's-it's-name." A newsboy went by shouting something about the Waterbury trial.

—"Perhaps this will refresh your memory." The District Attorney suddenly thrust a heavy automatic at the quiet figure on the witness stand. "Have you ever seen this before?" Walter Mitty took the gun and examined it expertly. "This is my Webley-Vickers 50.80," he said calmly. An excited buzz ran around the courtroom. The Judge rapped for order.

"You are a crack shot with any sort of firearms, I believe?" said the District Attorney, insinuatingly. "Objection!" shouted Mitty's attorney. "We have shown that the defendant could not have fired the shot. We have shown that he wore his right arm in a sling on the night of the fourteenth of July." Walter Mitty raised his hand briefly and the bickering attorneys were stilled. "With any known make of gun," he said evenly, "I could have killed Gregory Fitzhurst at three hundred feet *with my left hand*." Pandemonium broke loose in the courtroom. A woman's scream rose above the bedlam and suddenly a lovely, dark-haired girl was in Walter Mitty's arms. The District Attorney struck at her savagely. Without rising from his chair, Mitty let the man have it on the point of the chin. "You miserable cur!"—

"Puppy biscuit," said Walter Mitty. He stopped walking and the buildings of Waterbury rose up out of the misty courtroom and surrounded him again. A woman who was passing laughed. "He said 'Puppy biscuit'," she said to her companion. "That man said 'Puppy biscuit' to himself." Walter Mitty hurried on. He went into an A. & P., not the first one he came to but a smaller one farther up the street. "I want some biscuit for small, young dogs," he said to the clerk. "Any special brand, sir?" The greatest pistol shot in the world thought a moment. "It says 'Puppies Bark for It' on the box," said Walter Mitty.

His wife would be through at the hairdresser's in fifteen minutes, Mitty saw in looking at his watch, unless they had trouble drying it; sometimes they had trouble drying it. She didn't like to get to the hotel first; she would want him to be there waiting for her as usual. He found a big leather chair in the lobby, facing a window, and he put the overshoes and the puppy biscuit on the floor beside it. He picked up an old copy of *Liberty* and sank down in the chair. "Can Germany Conquer the World Through the Air?" Walter Mitty looked at the pictures of bombing planes and of ruined streets.

—"The cannonading has got the wind up in young Raleigh, sir," said the sergeant. Captain Mitty looked up at him through tousled hair. "Get him to bed," he said wearily. "With the others. I'll fly alone." "But you can't, sir," said the sergeant anxiously. "It takes two men to handle that bomber and the Archies are pounding hell out of the air. Von Richtman's circus is between here and Saulier." "Somebody's got to get that ammunition dump," said Mitty. "I'm going over. Spot of brandy?" He poured a drink for the sergeant and one for himself. War thundered and whined around the dugout and battered at the door. There was a rending of wood, and splinters flew through the room. "A bit of a near thing," said Captain Mitty carelessly. "The box barrage is closing in," said the sergeant. "We only live once, Sergeant," said Mitty, with his faint, fleeting smile. "Or do we?" He poured another brandy and tossed it off. "I never see a man could hold his brandy like you, sir," said the sergeant. "Begging your pardon, sir." Captain Mitty stood up and strapped on his huge Webley-Vickers automatic. "It's forty kilometers through hell, sir," said the sergeant. Mitty finished one last brandy. "After all," he said softly, "what isn't?" The pounding of the cannon increased; there was the rat-tat-tatting of machine guns, and from somewhere came the menacing pocketa-pocketa-pocketa of the new flame-throwers. Walter Mitty walked to the door of the dugout humming "Auprès de Ma Blonde." He turned and waved to the sergeant. "Cheerio!" he said.—

Something struck his shoulder. "I've been looking all over this hotel for you," said Mrs. Mitty. "Why do you have to hide in this old chair? How did you expect me to find you?" "Things close in," said Walter Mitty vaguely. "What?" Mrs. Mitty said. "Did you get the what's-its-name? The puppy biscuit? What's in that box?" "Overshoes," said Mitty. "Couldn't you have put them on in the store?" "I was thinking," said Walter Mitty. "Does it ever occur to you that I am sometimes thinking?" She looked at him. "I'm going to take your temperature when I get you home," she said.

They went out through the revolving doors that made a faintly derisive whistling sound when you pushed them. It was two blocks to the parking lot. At the drugstore on the corner she said, "Wait here for me. I forgot something. I won't be a minute." She was more than a minute. Walter Mitty lighted a cigarette. It began to rain, rain with sleet in it. He stood up against the wall of the drugstore, smoking.— He put his shoulders back and his heels together. "To hell with the handkerchief," said Walter Mitty scornfully. He took one last drag on his cigarette and snapped it away. Then, with that faint, fleeting smile playing about his lips, he faced the firing squad; erect and motionless, proud and disdainful, Walter Mitty the Undefeated, inscrutable to the last.

James Thurber (1894–1961) was a popular American writer, humorist, and cartoonist. "The Secret Life of Walter Mitty" was published in a collection of stories (1942), and was later adapted as a film (1947). Thurber, after reading the script, is said to have offered ten thousand dollars to *prevent* the film from being made; however, it proved to be very successful at the box office.

1. *Response*

a. Each of Mitty's five fantasies is initiated by a specific stimulus in the real world. For each daydream, find the stimulus.
b. Describe Walter Mitty's real life and real character. Contrast this to his secret lives and characters.
c. Provide at least three good reasons why the author would end the story with a fantasy sequence. Which do you think is the best reason? Why?
d. Did you find it necessary to look up the uncommon medical and military terms in the story? Explain.

2. *Literature Studies* *Climax and Resolution* Conventional short stories contain a **climax**. In your opinion, does "The Secret Life of Walter Mitty" contain a climax and/or **resolution**? Explain your answer using examples from the story. Speculate on why James Thurber did or did not include these conventional short story elements.

The **climax** of a story is the high point of the action, where something decisive occurs. The **resolution** follows the climax and traces the final outcome of the central conflict.

3. *Writing* *Short Story* Because Thurber provides us with only Mitty's point of view, the wife does not come across as a sympathetic character. Write a short story in which we are presented with the wife's view of Walter and their relationship. You can either invent a plot sequence or retell parts of Thurber's tale.

4. *Critical Thinking* "The Secret Life of Walter Mitty" contains obvious stereotypes of male and female roles and behaviours. These stereotypes were common in 1942 when the story was written. In a small group, identify and comment on the stereotypes. Do you think the same stereotypes would appear in an updated version of the story? Why or why not? Present your conclusions to the class.

In China, the revolution demanded self-sacrifice, and there were those who put their country before everything else—even love.

Love Must Not Be Forgotten

By Zhang Jie

Translated by Gladys Yang

I am thirty, the same age as our People's Republic. For a republic thirty is still young. But a girl of thirty is virtually on the shelf.

Actually, I have a bona fide suitor. Have you seen the Greek sculptor Myron's *Discobolos*? Qiao Lin is the image of that discus thrower. Even the padded clothes he wears in winter fail to hide his fine physique. Bronzed, with clear-cut features, a broad forehead, and large eyes, his appearance alone attracts most girls to him.

But I can't make up my mind to marry him. I'm not clear what attracts me to him, or him to me.

I know people are gossiping behind my back: "Who does she think she is, to be so choosy?"

To them, I'm a nobody playing hard to get. They take offence at such preposterous behaviour.

Of course, I shouldn't be captious. In a society where commercial production still exists, marriage like most other transactions is still a form of barter.

I have known Qiao Lin for nearly two years, yet still cannot fathom whether he keeps so quiet from aversion to talking or from having nothing to say. When, by way of a small intelligence test, I demand his opinion of this or that, he says "good" or "bad" like a child in kindergarten.

Once I asked, "Qiao Lin, why do you love me?" He thought the question over seriously for what seemed an age. I could see from his normally smooth but now wrinkled forehead that the little grey cells in his handsome head were hard at work cogitating. I felt ashamed to have put him on the spot.

Finally he raised his clear childlike eyes to tell me, "Because you're good!"

Loneliness flooded my heart. "Thank you, Qiao Lin!" I couldn't help wondering, if we were to marry, whether we could discharge our duties to each other as husband and wife. Maybe, because law and morality would have bound us together. But how tragic simply to comply with law and morality! Was there no stronger bond to link us?

When such thoughts cross my mind I have the strange sensation that instead of being a girl contemplating marriage I am an elderly social scientist.

Perhaps I worry too much. We can live like most married couples, bringing up children together, strictly true to each other according to the law.... Although living in the seventies of the twentieth century, people still consider marriage the way they did millennia ago, as a means of continuing the race, a form of barter, or a business transaction in which love and marriage can be separated. As this is the common practice, why shouldn't we follow suit?

But I still can't make up my mind. As a child, I remember, I often cried all night for no rhyme or reason, unable to sleep and disturbing the whole household. My old nurse, a shrewd though uneducated woman, said an ill wind had blown through my ear. I think this judgement showed prescience, because I still have that old weakness. I upset myself over things which really present no problem, upsetting other people at the same time. One's nature is hard to change.

I think of my mother too. If she were alive, what would she say about my attitude to Qiao Lin and my uncertainty about marrying him?

My thoughts constantly turn to her, not because she was such a strict mother that her ghost is still watching over me since her death. No, she was not just my mother but my closest friend. I loved her so much that the thought of her leaving me makes my heart ache.

She never lectured me, just told me quietly in her deep, unwomanly voice about her successes and failures, so that I could learn from her experience. She had evidently not had many successes—her life was full of failures.

During her last days she followed me with her fine, expressive eyes, as if wondering how I would manage on my own and as if she had some important advice for me but hesitated to give it. She must have been worried by my naiveté and sloppy ways. She suddenly blurted out, "Shanshan, if you aren't sure what you want, don't rush into marriage—better live on your own!"

Other people might think this strange advice from a mother to her daughter, but to me it embodied her bitter experience. I don't think she underestimated me or my knowledge of life. She loved me and didn't want me to be unhappy.

"I don't want to marry, mum!" I said, not out of bashfulness or a show of coyness. I can't think why a girl should pretend to be coy. She had long since taught me about things not generally mentioned to girls.

"If you meet the right man, then marry him. Only if he's right for you!"

"I'm afraid no such man exists!"

"That's not true. But it's hard. The world is so vast, I'm afraid you may never meet him." Whether I married or not was not what concerned her, but the quality of the marriage.

"Haven't you managed fine without a husband?"

"Who says so?"

"I think you've done fine."

"I had no choice...." She broke off, lost in thought, her face wistful. Her wistful lined face reminded me of a withered flower I had pressed in a book.

"Why did you have no choice?"

"You ask too many questions," she parried, not ashamed to confide in me but afraid that I might reach the wrong conclusion. Besides, everyone treasures a secret to carry to the grave. Feeling a bit put out, I demanded bluntly, "Didn't you love my dad?"

"No, I never loved him."

"Did he love you?"

"No, he didn't."

"Then why get married?"

She paused, searching for the right words to explain this mystery, then answered bitterly, "When you're young you don't always know what you're looking for, what you need, and people may talk you into getting married. As you grow older and more experienced you find out your true needs. By then, though, you've done many foolish things for which you could kick yourself. You'd give anything to be able to make a fresh start and live more wisely. Those content with their lot will always be happy, they say, but I shall never enjoy that happiness." She added self-mockingly, "A wretched idealist, that's all I am."

Did I take after her? Did we both have genes which attracted ill winds?

"Why don't you marry again?"

"I'm afraid I'm still not sure what I really want." She was obviously unwilling to tell me the truth.

I cannot remember my father. He and Mother split up when I was very small. I just recall her telling me sheepishly that he was a fine handsome fellow. I could see she was ashamed of having judged by appearances and made a futile choice. She told me, "When I can't sleep at night, I force myself to sober up by recalling all those stupid blunders I made. Of course it's so distasteful that I often hide my face in the sheet for shame, as if there were eyes watching me in the dark. But distasteful as it is, I take some pleasure in this form of atonement."

I was really sorry that she hadn't remarried. She was such a fascinating character, if she'd married a man she loved, what a happy household ours would surely have been. Though not beautiful, she had the simple charm of an ink landscape. She was a fine writer too. Another author who knew her well used to say teasingly, "Just reading your works is enough to make anyone love you!"

She would retort, "If he knew that the object of his affection was a white-haired old crone, that would frighten him away."

At her age, she must have known what she really wanted, so this was obviously an evasion. I say this because she had quirks which puzzled me.

For instance, whenever she left Beijing on a trip, she always took with her one of the twenty-seven volumes of Chekhov's stories published between 1950 and 1955. She also warned me, "Don't touch these books. If you want to read Chekhov, read that set I bought you." There was no need to caution me. Having a set of my own why should I touch hers? Besides, she'd told me this over and over again. Still she was on her guard. She seemed bewitched by those books.

So we had two sets of Chekhov's stories at home. Not just because we loved Chekhov, but to parry other people like me who loved Chekhov. Whenever anyone asked to borrow a volume, she would lend one of mine. Once, in her absence, a close friend took a volume from her set. When she found out she was frantic, and at once took a volume of mine to exchange for it.

Ever since I can remember, those books were on her bookcase. Although I admire Chekhov as a great writer, I was puzzled by the way she never tired of reading him. Why, for over twenty years, had she had to read him every single day?

Sometimes, when tired of writing, she poured herself a cup of strong tea and sat down in front of the bookcase, staring raptly at that set of books. If I went into her room then it flustered her, and she either spilt her tea or blushed like a girl discovered with her lover.

I wondered: Has she fallen in love with Chekhov? She might have if he'd still been alive.

When her mind was wandering just before her death, her last words to me were: "That set...." She hadn't the strength to give it its complete title. But I knew what she meant. "And my diary ... 'Love Must Not Be Forgotten' .... Cremate them with me."

I carried out her last instruction regarding the works of Chekhov, but couldn't bring myself to destroy her diary. I thought, if it could be published, it would surely prove the most moving thing she had written. But naturally publication was out of the question.

At first I imagined the entries were raw material she had jotted down. They read neither like stories, essays, a diary, or letters. But after reading the whole I formed a hazy impression, helped out by my imperfect memory. Thinking it over, I finally realized that this was no lifeless manuscript I was holding, but an anguished, loving heart. For over twenty years one man had occupied her heart, but he was not for her. She used these diaries as a substitute for him, a means of pouring out her feelings to him, day after day, year after year.

No wonder she had never considered any eligible proposals, had turned a deaf ear to idle talk whether well-meant or malicious. Her heart was already full, to the exclusion of anybody else. "No lake can compare with the ocean, no cloud with those on Mount Wu." Remembering those lines I often reflected sadly that few people in real life could love like this. No one would love me like this.

I learned that towards the end of the thirties, when this man was doing underground work for the Party in Shanghai, an old worker had given his life to cover him, leaving behind a helpless wife and daughter. Out of a sense of duty, of gratitude to the dead and deep class feeling, he had unhesitatingly married the girl. When he saw the endless troubles caused by "love" of couples who had married for "love," he may have thought, "Thank Heaven, though I didn't marry for love, we get on well, able to help each other." For years, as man and wife they lived through hard times.

He must have been my mother's colleague. Had I ever met him? He couldn't have visited our home. Who was he?

In the spring of 1962, Mother took me to a concert. We went on foot, the theatre being quite near.

A black limousine pulled up silently by the pavement. Out stepped an elderly man with white hair in a black serge tunic-suit. What a striking shock of white hair! Strict, scrupulous, distinguished, transparently honest—that was my impression of him. The cold glint of his flashing eyes reminded me of lightning or swordplay. Only ardent love for a woman really deserving his love could fill cold eyes like those with tenderness.

He walked up to Mother and said, "How are you, Comrade Zhong Yu? It's been a long time."

"How are you!" Mother's hand holding mine suddenly turned icy cold and trembled a little.

They stood face to face without looking at each other, each appearing upset, even stern. Mother fixed her eyes on the trees by the roadside, not yet in leaf. He looked at me. "Such a big girl already. Good, fine—you take after your mother."

Instead of shaking hands with Mother he shook hands with me. His hand was as icy as hers and trembling a little. As if transmitting an electric current, I felt a sudden shock. Snatching my hand away I cried, "There's nothing good about that!"

"Why not?" he asked with a surprised expression grown-ups always have when children speak out frankly.

I glanced at Mother's face. I did take after her, to my disappointment. "Because she's not beautiful!"

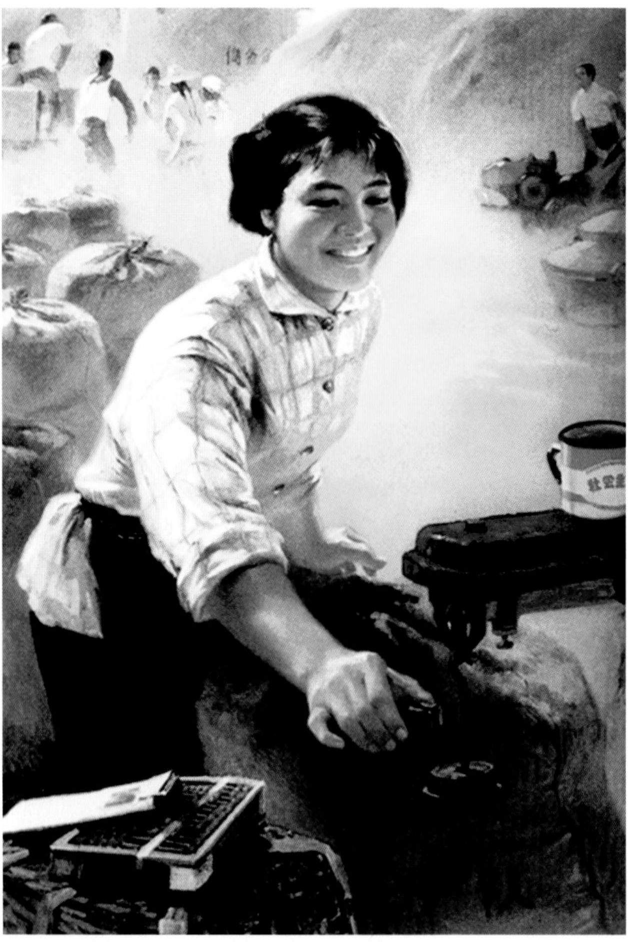

This is one of a series of postcards produced in China during the Cultural Revolution. How does this artist use colour to create mood? What messages, explicit or implicit, are sent by this postcard?

Untitled postcard by an unknown artist

He laughed, then said teasingly, "Too bad that there should be a child who doesn't find her own mother beautiful. Do you remember in '53, when your mum was transferred to Beijing, she came to our ministry to report for duty? She left you outside on the verandah, but like a monkey you climbed all the stairs, peeped through the cracks in doors, and caught your finger in the door of my office. You sobbed so bitterly that I carried you off to find her."

"I don't remember that." I was annoyed at his harking back to a time when I was still in open-seat pants.

"Ah, we old people have better memories." He turned abruptly and remarked to Mother, "I've read that last story of yours. Frankly speaking, there's something not quite right about it. You shouldn't have condemned the heroine.... There's nothing wrong with falling in love, as long as you don't spoil someone else's life.... In fact, the hero might have loved her too. Only for the sake of a third person's happiness, they had to renounce their love...."

A policeman came over to where the car was parked and ordered the driver to move on. When the driver made some excuse, the old man looked round. After a hasty "Goodbye" he strode to the car and told the policeman, "Sorry. It's not his fault, it's mine...."

I found it amusing watching this old cadre listening respectfully to the policeman's strictures. When I turned to Mother with a mischievous smile, she looked as upset as a first-form primary schoolchild standing forlornly in front of the stern headmistress. Anyone would have thought she was the one being lectured by the policeman.

The car drove off, leaving a puff of smoke. Very soon even this smoke vanished with the wind, as if nothing at all had happened. But the incident stuck in my mind.

Analyzing it now, he must have been the man whose strength of character won Mother's heart. That strength came from his firm political convictions, his narrow escapes from death in the Revolution, his active brain, his drive at work, his well-cultivated mind. Besides, strange to say, he and Mother both liked the oboe. Yes, she must have worshipped him. She once told me that unless she worshipped a man, she couldn't love him even for one day.

But I could not tell whether he loved her or not. If not, why was there this entry in her diary?

> "This is far too fine a present. But how did you know that Chekhov's my favourite writer?"
>
> "You said so."
>
> "I don't remember that."

"I remember. I heard you mention it when you were chatting with someone."

So he was the one who had given her the *Selected Stories of Chekhov*. For her that was tantamount to a love letter.

Maybe this man, who didn't believe in love, realized by the time his hair was white that in his heart was something which could be called love. By the time he no longer had the right to love, he made the tragic discovery of this love for which he would have given his life. Or did it go deeper than that?

This is all I remember about him.

How wretched Mother must have been, deprived of the man to whom she was devoted! To catch a glimpse of his car or the back of his head through its rear window, she carefully figured out which roads he would take to work and back. Whenever he made a speech, she sat at the back of the hall watching his face rendered hazy by cigarette smoke and poor lighting. Her eyes would brim with tears, but she swallowed them back. If a fit of coughing made him break off, she wondered anxiously why no one persuaded him to give up smoking. She was afraid he would get bronchitis again. Why was he so near yet so far?

He, to catch a glimpse of her, looked out of the car window every day, straining his eyes to watch the streams of cyclists, afraid that she might have an accident. On the rare evenings on which he had no meetings, he would walk by a roundabout way to our neighbourhood, to pass our compound gate. However busy, he would always make time to look in papers and journals for her work.

His duty had always been clear to him, even in the most difficult times. But now confronted by this love he became a weakling, quite helpless. At his age it was laughable. Why should life play this trick on him?

Yet when they happened to meet at work, each tried to avoid the other, hurrying off with a nod. Even so, this would make Mother blind and deaf to everything around her. If she met a colleague named Wang she would call him Guo and mutter something unintelligible.

It was a cruel ordeal for her. She wrote:

> We agreed to forget each other. But I deceived you, I have never forgotten. I don't think you've forgotten either. We're just deceiving each other, hiding our misery. I haven't deceived you deliberately, though; I did my best to carry out our agreement. I often stay far away from Beijing, hoping time and distance will help me to forget you. But on my

return, as the train pulls into the station, my head reels. I stand on the platform looking round intently, as if someone were waiting for me. Of course there is no one. I realize then that I have forgotten nothing. Everything is unchanged. My love is like a tree the roots of which strike deeper year after year—I have no way to uproot it.

At the end of every day, I feel as if I've forgotten something important. I may wake with a start from my dreams wondering what has happened. But nothing has happened. Nothing. Then it comes home to me that you are missing! So everything seems lacking, incomplete, and there is nothing to fill up the blank. We are nearing the ends of our lives, why should we be carried away by emotion like children? Why should life submit people to such ordeals, then unfold before you your lifelong dream? Because I started off blindly I took the wrong turning, and now there are insuperable obstacles between me and my dream.

Yes, Mother never let me go to the station to meet her when she came back from a trip, preferring to stand alone on the platform and imagine that he had met her. Poor mother with her greying hair was as infatuated as a girl.

Not much space in the diary was devoted to their romance. Most entries dealt with trivia: Why one of her articles had not come off; her fear that she had no real talent; the excellent play she missed by mistaking the time on the ticket; the drenching she got by going out for a stroll without her umbrella. In spirit they were together day and night, like a devoted married couple. In fact, they spent no more than twenty-four hours together in all. Yet in that time they experienced deeper happiness than some people in a whole lifetime. Shakespeare makes Juliet say, "I cannot sum up half my sum of wealth." And probably that is how Mother felt.

He must have been killed in the Cultural Revolution. Perhaps because of the conditions then, that section of the diary is ambiguous and obscure. Mother had been so fiercely attacked for her writing, it amazed me that she went on keeping a diary. From some veiled allusions I gathered that he had queried the theories advanced by that "theoretician" then at the height of favour, and had told someone, "This is sheer Rightist talk." It was clear from the tear-stained pages of Mother's diary that he had been harshly denounced; but the steadfast old man never knuckled under to the authorities. His last words were, "When I go to meet Marx, I shall go on fighting my case!"

That must have been in the winter of 1969, because that was when Mother's hair turned white overnight, though she was not yet fifty. And she put on a black arm-band. Her position then was extremely difficult. She was criticized for wearing this old-style mourning, and ordered to say for whom she was in mourning.

"For whom are you wearing that, mum?" I asked anxiously.

"For my lover." Not to frighten me she explained, "Someone you never knew."

"Shall I put one on too?" She patted my cheeks, as she had when I was a child. It was years since she had shown me such affection. I often felt that as she aged, especially during these last years of persecution, all tenderness had left her, or was concealed in her heart, so that she seemed like a man.

She smiled sadly and said, "No, you needn't wear one."

Her eyes were as dry as if she had no more tears to shed. I longed to comfort her or do something to please her. But she said, "Off you go."

I felt an inexplicable dread, as if dear Mother had already half left me. I blurted out, "Mum!"

Quick to sense my desolation, she said gently, "Don't be afraid. Off you go. Leave me alone for a little." I was right. She wrote:

> You have gone. Half my soul seems to have taken flight with you. I had no means of knowing what had become of you, much less of seeing you for the last time. I had no right to ask either, not being your wife or friend.... So we are torn apart. If only I could have borne that inhuman treatment for you, so that you could have lived on! You should have lived to see your name cleared and take up your work again, for the sake of those who loved you. I knew you could not be a counter-revolutionary. You were one of the finest men killed. That's why I love you—I am not afraid now to avow it.
>
> Snow is whirling down. Heavens, even God is such a hypocrite, he is using this whiteness to cover up your blood and the scandal of your murder.
>
> I have never set store by my life. But now I keep wondering whether anything I say or do would make you contract your shaggy eyebrows in a frown. I must live a worthwhile life like you, and do some honest work for our country. Things can't go on like this—those criminals will get what's coming to them.
>
> I used to walk alone along that small asphalt road, the only

> place where we once walked together, hearing my footsteps in the silent night.... I always paced to and fro and lingered there, but never as wretchedly as now. Then, though you were not beside me, I knew you were still in this world and felt that you were keeping me company. Now I can hardly believe that you have gone.
>
> At the end of the road I would retrace my steps, then walk along it again.
>
> Rounding the fence I always looked back, as if you were still standing there waving goodbye. We smiled faintly, like casual acquaintances, to conceal our undying love. That ordinary evening in early spring, a chilly wind was blowing as we walked silently away from each other. You were wheezing a little because of your chronic bronchitis. That upset me. I wanted to beg you to slow down, but somehow I couldn't. We both walked very fast, as if some important business were waiting for us. How we prized that single stroll we had together, but we were afraid we might lose control of ourselves and burst out with "I love you"—those three words which had tormented us for years. Probably no one else could believe that we never once even clasped hands!

No, Mother, I believe it. I am the only one able to see into your locked heart.

Ah, that little asphalt road, so haunted by bitter memories. We shouldn't overlook the most insignificant spots on earth. For who knows how much secret grief and joy they may hide.

No wonder that when tired of writing, she would pace slowly along that little road behind our window. Sometimes at dawn after a sleepless night, sometimes on a moonless, windy evening. Even in winter during howling gales which hurled sand and pebbles against the window pane.... I thought this was one of her eccentricities, not knowing that she had gone to meet him in spirit.

She liked to stand by the window too, staring at the small asphalt road. Once I thought from her expression that one of our closest friends must be coming to call. I hurried to the window. It was a late autumn evening. The cold wind was stripping dead leaves from the trees and blowing them down the small empty road.

She went on pouring out her heart to him in her diary as she had when he was alive. Right up to the day when the pen slipped from her fingers. Her last message was:

> I am a materialist, yet I wish there were a Heaven. For then, I know, I would find you there waiting for me. I am going there to join you, to be together for eternity. We need never be parted again or keep at a distance for fear of spoiling someone else's life. Wait for me, dearest, I am coming—

I do not know how Mother, on her deathbed, could still love so ardently with all her heart. To me it seemed not love but a form of madness, a passion stronger than death. If undying love really exists, she reached its extreme. She obviously died happy, because she had known true love. She had no regrets.

Now these old people's ashes have mingled with the elements. But I know that, no matter what form they may take, they still love each other. Though not bound together by earthly laws or morality, though they never once clasped hands, each possessed the other completely. Nothing could part them. Centuries to come, if one white cloud trails another, two grasses grow side by side, one wave splashes another, a breeze follows another ... believe me, that will be them.

Each time I read that diary "Love Must Not Be Forgotten" I cannot hold back my tears. I often weep bitterly, as if I myself experienced their ill-fated love. If not a tragedy it was too laughable. No matter how beautiful or moving I find it, I have no wish to follow suit!

Thomas Hardy wrote that "the call seldom produces the comer, the man to love rarely coincides with the hour for loving." I cannot censure them from conventional moral standards. What I deplore is that they did not wait for a "missing counterpart" to call them.

If everyone could wait, instead of rushing into marriage, how many tragedies could be averted!

When we reach communism, will there still be cases of marriage without love? Maybe, because since the world is so vast, two kindred spirits may be unable to answer each other's call. But how tragic! However, by that time, there may be ways to escape such tragedies.

Why should I split hairs?

Perhaps after all we are responsible for these tragedies. Who knows? Maybe we should take the responsibility for the old ideas handed down from the past. Because if someone never marries, that is a challenge to these ideas. You will be called neurotic, accused of having guilty secrets or having made political mistakes. You may be regarded as an eccentric who looks down on ordinary people, not respecting age-old customs—a heretic. In short they will trump up endless vulgar and futile charges to ruin your reputation. Then you have to knuckle under to those ideas and marry willy-nilly. But once you put the chains of a loveless marriage around your neck, you will suffer for it for the rest of your life.

I long to shout: "Mind your own business! Let us wait patiently for our counterparts. Even waiting in vain is better than willy-nilly marriage. To live single is not such a fearful disaster. I believe it may be a sign of a step forward in culture, education, and the quality of life."

Zhang Jie was born in 1937 in Beijing, China. She studied economics, but turned to writing, beginning with scripts for the Beijing Film Studio. She has written many short stories since the end of the Cultural Revolution in 1976, and these have established her as a popular and controversial writer.

1. ***Response***
   a. Were you able to make personal connections to the characters and situations in the story? Explain your response.
   b. Describe some of the different ways in which the mother nurtures her love for the nameless man. Do you think her devotion is admirable or foolish? Explain.
   c. Why do you think the author, Zhang Jie, chose to narrate the story from the daughter's point of view?

2. ***Research and Inquiry*** Compile some background information that would help a reader better appreciate the historical and cultural context of "Love Must Not Be Forgotten." First, look through the story for dates, places, and key terms that you can use to guide your research. Summarize your findings in a page or less of background information.

3. ***Language Conventions*** *Personal Pronouns* Read the mother's speech on page 41 ("She paused, searching for the right words ..."). Note the shift in the personal pronouns she uses in this paragraph. What does the shift reveal about her character?

4. ***Critical Thinking*** What social message does the author, Zhang Jie, convey in her story? Do you think the message is relevant to contemporary Canadians? Present your answer in a brief opinion piece. State your viewpoint clearly and articulate the reasons for your position.

Saturday Climbing

By W.D. Valgardson

"Gradually, as a dozen Saturdays passed, what had seemed impossible was reduced to the merely difficult."

Sixty feet up the cliff, the toe of his climbing boot resting on a ledge no wider than a dime, two fingers curled around a nubbin of rock, Barry was suddenly afraid that he would fall.

"Rope," he called.

At the foot of the cliff, his daughter let out the golden line of rope that joined them.

As Barry felt the rope go slack, he raised his right knee and pressed his toe into a shallow depression. Grunting with the strain, he stood up on his right leg, then paused, uncertain of his next move.

The cliff had proven to be deceptive. The conglomerate, with its rough, gravel-like surface, had looked easy. Close to the base, there were large handholds, so that at first the climbing was little more difficult than walking up stairs. Then, unexpectedly, the surfaces smoothed; the places where he could get a secure hold were spread farther and farther apart. At the same time, the numerous cracks dwindled until there was no place to set any protection. Unable to go back because of his pride, he had continued on until he now found himself dangerously far above his last piton. If he fell, he would drop twenty-five feet to the piton, then twenty-five feet past it before his rope came taut and held him. There was, because of the elasticity of the rope, a chance that he would ground out.

The thought flitted through his mind that it would be like falling from the top of a six-storey building. Tensing his fingers, he straightened his elbow and leaned back from the rock so that he could search for his next hold. Above him, there was a half-inch ledge. He reached up, got a good grip, then lifted his left leg higher than he had ever imagined he could and set his foot on a rough patch that would provide the necessary friction to hold his weight.

He had been scared many times but never like this. Never before had he been this close to paralysis, to a sensation of letting go so that the tension and the fear would be over. The way he felt, he imagined, was the way a wounded animal felt when it finally gave up fleeing and allowed itself to be killed.

Six inches from his left hand there was a vertical crack that seemed hardly wider than a fingernail. Cautiously, he explored it with his fingers. Just within his reach it widened slightly. He ran his hand over his rack and unsnapped the smallest chock nut. He forced the aluminum wedge deep into the crack. From the wedge there hung a wire loop and from that a carabiner. Catching hold of the rope tied to his harness, he lifted it up, forced open the spring-loaded gate of the carabiner and fitted the rope into the aluminum oval.

Once the gate snapped shut, he sighed with relief. The chock nut, the wire loop, the carabiner, the rope, fragile as they looked, would hold ten times his weight. If he wanted to, he could let go and simply hang in space.

"You all right?" his daughter called. "Yeah," he lied. "Just resting."

His voice sounded faint and breathy. He was glad she could not see his momentary weakness. He could not control the trembling of his legs. The muscle of his right arm jerked spasmodically. Ever since his wife had left him, he had tried to compensate by providing unhesitating leadership for his daughter. He did his best to keep life simple and uncomplicated. It was, he thought, the way to provide security.

He glanced down. Among the scattered grey boulders, Moira's red hair gleamed like a burnished cap.

"You're doing fine," she hollered. The crosscurrents of air that played over the cliff face blurred her voice, making it seem farther away than it really was. To hear what she said, he had to strain toward the sound. "You've got another twenty feet to a big ledge. You can do it easy."

He was grateful for her confidence. Before they had started climbing, there had crept into his daughter's voice a constant note of disparagement and disappointment. The times he had managed to overcome his own insecurity and had asked her what was the matter, she had turned her back on him, answering, "Nothing," with a tightly controlled voice.

Bewildered, he had sought the advice of women at work who had teenage daughters. They had been no help. Behind their competent, efficient professional selves, they too, he realized, were just as confused as he was. In desperation, he had gone so far as to pose the question of the relationship of fathers and daughters to his class. He had not been prepared for the reaction he got. From every corner of the room came cries of bitter disappointment and resentment.

As he had left the classroom, one student had called to him. He had stopped to wait for her. She had frizzy dark hair, wore long dresses that might have come from a western movie set, a rainbow assortment of beads, and a nose ring. She always talked as if she was thinking in some exotic language and was translating it badly. She was the only student he'd ever had who insisted on analysing *War and Peace*[1] by consulting the *I Ching*.[2]

"The caged bird proves nothing but the power of the captor," she had intoned.

For a moment, he suffered vertigo, and the cliff seemed to sway as if in an earthquake. He pressed his forehead to the cool stone and shut his eyes. Inside his flesh, his bones trembled.

Taking up rock-climbing had been an act of desperation. All the past activities Moira and he had done together—going to foreign films, visiting Seattle, beachcombing—she dismissed with a contemptuous shrug of her shoulders. At one time, they had played chess nearly every day. Lately, she pretended she had never seen the game. When he had noticed an advertisement for rock-climbing, he remembered that she had spoken admiringly of classmates who had hiked the West Coast Trail. He had registered them and paid their fees. Then he informed her.

He hoped she would be pleased. Instead, she was incensed that he had committed her to something without her consent. He knew she was right to be angry but he was too frantic to care. Over the previous month, she had come home late a number of times. Each time, the sweet-sour smell of marijuana clung to her, and her pupils seemed unnaturally large. He had not dared to accuse her of smoking dope. If he was wrong, she would never forgive him for being unjust. Being right frightened him even more. If she said, "That's right, I'm smoking dope, six joints a day, and sniffing coke and participating in orgies," he didn't know what he would do. Ranting and raving had ceased to work. Reasoning with her had no effect. He felt utterly helpless.

By emphasizing that the money was spent and there was no refund, he won the argument over rock-climbing. However, he took the car to the first class while she took her bike. She went prepared to sneer at everything, but once she saw her classmates, her attitude changed. Instead of Moira being isolated by her youth, Barry was isolated because of his age. Of the fifteen members, eleven were under twenty. The instructor still didn't need to shave more than once a week.

By the time the three hours were over and he realized that rock-

[1]***War and Peace:*** novel by the Russian author Leo Tolstoy
[2]***I Ching:*** ancient Chinese book used to foretell the future

climbing wasn't going to be rough hiking, it was too late to back out. There were only three girls in the class. In return for the attention of one-third of the young men, Moira was prepared to scale the Himalayas.

Barry began with an attitude that was typical of someone raised on the Prairies. Anything over three feet was a substantial elevation. During the second class, he was expected to climb vertical cliffs. He gave some thought to dropping out of the class but realized that, after the fuss he had made about the fees, he would look like a dreadful hypocrite.

Gradually, as a dozen Saturdays passed, what had seemed impossible was reduced to the merely difficult. Cliffs that had looked flat and smooth as polished marble became a series of problems and solutions. The names of the unfamiliar equipment became a part of his vocabulary. Young men in climbing boots frequented his backyard and kitchen. To his relief, Moira accepted him enough to spend an occasional hour practising knot-tying with him.

This weekend there had been no class. In an attempt to heal a rift caused by an argument over her going away to college—she was two years ahead of herself in school and, therefore, in spite of being in grade 12 was only 16—he had offered to go climbing with her. To his surprise, she'd accepted.

"Climbing," he called.

"Climb on," Moira answered.

He stepped up, away from the safety of his perch. His life, he realized, was in her hands. If he fell, she was his protection.

The thought of giving her so much responsibility was like the prick of a thorn. In all other things, he had been trying to keep her from rushing headlong into taking on too much responsibility at once. The result had been a long series of disagreements. She did not have the decency to let one dispute finish before she began another. Sometimes three or four overlapped.

On Fridays, when he went to the faculty club, he ordered double brandies and brooded over whether he shouldn't have insisted on Sunday school in a good fundamentalist church all the past years. His colleagues, the majority of whom were the epitome of liberal tolerance about most things, when they talked about their teenage children reverted to wistful fantasies about convents and boarding schools in inaccessible locations.

The weekend past, Moira had wanted to go to an all-night party with a boy he just vaguely recognized as having drifted through the house two or three times. Barry was dumbfounded. At the same age, he'd had to have his girlfriends in before midnight. If he had kept a girl out all night, her father would have met them with a shotgun.

"Good girls," he said, quoting something he'd heard in adolescence, "don't stay out all night."

"Good fathers," she shot back, "don't think the worst of their daughters."

That afternoon was filled with slamming doors, weeping and raised voices. He found himself fighting so hard against her staying out all night that he compromised on three o'clock and afterward, when he had calmed down, wondered how it had happened. He had been determined to start with a deadline of midnight and let himself be persuaded to accept one o'clock. Although Moira claimed not to remember the chess moves, he had the distinct feeling that he'd been checkmated.

The final blow had been her insistence on going away to college. They had the money, he admitted. It just wasn't sensible, at sixteen, to travel 2,000 miles to attend a school when the local university was every bit as good, even if it did have him on the faculty. He suspected the choice had more to do with her all-night-party boy than with academic excellence.

Now, as he worked his way up toward the large ledge where he was to set up a belay station, it was as if Barry were in danger of being pulled backward by the sheer weight of his memories. It was with a sense of relief that he heaved himself onto the ledge. He paused to catch his breath, then anchored himself to a boulder.

"On belay," he shouted down, giving Moira the signal that he was ready.

His daughter, eighty feet below, seemed so small that Barry felt he could lift her into his arms. She looked no larger than she had been when, at three, she had eaten a bottle of aspirin. He had scooped her up and run with her four blocks to the hospital. After that desperate race and the struggle to hold her down—it had taken both him and a nurse to control her flailing limbs while the doctor had pumped her stomach—he was acutely aware of how tenuous her life was, of how much he would suffer if he lost her. For a long time afterward, he thought of her as being intricately constructed of fragile paper.

"Climbing," Moira answered.

"Climb on," he shouted.

From time to time, she paused to pull loose the chock nuts and

People create stories create people; or rather
stories create people create stories.

Chinua Achebe

pitons her father had left behind. These, since they would be needed later, she clipped to a sling that hung over her shoulder. Once, when she deviated from the route her father had taken, she became stuck at an overhang. Not having dealt with the obstacle himself, Barry could not help and had to leave her to find her own solution.

The climb seemed agonizingly slow, as if it would never be completed. Then, when it was over, and his daughter, grinning, breathless, was climbing over the edge, it was as if hardly any time had passed.

They sat side by side, sipping orange juice, their feet dangling in space.

"I thought you were in trouble," Moira said.

"I thought you were too," he replied, matching his weakness with hers. Then, ashamed, he admitted, "I gripped."

Moira twisted about. Her red hair was snugged at the back with a rubber band. Being outside had sprinkled her nose with light freckles.

She studied the cliff face. It rose another hundred feet. There was a crack that ran more than halfway, then a small series of outcrops. He tried to see the route they should take, but the last ten or fifteen feet seemed impossible.

"I'd come home for Christmas," she said in a rush, "and classes are out in April. It's not as if it was such a long time to be away."

She had caught him unawares, and none of his carefully prepared arguments were at hand.

"It's just so unexpected," was all that he could manage.

"I've got to leave sometime."

The house will be so empty, he wanted to say. How will I get used to being alone? It is as if you lost your first tooth only last year. As if I took you to kindergarten six months ago. You're barely rid of your braces.

She lifted her index finger and rubbed the side of her nose. She had done it as long as he could remember. It was her signal that she was going to impart a confidence or confess a wrongdoing—that she liked some boy in her class, that she had got a detention or spent all her allowance before the end of the week and needed more money.

"I'm not innocent, you know."

He wondered what she meant by that but was afraid to ask.

"I mean," she continued, "Vic Hi's a big school. You hear a lot. Everybody's on the Pill. The dope's there if you want it. There's lots of opportunity."

He was tempted to let loose his anxiety in a lecture, but the memory of the frizzy-haired student in his class stopped him. She had stood on one foot all the time they were talking, the sole of her left sandal pressed to her right knee. She had passed her hand before his face in an affected arc. He'd heard her father was a prominent lawyer in the East but found it hard to believe.

She had talked in aphorisms and riddles, then a silence had fallen between them. He'd wondered why she had bothered to call after him, what she had really wanted to say. He had left her but, after a few steps, glanced back. She had given up her storklike stance and was standing with feet together, shoulders slumped, her face slack beneath her gaudy makeup. For the first time, he had seen how much younger she was than he had thought. If he had not known better, he'd have said she was a lost child.

Just then, she had seen him watching her. Immediately, she had drawn up her shoulders, flung back her head, given an exaggerated sway of her hips and pranced away. That had been the last time he'd seen her. She had never come back to his class, and one day a yellow drop-slip with her name on it had appeared in his mailbox.

"I want to lead this pitch," Moira said.

Barry was startled. She had never led. Always before she'd been second or third on a rope.

"I was thinking of rappelling down," he answered. "I can't see a clear route up."

"There," she said. "There and there and there." She jabbed her fingertip at a series of holds.

"But where would you set your protection?"

Her hand wove a series of stitches in the air. "There. Up there. To the side. Back across. Up about six feet."

His fear for her was not without reason. The climbing, after seeming so dangerous at first, had begun to lose its aura of hazard. They all fell from time to time, but their ropes kept them from suffering more than bruised knees and elbows. Then, one of the climbers who was leading had ignored instructions and, overconfident, had put in only one piece of protection. He placed it improperly, and when he slipped and fell, his weight jerked it loose. For a moment, no one had been able to move, then those who were not belaying or climbing had run toward the boy who lay sprawled on his back. Bright red blood seeped from his nose and ear.

"Jackets," Barry had demanded. Red Cross training that he'd not thought about in years came back with an intense clarity. "Every piece of clothing you can spare. We mustn't let him get cold."

They all had moved automatically, clumsily, unable to think. Having done as he instructed, they all stood stupefied. Their faces were shocked white beneath their tans.

He sent two of the students racing down the hill for help.

For an hour, they huddled in a ragged circle around the boy whose hair was paler than the sun-drenched grass and whose skin might have been moulded from wax. He slipped in and out of consciousness. Each time his eyes shut, they all tensed, afraid that he had died. But then, he would groan or let out his breath harshly, and the moment would pass. Someone, Barry had not noticed who, had started collecting gear. One, and then another, began to pack. They moved slowly, silently, as if any noise would disturb the delicate balance between life and death.

Grounded out. That was what they called it. Because his safety had not been properly set, he had grounded out. Barry remembered that the air force had been like that too. Pilots never failed. They washed out. They never died. They bought it. *Grounded out.* The semantics covered up the fear.

Now, for a moment, it was as if, once again, he could hear the sharp startled cry; see the backward arc, the body, falling without grace or beauty, the rope writhing and twisting, the red-shirted boy settling in a cloud of unexpected dust.

"Ron," Barry protested, surprising himself at remembering the boy's name.

"Do you think I'd be so careless?"

It was asked in a tone that allowed no argument.

Stiffly, he stood up and tested his belay.

Don't climb, he thought, *it's too dangerous. Let us go back the way we came and find somewhere that'll always be safe.* But even as he thought it, he knew that it was impossible.

Once again, it was as if he were standing before the frizzy-haired girl, watching her long green nails sweep slowly before his face. At the time, he had not wanted to understand. "The world seeks balance," she'd said. "Extremism begets extremism."

"On belay," he said.

"Climbing," Moira replied.

His daughter, easily, with the supreme confidence of youth, grasped a handhold and pulled herself onto a flake. Smoothly, she worked her way up one side of the crack, straddled it and crossed over.

Below her, her father, ever watchful, full of fear, smoothly payed out the rope, determined to give her all the slack she needed while, at the same time, keeping his hands tensed, ready to lock shut, ready to absorb the shock of any fall. ◗

W.D. Valgardson was born in 1939 and grew up in Gimli, Manitoba. He now lives in British Columbia. He is a poet, novelist, short story writer, and playwright, and teaches writing at the University of Victoria. For "Saturday Climbing," Valgardson drew on personal experience—his hobbies include rock climbing and hiking.

1. ***Response***
   a. The protagonist of a story is the main character. Who do you think is the protagonist of "Saturday Climbing"? Explain.
   b. "Saturday Climbing" tells the story of a parent-teenager relationship from the perspective of the parent. As a teenager, what is your reaction? Do you think W.D. Valgardson does a good job of capturing some of the challenges that parents and teenagers face? Is Moira's perspective fairly represented? Give reasons for your opinions.
   c. What does the ending of the story suggest about the changes that are occurring in the relationship between the father and daughter? Use specific details to support your answer.

2. ***Literature Studies*** *Plot* A short story often contains more than one plot. In a small group, identify the different plots in "Saturday Climbing" and show the parallels among them. Why do you think the author chose to tell this story using multiple plots?

3. ***Media*** *Poster* In "Saturday Climbing," Valgardson uses setting in a symbolic way; rock climbing becomes a metaphor for a parent–teenager relationship. Create a poster that also uses rock climbing imagery to express one of the themes or messages in the story. The image(s) you select for your poster should complement the title, caption, and/or text you use to convey the message.

Folk tales are rich in character, plot, and theme. They originated in the oral tradition, as tales told around the fire to delight listeners but also to convey serious moral lessons. Most cultures have folk tales that go back hundreds, even thousands, of years. Yet these tales have characters and themes that remain relevant even today. Folk tales are the true predecessors of the short story form.

The following tale is part of the Balkan oral tradition, but similar stories are found in many other cultures.

The Maiden Wiser Than the Tsar

Traditional tale retold by Idries Shah

ONCE UPON A TIME THERE WAS A poor man who had one daughter.

Now, this girl was amazingly wise, seemed to have knowledge far beyond her years, and often said things which surprised her own father.

One day, being without a penny, the poor man went to the Tsar to beg.

The Tsar, astonished at the man's cultivated way of saying things, asked him where he had learned such phrases.

"From my daughter," he replied.

"But where was your daughter taught?" asked the Tsar.

"God and our poverty have made her wise," was the answer.

"Here is some money for your immediate needs," said the Tsar, "and here are thirty eggs; command your daughter in my name to hatch them for me. If she does this successfully, you shall both have rich presents, but if she does not, you will be put to the torture."

The man went home and took the eggs to his daughter. She examined them, and weighed one or two in her hands. Then she realised that they were hard-boiled. So, she said "Father, wait until tomorrow, maybe I can think what can be done about this."

Next day, she was up early, having thought of a solution, and boiled some beans. She gave her father a small bag of the beans, and said:

"Go with the plough and oxen, father, and start ploughing beside the road where the Tsar will pass on his way to church. When he puts his head out of the carriage window, call out 'Go on, good oxen, plough the land so that these boiled beans will grow well!'"

The father did as she told him, and sure enough, the Tsar put his head out of the window of his carriage to watch the man at work, and, hearing what was being shouted, said "Stupid Fellow, how can you expect boiled beans to produce anything?"

Primed by his daughter, the simple man called out, "Just as from boiled eggs chickens can be produced!"

So, laughing, the Tsar went on his way, knowing that the girl had outwitted him.

But it was not to end there.

The next day the Tsar sent a courtier to the poor man with a bundle of flax, saying "This flax must be made into sails for my ship by tomorrow; otherwise, you will be executed."

Weeping, the man went home, but his daughter said "Have no fear, I shall think of something."

In the morning she came to him and gave him a small block of wood, and said "Tell the Tsar that if he can have all the tools necessary for spinning and weaving made out of this piece of wood, I will do the material for his sails out of the bunch of flax."

He did so, and the Tsar was further impressed by the girl's answer. But he put a small glass into the man's hand and said:

"Go, take this to your daughter, and ask her to empty the sea with this so that I may enlarge my dominions with precious new pastures."

The man went home, and gave his daughter the glass, telling her that the ruler had demanded yet another impossibility.

"Go to bed!" she said, "I will think of something by bringing my mind to bear upon it all night."

In the morning she said "Go to the Tsar and tell him that if he can dam up all the rivers of the world with this bundle of tow, then I will empty the sea for him."

The father went back to the Tsar and told him what his daughter had said. The Tsar, seeing that she was wiser than himself, asked that she be brought to court forthwith. When she appeared he asked her:

"What is it that can be heard at the greatest distance?" Without any hesitation she replied at once:

"The thunder and the lie can be heard at the greatest distance,

O Tsar." Astonished, the Tsar grasped his beard, and then, turning to his courtiers asked:

"What is my beard worth, do you think?" Each of them began to say what they thought the Tsar's beard was worth, making the value higher and higher, hoping to curry favour with His Majesty. Then, he said to the maiden:

"And what do *you* think my beard is worth, my child?" Everyone looked on in amazement as she replied:

"Your Majesty's beard is worth every bit as much as three summer rains!" The Tsar, greatly astonished, said:

"You have guessed rightly; I shall marry you and make you my wife this very day." So the girl became the Tsarina. But just when the wedding was over, she said to the Tsar:

"I have one request to make; be graciously pleased to write with your own hand that if you, or anyone in your court be displeased with me, and I had to go away, I should be allowed to take with me any one thing which I liked best." Enamoured of the beautiful maiden, the Tsar asked for pen and parchment, and at once wrote, sealing the document with his own ruby ring, as she had requested.

The years passed most happily for both of them, then one day the Tsar had a heated argument with the Tsarina and said:

"Go, I desire that you leave this palace, never to return!"

"I shall go tomorrow, then," said the young Tsarina dutifully. "Only allow me one more night here to prepare myself for the journey home." The Tsar agreed, and she gave him his bedtime herbal drink with her usual care.

No sooner had the Tsar drunk the potion than he fell asleep. The Tsarina had the Tsar carried to a coach, and they went to her father's cottage.

When the morning came, the Tsar, who had spent a tranquil night, woke, and looked around him in amazement.

"Treason!" he roared, "Where am I, and whose prisoner?"

"Mine, your Majesty," said the Tsarina sweetly, "Your parchment, written with your own hand is here," and she showed him where he had written that if she had to leave the palace she could take with her that which she liked best.

Hearing this, the Tsar laughed heartily, and declared that his affection for her had returned. "My great love for you, O Tsar," said she "has made me do this bold thing, but I risked death to do it, so you must see that my love is indeed very great."

Then they were united, and lived happily together for the rest of their lives. ◗

Idries Shah (1924–1996) was born in India but lived much of his life in England. He was fascinated by cross-cultural studies, and collected and published stories and tales from many different cultures. His many books about Sufi spirituality were his best-known works, and helped to spread knowledge of some aspects of Islamic thought to readers in the West.

1. ***Response***
   a. In addition to being entertaining, many folk tales express a moral lesson. What lesson or reminder does "The Maiden Wiser Than the Tsar" provide?
   b. Create a line graph to represent the plot of this tale in a visual way. Your graph should somehow indicate the various complications that arise, as well as the turning point of the story. Compare your graph with someone else's. Did you use similar or different approaches?

2. ***Literature Studies*** *Elements of Folklore* There are thousands of different folk tales, but they have many elements in common. Working in a group, identify elements in "The Maiden Wiser Than the Tsar" that appear in other folk tales with which you are familiar. Compare your ideas with those of other groups. If it is true that folk tales from around the world share common elements, what inferences might you make?

3. ***Writing*** *Modern Folk Tale* Write an updated version of "The Maiden Wiser Than the Tsar" using a modern setting and characters. You are free to change the details of all the impossible tasks set by the Tsar.

4. ***Oral Language*** *Presentation* Research the folklore of a culture that interests you. Prepare a presentation in which you summarize the unique or interesting aspects of that culture's folk tales. Complete your presentation with a dramatic reading of one tale.

The Storyteller

By Saki

Have you ever been annoyed by noisy children on a long trip? Here's one man's solution.

It was a hot afternoon, and the railway carriage was correspondingly sultry, and the next stop was at Templecombe, nearly an hour ahead. The occupants of the carriage were a small girl, and a smaller girl, and a small boy. An aunt belonging to the children occupied one corner seat, and the further corner seat on the opposite side was occupied by a bachelor who was a stranger to their party, but the small girls and the small boy emphatically occupied the compartment. Both the aunt and the children were conversational in a limited, persistent way, reminding one of the attentions of a housefly that refused to be discouraged. Most of the aunt's remarks seemed to begin with "Don't," and nearly all of the children's remarks began with "Why?" The bachelor said nothing out loud.

"Don't, Cyril, don't," exclaimed the aunt, as the small boy began smacking the cushions of the seat, producing a cloud of dust at each blow.

"Come and look out of the window," she added.

The child moved reluctantly to the window.

"Why are those sheep being driven out of that field?" he asked.

"I expect they are being driven to another field where there is more grass," said the aunt weakly.

"But there is lots of grass in that field," protested the boy. "There's nothing else but grass there. Aunt, there's lots of grass in that field."

"Perhaps the grass in the other field is better," suggested the aunt fatuously.

"Why is it better?" came the swift, inevitable question.

"Oh, look at those cows!" exclaimed the aunt. Nearly every field along the line had contained cows or bullocks, but she spoke as though she were drawing attention to a rarity.

"Why is the grass in the other field better?" persisted Cyril.

The frown on the bachelor's face was deepening to a scowl. He was a hard, unsympathetic man, the aunt decided in her mind. She was utterly unable to come to any satisfactory decision about the grass in the other field.

The smaller girl created a diversion by beginning to recite "On the Road to Mandalay." She only knew the first line, but she put her limited knowledge to the fullest possible use. She repeated the line over and over again in a dreamy but resolute and very audible voice; it seemed to the bachelor as though someone had had a bet with her that she could not repeat the line aloud two thousand times without stopping. Whoever it was who had made the wager was likely to lose his bet.

"Come over here and listen to a story," said the aunt, when the bachelor had looked twice at her and once at the communication cord.

The children moved listlessly toward the aunt's end of the carriage. Evidently her reputation as a storyteller did not rank high in their estimation.

In a low, confidential voice, interrupted at frequent intervals by loud, petulant questions from her listeners, she began an unenterprising and deplorably uninteresting story about a little girl who was good, and made friends with everyone on account of her goodness, and was finally saved from a mad bull by a number of rescuers who admired her moral character.

"Wouldn't they have saved her if she hadn't been good?" demanded the bigger of the small girls. It was exactly the question that the bachelor had wanted to ask.

"Well, yes," admitted the aunt lamely, "but I don't think they would have run quite so fast to her help if they had not liked her so much."

"It's the stupidest story I've ever heard," said the bigger of the small girls, with immense conviction.

"I didn't listen after the first bit, it was so stupid," said Cyril.

The smaller girl made no actual comment on the story, but she had long ago recommenced a murmured repetition of her favourite line.

"You don't seem to be a success as a storyteller," said the bachelor suddenly from his corner.

The aunt bristled in instant defence at this unexpected attack.

"It's a very difficult thing to tell stories that children can both understand and appreciate," she said stiffly.

"I don't agree with you," said the bachelor.

"Perhaps *you* would like to tell them a story," was the aunt's retort.

"Tell us a story," demanded the bigger of the small girls.

> The universe is made up of stories, not of atoms.
>
> Muriel Rukeyser

"Once upon a time," began the bachelor, "there was a little girl called Bertha, who was extraordinarily good."

The children's momentarily aroused interest began at once to flicker; all stories seemed dreadfully alike, no matter who told them.

"She did all that she was told, she was always truthful, she kept her clothes clean, ate milk puddings as though they were jam tarts, learned her lessons perfectly, and was polite in her manners."

"Was she pretty?" asked the bigger of the small girls.

"Not as pretty as any of you," said the bachelor, "but she was horribly good."

There was a wave of reaction in favor of the story; the word *horrible* in connection with goodness was a novelty that commended itself. It seemed to introduce a ring of truth that was absent from the aunt's tales of infant life.

"She was so good," continued the bachelor, "that she won several medals for goodness, which she always wore pinned onto her dress. There was a medal for obedience, another medal for punctuality, and a third for good behaviour. They were large metal medals, and they clicked against one another as she walked. No other child in the town where she lived had as many as three medals, so everybody knew that she must be an extra good child."

"Horribly good," quoted Cyril.

"Everybody talked about her goodness, and the Prince of the country got to hear about it, and he said that as she was so very good she might be allowed once a week to walk in his park, which was just outside the town. It was a beautiful park, and no children were ever allowed in it, so it was a great honour for Bertha to be allowed to go there."

"Were there any sheep in the park?" demanded Cyril.

"No," said the bachelor, "there were no sheep."

"Why weren't there any sheep?" came the inevitable question arising out of that answer.

The aunt permitted herself a smile, which might almost have been described as a grin.

"There were no sheep in the park," said the bachelor, "because the Prince's mother had once had a dream that her son would either be killed by a sheep or else by a clock falling on him. For that reason the Prince never kept a sheep in his park or a clock in his palace."

The aunt suppressed a gasp of admiration.

"Was the Prince killed by a sheep or by a clock?" asked Cyril.

"He is still alive, so we can't tell whether the dream will come true," said the bachelor unconcernedly. "Anyway, there were no sheep in the park, but there were lots of little pigs running all over the place."

"What colour were they?"

"Black with white faces, white with black spots, black all over, grey with white patches, and some were white all over."

The storyteller paused to let the full idea of the park's treasures sink into the children's imaginations; then he resumed:

"Bertha was rather sorry to find that there were no flowers in the park. She had promised her aunts, with tears in her eyes, that she would not pick any of the kind Prince's flowers, and she had meant to keep her promise, so of course it made her feel silly to find that there were no flowers to pick."

"Why weren't there any flowers?"

"Because the pigs had eaten them all," said the bachelor promptly. "The gardeners had told the Prince that you couldn't have pigs and flowers, so he decided to have pigs and no flowers."

There was a murmur of approval at the excellence of the Prince's decision; so many people would have decided the other way.

"There were lots of other delightful things in the park. There were ponds with gold and blue and green fish in them, and trees with beautiful parrots that said clever things at a moment's notice, and humming birds that hummed all the popular tunes of the day. Bertha walked up and down and enjoyed herself immensely, and thought to herself, 'If I were not so extraordinarily good I should not have been allowed to come into this beautiful park and enjoy all there is to be seen in it,' and her three medals clinked against one another as she walked and helped to remind her how very good she really was. Just then an enormous wolf came prowling into the park to see if it could catch a fat little pig for its supper."

"What colour was it?" asked the children, amid an immediate quickening of interest.

"Mud-colour all over, with a black tongue and pale grey eyes that gleamed with unspeakable ferocity. The first thing that it saw in the park was Bertha; her pinafore[1] was so spotlessly white and clean that it could be seen from a great distance. Bertha saw the wolf and saw that it was stealing toward her, and she began to wish that she had never been allowed to come into the park. She ran as hard as she could, and the wolf came after her with huge leaps and bounds. She managed to reach a shrubbery of myrtle bushes, and she hid herself in one of the thickest of the bushes. The wolf came sniffing among the branches, its black tongue lolling out of its mouth and its pale grey eyes glaring with rage.

---

[1]**pinafore:** a sleeveless dress

Bertha was terribly frightened, and thought to herself: 'If I had not been so extraordinarily good, I should have been safe in town at this moment.'

"However, the scent of the myrtle was so strong that the wolf could not sniff out where Bertha was hiding, and the bushes were so thick that he might have hunted about in them for a long time without catching sight of her; so he thought he might as well go off and catch a little pig instead. Bertha was trembling very much at having the wolf prowling and sniffing so near her, and as she trembled the medal for obedience clinked against the medals for good conduct and punctuality. The wolf was just moving away when he heard the sound of the medals clinking and stopped to listen; they clinked again in a bush quite near him. He dashed into the bush, his pale grey eyes gleaming with ferocity and triumph, and dragged Bertha out and devoured her to the last morsel. All that was left of her were her shoes, bits of clothing, and the three medals for goodness."

"Were any of the little pigs killed?"

"No, they all escaped."

"The story began badly," said the smaller of the two girls, "but it had a beautiful ending."

"It is the most beautiful story that I ever heard," said the bigger of the small girls, with immense decision.

"It is the *only* beautiful story I have ever heard," said Cyril.

A dissentient opinion came from the aunt.

"A most improper story to tell to young children! You have undermined the effect of years of careful teaching."

"At any rate," said the bachelor, collecting his belongings preparatory to leaving the carriage, "I kept them quiet for ten minutes, which was more than you were able to do."

"Unhappy woman!" he observed to himself as he walked down the platform of Templecombe station. "For the next six months or so those children will assail her in public with demands for an improper story!"

Saki (1870–1916) was the pen name of Hector Hugh Munro. He was born in Burma, but spent most of his childhood in England. Best known as a short story writer, Munro was also a satirist and a journalist.

His career as a writer was promising but brief. When World War I began in 1914 he enlisted as a soldier. On the 14th of November, 1916, while stationed in France, he was killed by a sniper.

"The Storyteller" was first published in 1914.

1. ***Response***

a. What are the first lines in the story that suggest "The Storyteller" is meant to be humorous?

b. When and where do you think "The Storyteller" takes place? List some specific words and phrases that help the reader draw conclusions about the setting.

c. The aunt's story is *didactic*—its purpose is to teach a moral lesson. How do the children react to her story? Why?

d. Reflect on your own reading and viewing habits. What kinds of stories do you prefer? Why? What do you think of works whose purpose is to illustrate that virtue and goodness are rewarded?

2. ***Oral Language*** *Group Discussion* Long ago, all stories were spoken aloud to the audience. As a group, discuss where stories are found today and how they are delivered. Which methods of storytelling do you prefer? Explain.

3. ***Literature Studies*** *Principles of Storytelling* Reread "The Storyteller" carefully and create five guidelines for storytelling that the bachelor would accept. Are these guidelines enough, or do you think more are required? Why?

Bluffing

By Gail Helgason

"In the end, Gabriella felt she'd fooled them all. Oh, she'd answered all the questions, but that wasn't the same as telling the whole story."

She reaches for her double-faced pile jacket in the hallway, opens the front door, and runs down the sidewalk as fast as she dares. It's only three blocks to the Jasper hospital. Wind-driven rivers of ice have formed on the hospital steps and Gabriella almost loses her footing. She grips the railing. She wonders what her grade ten students would think if they could see her, clutching the rail, as if the slightest breeze could blow her down.

Inside the hospital, equilibrium returns. The tiled floor feels cold, even through her vibram soles. The hospital is modern and all on one level. The corridors are eggshell white, full of promise, Gabriella thinks. She would have preferred vomit green. Even the reassuring medicinal smell seems diluted. The scent reminds her of the home-made cleaning solution she prepared at Liam's insistence. She used the mixture for a week, until she noticed that it took twice as long to remove grime as the concentrate she bought at the janitorial supply store. Liam hadn't noticed that she'd stopped using it.

The nurse at the station nods to Gabriella. "It will just be a few minutes," she says. "Won't you have a seat?" She can't be more than twenty-two, thinks Gabriella, three years younger than she is. She sinks into the vinyl couch. Only three weeks since the accident, and it seems as if she's been waiting forever.

On that morning three weeks ago, a light frost had silvered the club-moss along the trail. Ahead, the plum-coloured peaks of the Maligne Range cut razor-sharp silhouettes against the sky. Gabriella noticed how Liam's thick black hair was cut as fashionably as ever, unusual for a climber, although his face appeared lined and travel-worn.

Gabriella hadn't proposed the hike until the night before. She'd called it "one last outing before the snow comes." She didn't want to let on that it might mean anything much to her. At the lake, she planned to bring up the subject of the lease. The landlord said he'd have to know by October 31 if they would sign for a year. Housing was so tight in Jasper; he had at least three people who would take the house sight unseen. Would they sign the lease or not? He always speaks to her about these matters, not Liam.

The morning sky began to cream with cumulus clouds. Below, in the valley, the dark greens of white spruce and tarnished golds of the poplars wove an intricate montane tartan.

Liam stayed in the lead. At times, Gabriella had to run, the way her students sometimes did to keep up with her on field trips to nearby bogs and meadows. But she didn't mind Liam's pace. She sensed a special energy to the day. They'd be able to firm things up at the lake, the way they never could in town, knocking elbows, rushing about. She couldn't take the uncertainty much longer, now that Liam was talking about going off again for the winter, and she couldn't afford to keep the house herself. She thought that signing a one-year lease demanded a certain courage, a certain faith that the earth will keep holding them up, a certain commitment. She planned to introduce the subject in this way, as a challenge.

"Should get the lake all to ourselves," Liam said.

His boots left the partial prints of an expensive trademark on the soft loamy trail. His jacket was new, too. He spent most of his money on outdoor gear—the little he made guiding American and German tourists up easy climbs in the Rockies. Liam liked to joke that one day he would have his photo in glossy magazines for high-tech outdoor gear. Prestigious companies would seek his endorsement. He always laughed when he said this, but there was a steel edge to his voice. He really believed it. She thought he was getting a little long in the tooth for this kind of fantasy.

When they were half-way to the lake, they stopped for a short break on a fallen log. They heard a man's laughter from somewhere below. Liam turned to Gabriella, his eyes vigilant. She had seen that expression once before, when Clive, one of the other mountain guides in the town, asked Liam if the rumours were true. Had he almost lost his nerve on Mt. Robson last year, when he realized the American climber he was guiding couldn't set up a belay that gave Liam adequate protection? Liam told Clive to go to hell. But Liam was secretly jealous of Clive. Liam has never been asked to join a big expedition; Clive was invited to Mt. McKinley last year.

"I'll handle it," Liam whispered.

Two young men approached. They looked to be in their late teens or early twenties. They took big elastic steps, as if springs were attached to the soles of their boots. Grey jays emitted staccato cries into the spruce air.

"Planning on going up to the lake?" Liam asked.

"You bet," one of them replied.

"Might not be such a good idea," Liam said, his voice thick with sympathy. "We're turning back ourselves. Came across an elk carcass by the lake. Some grizzly had himself a dandy breakfast."

"Grizzly, eh?" said the hiker. "Sure it was a grizzly?"

"Can't mistake those long front claws," Liam said. "They usually come back to the kill, you know."

"Guess you're right. Doesn't sound like a great place to be."

The pair turned around on the trail; the spring was missing from their step. When they were out of sight, Liam and Gabriella continued on to the lake. The grey jays had stopped shrieking.

Gabriella hears footsteps in the hospital corridor and looks up from a *Canadian Living* magazine to see the young nurse coming out of Liam's room.

"He's sleeping but I'll wake him in a minute," she says. Gabriella thinks she catches a quizzical look on her face. The nurse seems to be weighing whether to say anything more, then shows her straight teeth in a smile. "He really wants you to be here today, doesn't he?"

Gabriella nods. She doesn't know what to say. The nurse leaves her and pads down the corridor. Gabriella draws her legs under her. Her feet still feel icy.

Tell us what happened, the strangers said, pressing in on her with their uniforms, badges, khaki jackets, and pressed pants. All of them urged her to tell. "To aid in our understanding of how these attacks occur," said one warden, a safety specialist, with a smooth chin and a particularly insistent manner.

In the end, Gabriella felt she'd fooled them all. Oh, she'd answered all the questions, but that wasn't the same as telling the whole story. How could she, when it still wasn't clear?

Gabriella watches as a merlin alights on a bare branch outside the window. Odd that he'd get so close. Then she sees the streaky yellow plumage. Just a baby. He thinks the world is a nurturing place.

Where is that nurse?

Gabriella looks again at the merlin and remembers how she taught Liam to spot wildlife. He said he hadn't really taken much notice up till then, his eyes were always on the peaks. But he wanted to know more. This was after they'd moved in together, before he'd gone off to Leavenworth with Clive for two weeks' climbing that turned into six weeks.

She and Liam had been looking for wildlife up on the Pyramid Bench. Liam couldn't see anything. Gabriella said the problem was that he was trying to focus on a single object. Instead, he should try to soften his eyes and take in the entire horizon. Liam tried this. He wasn't always willing to learn from people who might know more than he did, but she hoped he'd recognize her authority here. After all, she was the biology teacher.

They crouched behind a stand of young spruce. In a few minutes, they observed movement at the edge of the forest: a cow moose, holding her head high, ears up instead of out.

"Means she senses danger," Gabriella said. "She probably has a calf around here. Better freeze. The worst thing to do would be to run."

They both froze. Afterwards, Liam said he'd learned a lot being out with her. It opened his eyes, he said.

At noon, Gabriella and Liam reached the lake. She found a rock of flat limestone along the shore and they spread their foam pads to sit on. Liam dug into his pack and pulled out a small bottle of Remy Martin, French bread, a wedge of Camembert, and chocolate-covered almonds.

She felt a small rush of pleasure. He never lost the ability to surprise her, sometimes through astonishing small deceits, sometimes through extravagant gestures. In a way he reminded her of the plants and animals she so loved teaching her students about: organized, coded, identifiable as a type, but ultimately unknowable. Gabriella decided not to mention the foil-wrapped egg sandwiches in her day pack; she wouldn't dream of spoiling his surprise.

"To celebrate," Liam said. He didn't say right away what they would be celebrating, but Gabriella took this as an encouraging sign. She planned to mention the lease after lunch. She imagined winter nights with Liam hunkered over topographical maps at the yellow kitchen table. Only this time, she saw him studying places they could explore together, high meadows and alpine lakes. She smiled up at him.

"Clive and I worked it out last week," Liam said. He shook his crop of black hair and his voice pranced. "If we pool our resources, live in his old van, we've got just enough to get by for three months over the winter. So we're gonna head down south."

The words hit Gabriella like small, sharp rocks.

"I've had enough of this limestone," Liam continued. "Three months of good, technical rock—I'm talking Yosemite, maybe New

Mexico—is gonna make all the difference for me."

Gabriella grabbed for her pack and pushed herself off the rock. She strode as fast as she could without running. She didn't care where. Once she looked back. Liam was following her. Let him hoof it a little, she thought. She willed herself to walk fast and stay angry, because she didn't want to think about what might happen to her if she relented one more time. Maybe there would be nothing left of her except endurance, maybe all her other strengths would be sucked away. She'd seen it happen.

The sandy shore of the lake ended and Gabriella crashed through a thick stand of dwarf birch and rock willows. A twig snapped and cut into her cheek. She hauled herself through one last bush to the end of the lake, where the willows gave way to huckleberries.

The grizzly sow stood twenty paces ahead. The bear's hump and dished-in face were unmistakable. There was not a climbing tree within reach.

In that instant, every cell in Gabriella's body yearned to turn and flee. But some inner force held her, a force she'd never before sensed.

Gabriella dropped her eyes from the bear's stare and slumped her body forwards. She noticed how scuffed her boots were. She knew that if she retreated too quickly, the bear could be on her like a cat on a wounded bumblebee. She tried moving one foot back. The bear stepped forwards a foot or two. Gabriella froze. The bear stopped.

Behind her, she heard rustling in the shrubbery, and then Liam's voice. "Geez," he said.

It took all her willpower to stay where she was. "Try backing off slowly," she said. "Bluff him, remember?"

And now, as Gabriella sits on the hospital couch, the part that was missing comes back. How she waited to hear Liam take one or two cautious steps backwards. How instead, after one long minute, she heard the rustle of footsteps through shrubbery. Liam wasn't just stepping back. He was running away as fast as he could.

Gabriella hit the ground as the bear lunged forwards. She intertwined her fingers behind her neck, legs drawn up over her vitals. But even as her forehead pressed against the gravelly earth, she felt the powerful sweep of the bear hurtling past. It was giving full chase.

The nurse is back. She bends down to Gabriella.

"He'll be counting on your reaction," she says. "Are you sure you feel up to it?"

Gabriella nods, but as she is ushered into Liam's private room, she is no longer so sure. He sits propped up in bed beside a table brimming with gladioli, carnations, cards from the climbing team. He looks a bit like pictures she has seen of mummified Egyptian princes. Bandages wind round his scalp, over his cheeks and forehead and chin. Only his blue eyes, nostrils, and mouth are visible.

What was it the doctor had told her after they airlifted him to the hospital? "No damage to the vital organs, that's the main thing." Then he'd listed the injuries. Gabriella had to bite down on her fist to keep from screaming.

"Gabriella," Liam whispers. She goes to his side. Broad beams of light penetrate the room from the west window and hurt her eyes.

"I'm here," she says. She places her palm lightly over one of his bandaged hands.

"I'm glad." Liam stares at her unflinchingly. "I thought you'd be here before this."

"I've been here every day for the last three weeks," Gabriella says. "You've been sleeping most of the time. It's just hard for you to remember."

"You know I wasn't trying to run away up there," Liam says. "You know that?"

"Of course."

"I meant the bear to come after me instead of you," he says.

Gabriella's mouth feels dry. She looks at her outstretched fingers, the irregular roof her knuckles and joints form over Liam's bandaged hand. She wonders if she could move her hand if she tries. For a moment, she hears Clive's accusing voice and the bear's low grunt.

The doctor sweeps into the room and the nurse announces that they are ready to begin. The nurse starts to snip at the facial bandage. Liam's forehead emerges, what is left of his eyebrows, just shadowy lines really, then his cheeks and chin. Beneath the bandages, the skin is all puffed up, mottled, with ridges of shiny, rubbery scar tissue criss-crossing like tributaries on a map. Gabriella's eyes linger on her feet.

When the last bandage is removed, she pulls her chair closer to the bed and stretches her lips into a smile. She knows in her bones that she can manage this way, for the rest of the afternoon, at least. She still has that much bluffing left in her.

Gail Helgason lives in Edmonton.
Her short story collection, *Fracture Patterns,* was shortlisted in 1996 for both the Writers Guild of Alberta Best First Book Award, and the City of Edmonton Book Prize.

1. ***Response***

   a. In the first three paragraphs of the story, what concrete information did you learn about Gabriella? At that point, what inferences were you able to draw about the relationship between her and Liam?

   b. What was your first impression of Liam? What process did you use to arrive at this impression? Do you think this is the same process that people use in everyday life when they meet someone new?

   c. Explain how the title of the story is important to an understanding of the final scene between Gabriella and Liam.

   d. "Bluffing" focusses on a conflict between two characters. What is the essential conflict? In your view, does the story present the conflict neutrally? Explain.

2. ***Literature Studies*** *Foreshadowing* Reread the story and identify specific lines that **foreshadow** some aspect of the story's conclusion. Find further examples of foreshadowing in this unit and compare these stories.

Foreshadowing is a plot technique in which a writer plants clues or subtle indications about events that will happen later in the narrative.

3. ***Language Conventions*** *Verb Tenses* What two main verb tenses does the author, Gail Helgason, use to tell her story? In a group, discuss why verb tense is an important part of the story's structure. Compare Helgason's use of verb tense with Coakley's in "Mirror Image." What are some of the advantages and disadvantages of each approach?

4. ***Research and Inquiry*** Working in a group, use the Internet and other resources to learn more about encounters between grizzlies and humans. Begin by brainstorming at least five questions you would like to answer. When you have gathered the required information, present your findings to the class. Are the findings of the various groups consistent, or are there obvious differences? Explain how your own group determined the reliability of the resources you accessed.

The Labrador Fiasco

By Margaret Atwood

**"We left behind ...
one by one our civilized
distinctions**

and entered a large darkness.

**It was our own
ignorance we entered."**
MARGARET ATWOOD, from
The Journals of Susanna Moodie

It's October, but which October? One of those Octobers with their quick intensities of light, their diminuendos, their red and orange leaves. My father is sitting in his armchair by the fire. He has on his black-and-white-checked dressing gown, over his other clothes, and his old leather slippers, with his feet propped up on a hassock. Therefore it must be evening.

My mother is reading to him. She fiddles with her glasses, and hunches over the page; or it looks like hunching. In fact, that is just the shape she is now.

My father is grinning, so this must be a part he enjoys. His grin is higher on the left side than on the right: six years ago he had a stroke, which we all pretend he's recovered from; and he has, mostly.

"What's happening now?" I say, taking off my coat. I already know the story, having heard it before.

"They've just set out," says my mother.

My father says, "They took the wrong supplies." This pleases him: he himself would not have taken the wrong supplies. In fact, he would never have gone on this ill-advised journey in the first place, or—although he was once more reckless, more impetuous, more sure of his ability to confront fate and transcend danger—this is his opinion now. "Darn fools," he says, grinning away.

But what supplies could they have taken, other than the wrong ones? White sugar, white flour, rice; that was what you took then. Peameal, sulphured apples, hardtack, bacon, lard. Heavy things. There was no freeze-drying then, no handy packaged soups; there were no nylon vests, no pocket-sized sleeping bags, no light-weight tarpaulins. Their tent was made of balloon silk, oiled to waterproof it. Their blankets were of wool. The packsacks were canvas, with leather straps and tumplines that went across the forehead to cut the strain on the back. They would have smelled of tar. In addition there were two rifles, two pistols, 1,200 rounds of ammunition, a camera, and a sextant; and then the cooking utensils and the clothing. Every pound of it had to be carried over each and every portage, or hauled upriver in the canoe, which was eighteen feet long, wood-framed, and canvas-covered.

None of this would have daunted the adventurers, however; or not at first. There were two of them, two young Americans; they'd been on camping expeditions before, although at warmer latitudes, with fragrant evening pipes smoked before cheerful blazes and a fresh-caught trout sizzling in the pan while the sunsets paled in the west. Each would have been able to turn a neat, Kiplingesque[1] paragraph or two on the lure of wild places, the challenge of the unknown. This was in 1903, when exploration was still in vogue as a test of manliness, and when manliness itself was still in vogue and was thought to couple naturally with the word *clean*. Manliness, cleanliness, the wilderness, where you could feel free. With gun and fishing rod, of course. You could live off the land.

The leader of the expedition, whose name was Hubbard, worked for a magazine dedicated to the outdoors. His idea was that he and his chum and cousin—whose name was Wallace—would penetrate the last unmapped Labrador wilds, and he would write a series of articles about their adventures, and thus make his name. (These were his very words: "I will make my name.") Specifically, they would ascend the Nascaupee River, said to flow out of Lake Michikamau, a fabled inland lake teeming with fish; from there they could make it to the George River, where the Indians congregated every summer for the caribou hunt, and from there to a Hudson's Bay post and out to the coast again. While among the Indians, Hubbard planned to do a little amateur anthropology, which he would also write up, with photographs—a shaggy-haired hunter with an old-fashioned rifle, his foot on a carcass; a cut-off head with spreading antlers; women with bead necklaces and gleaming eyes chewing the hide, or sewing it, or whatever they did.

[1]**Kiplingesque:** in the style of Rudyard Kipling, British writer

The Last Wild People. Something like that. There was a great interest in such subjects. He would describe the menus, too.

(But those Indians came from the north. No one ever took the river route from the west and south.)

In stories like this, there is always—there is supposed to be—an old Indian who appears to the white men as they are planning to set out. He comes to warn them, because he is kind at heart and they are ignorant. "Do not go there," he says. "That is a place we never go." Indians in these tales have a formal manner of speaking.

"Why not?" the white men say.

"Bad spirits live there," says the old Indian. The white men smile and thank him, and disregard his advice. Native superstition, they think. So they go where they've been warned not to, and then, after many hardships, they die. The old Indian shakes his head when he hears of it. Foolish white men, but what can you tell them? They have no respect.

There's no old Indian in this book—he somehow got left out—so my father takes the part upon himself. "They shouldn't have gone there," he says. "The Indians never went that way." He doesn't say *bad spirits*, however. He says, "Nothing to eat." For the Indians it would have been the same thing, because where does food come from if not from the spirits? It isn't just there, it is given; or else withheld.

Hubbard and Wallace tried to hire several Indians to come with them, at least on the first stages of the journey, and to help with the packs. None would go; they said they were "too busy." Really they knew too much. What they knew was that you couldn't possibly carry with you, in there, everything you would need to eat. And if you couldn't carry it, you would have to kill it. But most of the time there was nothing to kill. "Too busy" meant too busy to die. It also meant too polite to point out the obvious.

The two explorers did do one thing right. They hired a guide. His name was George, and he was a Cree Indian, or partly; what they called then a breed. He was from James Bay, too far away from Labrador to know the full and evil truth about it. George travelled south to meet his employers, all the way to New York City, where he had never been before. He had never been to the United States before, or even to a city. He kept calm; he looked about him; he demonstrated his resourcefulness by figuring out what a taxicab was and how to hire one. His ability to reason things through was to come in very handy later on.

"That George was quite a boy," says my father. George is his favourite person in the whole story.

Somewhere around the house there's a picture of my father himself

—at the back of a photo album, perhaps, with the snapshots that haven't yet been stuck in. It shows him thirty years younger, on some canoe trip or another—if you don't write these things down on the backs of the pictures, they get forgotten. He's evidently crossing a portage. He hasn't shaved, he's got a bandana tied around his head because of the blackflies and mosquitoes, and he's carrying a heavy pack, with the broad tumpline across his forehead. His hair is dark, his glistening face is deeply tanned and not what you'd call clean. He looks slightly villainous—like a pirate, or indeed like a northwoods guide, the kind who might suddenly vanish in the middle of the night, along with your best rifle, just before the wolves arrive on the scene. But like someone who knows what he's doing.

"That George knew what he was doing," says my father now.

Once he got out of New York, that is; while there, George wasn't much help, because he didn't know where to shop. It was in New York that the two men bought all the necessary supplies, except a gill net, which they thought they could find up north. They also failed to purchase extra moccasins. This may have been their worst mistake.

Then they set out, by train and then by boat and then by smaller boat. The details are tedious. The weather was bad, the meals were foul, none of the transportation was ever on time. They spent a lot of hours, and even days, waiting around on docks and wondering when their luggage would turn up.

"That's enough for tonight," says my mother.

"I think he's asleep," I say.

"He never used to go to sleep," says my mother. "Not with this story. Usually he's busy making up his list."

"His list?"

"His list of what he would take."

While my father sleeps, I skip ahead in the story. The three men have finally made it inland from the bleak northeastern shore of Labrador, and have left their last jumping-off place, and are voyaging in earnest.

It's the middle of July, but the short summer will soon be over, and they have five hundred miles to go.

Their task is to navigate Grand Lake, which is long and thin; at its extreme end, or so they've been told, the Nascaupee flows into it. The only map they've seen, crudely drawn by an earlier white traveller some fifty years before, shows Grand Lake with only one river emptying into it. One is all the Indians have ever mentioned: the one that goes somewhere. Why talk about the others, because why would anyone want to know about them? There are many plants that have no names because they cannot be eaten or used.

But in fact there are four other rivers.

During this first morning they are exhilarated, or so Wallace records. Their hopes are high, adventure calls. The sky is deep blue, the air is crisp, the sun is bright, the treetops seem to beckon them on. They do not know enough to beware of beckoning treetops. For lunch they have flapjacks and syrup, and are filled with a sense of well-being. They know they're going into danger, but they also know that they are immortal. Such moods do occur, in the North. They take pictures with their camera: of their laden canoe; of one another—moustached, be-sweatered, with puttee-shaped wrappings on their legs and things on their heads that look like bowler hats—leaning blithely on their paddles. Heartbreaking, but only when you know the end. As it is they're having the time of their lives.

There's another photo of my father, perhaps from the same trip as the one with the portage; or he's wearing the same bandana. This time he's grinning into the camera lens, pretending to shave himself with his axe. Two tall-tale points are being made: that his axe is as sharp as a razor, and that his bristles are so tough that only an axe could cut them. It's highjinks, a canoe-trip joke; although secretly, of course, he once believed both of these things.

On the second day the three men pass the mouth of the Nascaupee, which is hidden behind an island and looks like shoreline. They don't even suspect it is there. They continue on to the end of the lake, and enter the river they find there. They've taken the wrong turn.

I don't get back to Labrador for more than a week. When I return, it's a Sunday night. The fire is blazing away and my father is sitting in front of it, waiting to see what will happen next. My mother is rustling up the baking-powder biscuits and the decaffeinated tea. I forage for cookies.

"How is everything?" I say.

"Fine," she says. "But he doesn't get enough exercise." *Everything* means my father, as far as she is concerned.

"You should make him go for a walk," I say.

"*Make* him," she says.

"Well, suggest."

"He doesn't see the point of walking just to walk," she says. "If you're not going anywhere."

"You could send him on errands," I say. To this she does not bother even to reply.

"He says his feet hurt," she says. I think of the array of almost-new boots and shoes in the cupboard; boots and shoes that have proliferated lately. He keeps buying other ones. If only he can find the right pair, he must think, whatever it is that's causing his feet to hurt will go away.

I carry in the teacups, dole out the plates. "So, how are Hubbard and Wallace coming along?" I say. "Have you got to the place where they eat the owl?"

"Slim pickings," he says. "They took the wrong river. Even if they'd found the right one, it was too late to start."

Hubbard and Wallace and George toil upstream. The heat at midday is oppressive. Flies torment them, little flies like pinpricks, giant ones as big as your thumb. The river is barely navigable: they have to haul their laden canoe over gravel shallows, or portage around rapids, through forest that is harsh and unmarked and jumbled. In front of them the river unrolls; behind them it closes up like a maze. The banks of the river grow steeper; hill after hill, gentle in outline, hard at the core. It's a sparse landscape: ragged spruce, birch, aspen, all spindly; in some places burned over, the way forward blocked by charred and fallen tree trunks.

How long is it before they realize they've gone up the wrong river? Far too long. They cache some of their food so they won't have to carry it; they throw some of it away. They manage to shoot a caribou, which they eat, leaving the hoofs and head behind. Their feet hurt; their moccasins are wearing out.

At last Hubbard climbs a high hill, and from its top he sees Lake Michikamau; but the river they have been following does not go there. The lake is too far away; they can't possibly haul their canoe that far through the forest. They will have to turn back.

In the evening their talk is no longer of discovery and exploration. Instead they talk about what they will eat. What they'll eat tomorrow, and what they'll eat when they get back. They compose bills of fare, feasts, grand blowouts. George is able to shoot or catch this and that. A duck here, a grouse there. A whisky-jack. They catch sixty trout, painstakingly one by one, using a hook and line because they have no gill net. The trout are clear and fresh as icewater, but only six inches long. Nothing is nearly enough. The work of travelling uses up more energy than they can take in; they are slowly dissolving, wasting away.

> The answers you get from literature depend on the questions you pose.
>
> Hannah Arendt

Meanwhile, the nights become longer and longer and darker and darker. Ice forms on the edges of the river. Hauling the canoe over the shallows, through the rushing, stone cold water, leaves them shivering and gasping. The first snowflurries fall.

"It's rough country," says my father. "No moose; not even bears. That's always a bad sign, no bears." He's been there, or near it; same sort of terrain. He speaks of it with admiration and nostalgia, and a kind of ruefulness. "Now, of course, you can fly in. You can cover their whole route in a couple of hours." He waves his fingers dismissively. So much for planes.

"What about the owl?" I say.

"What owl?" says my father.

"The one they ate," I say. "I think it's where the canoe dumps, and they save their matches by sticking them in their ears."

"I think that was the others," says my father. "The ones who tried the same thing later. I don't think this bunch ate an owl."

"If they had eaten one, what sort of owl would it have been?" I say.

"Great horned or boreal," he says, "if they were lucky. More meat on those. But it may have been something smaller." He gives a series of thin, eerie barks, like a dog at a distance, and then he grins. He knows every bird up there by its call; he still does.

"He's sleeping too much in the afternoons," says my mother.

"Maybe he's tired," I say.

"He shouldn't be that tired," she says. "Tired, and restless as well. He's losing his appetite."

"Maybe he needs a hobby," I say. "Something to occupy his mind."

"He used to have a lot of them," my mother says.

I wonder where they've all gone, those hobbies. Their tools and materials are still around: the plane and the spirit level, the feathers for tying dry flies, the machine for enlarging prints, the points for making arrows. These bits and pieces seem to me like artifacts, the kind that are dug up at archaeological sites, and then pondered over and classified, and used for deducing the kind of life once lived.

"He used to say he wanted to write his memoirs," says my mother. "A sort of account; all the places he's been. He did begin it several times, but now he's lost interest. He can't see too well."

"He could use a tape recorder," I say.

"Oh, help," says my mother. "More gadgets!"

The winds howl and cease, the snow falls and stops falling. The three men have traversed across to a different river, hoping it will be better, but it isn't. One night George has a dream: God appears to him, shining and bright and affable, and speaks in a manner that is friendly but firm. "I can't spare any more of these trout," he says, "but if you stick to this river you'll get down to Grand Lake all right. Just you don't leave the river, and I'll get you out safe."

George tells the others of his dream. It is discounted. The men abandon their canoe and strike out overland, hoping to reach their old trail. After far too long they do reach it, and stumble along it down the valley of the river they first ascended, rummaging through their former campsites for any food they might have thrown away. They aren't counting in miles, but in days; how many days they have left, and how many it will take. But that will depend on the weather, and on their own strength; how fast they can go. They find a lump of mouldering flour, a bit of lard, a few bones, some caribou hoofs, which they boil. A little tin of dry mustard; they mix it into the soup, and find it encouraging.

In the third week of October, this is how things stand:

Hubbard has become too weak to go any farther. He's been left behind, wrapped in his blankets, in the tent, with a fire going. The other two have gone on; they hope to walk out, then send help back for him. He's given them the last of the peameal.

The snow is falling. For dinner he has some strong tea and bone broth, and some boiled rawhide, made from the last of his moccasins; he writes in his journal that it is truly delicious. Now he is without footgear. He has every hope that the others will succeed, and will return and save him; or so he records. Nevertheless, he begins a farewell message for his wife. He writes that he has a pair of cowhide mittens that he is looking forward to cooking and eating the next day.

After that he goes to sleep, and after that he dies.

Some days farther down the trail, Wallace too has to give up. He and George part company: Wallace intends to go back with the latest leavings they've managed to locate—a few handfuls of mouldy flour. He will find Hubbard, and together they will await rescue. But he's been caught in a blizzard, and has lost his bearings; at the moment he's in a shelter made of branches, waiting for the snow to let up. He is amazingly weak, and no longer hungry, which he knows is a bad sign. Every movement he makes is slow and deliberate, and at the same time unreal, as if his body is apart from him and he is only watching it. In the white light of day or the red flicker of the fire—for he still has fire—the patterns on the ends of his own fingers appear miraculous to him. Such clarity and detail; he follows the pattern of the woven blanket as if tracing a map.

His dead wife has appeared to him, and has given him several pieces of practical advice concerning his sleeping arrangement: a thicker layer of spruce boughs underneath, she's said, would be more comfortable. Sometimes he only hears her; sometimes he sees her as well. She's wearing a blue summer dress, her long hair pinned up in a shining coil. She appears perfectly at home; the poles of the shelter are visible through her back. Wallace has ceased to be surprised by this.

Even farther along, George continues to walk; to walk out. He knows more or less where he's going; he will find help and return with it. But he isn't out yet, he's still in. Snow surrounds him, the blank grey sky enfolds him; at one point he comes across his own tracks and realizes he's been walking in a circle. He too is thin and weak, but he's managed to shoot a porcupine. He pauses to think it through: he could turn around, retrace his steps, take the porcupine back to share with the others; or he could eat all of it himself and go forward. He knows that if he goes back it's likely that none of them will get out alive; but if he goes on, there's at least a possibility, at least for him. He goes on, hoarding the bones.

"That George did the right thing," says my father.

While sitting at the dinner table my father has another stroke. This time it knocks out half the vision in each eye, his short-term memory, and his sense of where he is. From one minute to the next, he has become lost; he gropes through the living room as if he's never been in such a place before. The doctors say this time it's unlikely he'll recover.

Time passes. Now the lilacs are in bloom outside the window, and he can see them, or parts of them. Despite this he thinks it's October. Still, the core of him is still there. He sits in his armchair, trying to figure things out. One sofa cushion looks much like another unless you have something to go by. He watches the sunlight gleaming on the hardwood floor; his best guess is that it's a stream. In extreme situations you have to use your wits.

"I'm here," I say, kissing his dry cheek. He hasn't gone bald, not in the least. He has silvery white hair, like an egret frozen.

He peers at me out of the left sides of his eyes, which are the ones that work. "You seem to have become very old all of a sudden," he says.

As far as we can tell, he's missing the last four or five years, and several blocks of time before that as well. He's disappointed in me: not because of anything I've done, but because of what I've failed to do. I've failed to remain young. If I could have managed that, I could have saved him; then he too could have remained as he was.

I wish I could think of something to amuse him. I've tried recordings of bird songs, but he doesn't like them: they remind him that there's something he once knew, but can't remember. Stories are no good, not even short ones, because by the time you get to the second page he's forgotten the beginning. Where are we without our plots?

Music is better; it takes place drop by drop.

My mother doesn't know what to do, and so she rearranges: cups and plates, documents, bureau drawers. Right now she's outside, yanking weeds out of the garden in a bewildered frenzy. Dirt and couch grass fly through the air: that at least will get done! There's a wind; her hair is wild, blown up around her head like feathers.

I've told her I can't stay long. "You can't?" she said. "But we could have tea, I could light a fire … "

"Not today," I said firmly.

He can see her out there, more or less, and he wants her to come back in. He doesn't like it that she's on the other side of the glass. If he lets her slip away, out of his sight, who knows where she might go? She might vanish forever.

I hold his good hand. "She'll come in soon," I say; but *soon* could be a year.

"I want to go home," he says. I know there's no point telling him that home is where he now is, because he means something else. He means the way he was before.

"Where are we now?" I say.

He gives me a crafty look: Am I trying to trip him up? "In a forest," he says. "We need to get back."

"We're all right here," I say.

He considers. "Not much to eat."

"We brought the right supplies," I say.

He is reassured. "But there's not enough wood." He's anxious about this; he says it every day. His feet are cold, he says.

"We can get more wood," I say. "We can cut it."

He's not so sure. "I never thought this would happen," he says. He doesn't mean the stroke, because he doesn't know he's had one. He means getting lost.

"We know what to do," I say. "Anyway, we'll be fine."

"We'll be fine," he says, but he sounds dubious. He doesn't trust me, and he is right. ◗

The story related within this story may be found in its original version in *The Lure of the Labrador Wild*, by Dillon Wallace, published in 1905 by Fleming H. Revell Company and reprinted by Breakwater Books, Newfoundland, in 1977.

Margaret Atwood was born in 1939 in Ottawa, Ontario. She is an internationally acclaimed poet, novelist, story writer, and essayist. "The Labrador Fiasco," published in 1996, incorporates two of her longstanding interests—Canadian history and the Canadian wilderness.

1. ***Response***
   a. In a group, discuss the challenges this story presents to the reader. Together, think of strategies that readers could use to overcome the challenges. Present your ideas to the class.
   b. What do you think the *fiasco* is that's referred to in the title?
   c. Describe the narrator's feelings towards the father and towards the explorers. How do you know?
   d. In your view, what does the narrator mean by the last sentence?

2. ***Research and Inquiry*** One of Margaret Atwood's early works was a book entitled *Survival: A Thematic Guide to Canadian Literature*. Use the Internet and other resources to learn about the main argument Atwood presented in that book and the controversy it caused. What connection do you see between "The Labrador Fiasco" and *Survival?*

3. ***Literature Studies*** *Story Within a Story* "The Labrador Fiasco" contains two stories, one nested inside the other. In a group, determine which is the *frame story*—the story that holds the second story. Why do you think Atwood includes the second story? What are the parallels between the two narratives? Design a visual way (a chart, diagram, or poster, for example) of presenting your conclusions.

4. ***Critical Thinking*** Choose three words that you think best describe nature as it is portrayed in "The Labrador Fiasco." Now choose three words that capture the way nature is portrayed in Judith Currelly's *Travelers.* Give reasons for your interpretations. Which attitude about nature comes closest to your own?

Travelers, Judith Currelly. Oil on wood panel.

How do the details of the painting reflect its title and the theme of undertaking a journey?

Snow

By Ann Beattie

"I know ten ways to move [a story] through time, and my interest is in finding the eleventh. I want to do something that I haven't done before," Ann Beattie claims. What conventions of short story writing does Beattie challenge in "Snow"?

I remember the cold night you brought in a pile of logs and a chipmunk jumped off as you lowered your arms. "What do you think *you're* doing in here?" you said, as it ran through the living room. It went through the library and stopped at the front door as though it knew the house well. This would be difficult for anyone to believe, except perhaps as the subject of a poem. Our first week in the house was spent scraping, finding some of the house's secrets, like wallpaper underneath wallpaper. In the kitchen, a pattern of white-gold trellises supported purple grapes as big and round as Ping-Pong balls. When we painted the walls yellow, I thought of the bits of grape that remained underneath and imagined the vine popping through, the way some plants can tenaciously push through anything. The day of the big snow, when you had to shovel the walk and couldn't find your cap and asked me how to wind a towel so that it would stay on your head—you, in the white towel turban, like a crazy king of snow. People liked the idea of our being together, leaving the city for the country. So many people visited, and the fireplace made all of them want to tell amazing stories: the child who happened to be standing on the right corner when the door of the ice cream truck came open and hundreds of Popsicles crashed out; the man standing on the beach, sand sparkling in the sun, one bit glinting more than the rest, stooping to find a diamond ring. Did they talk about amazing things because they thought we'd turn into one of them? Now I think they probably guessed it wouldn't work. It was as hopeless as giving a child a matched cup and saucer. Remember the night, out on the lawn, knee-deep in snow, chins pointed at the sky as the wind whirled down all that whiteness? It seemed that the world had been turned upside down, and we were looking into an enormous field of Queen Anne's lace. Later, headlights off, our car was the first to ride through the newly fallen snow. The world outside the car looked solarized.

You remember it differently. You remember that the cold settled in stages, that a small curve of light was shaved from the moon night after night, until you were no longer surprised the sky was black, that the chipmunk ran to hide in the dark, not simply to a door that led to its escape. Our visitors told the same stories people always tell. One night, giving me a lesson in storytelling, you said, "Any life will seem dramatic if you omit mention of most of it."

This, then, for drama: I drove back to that house not long ago. It was April, and Allen had died. In spite of all the visitors, Allen, next door, had been the good friend in bad times. I sat with his wife in their living room, looking out the glass doors to the backyard, and there was Allen's pool, still covered with black plastic that had been stretched across it for winter. It had rained, and as the rain fell, the cover collected more and more water until it finally spilled onto the concrete. When I left that day, I drove past what had been our house. Three or four crocus were blooming in the front—just a few dots of white, no field of snow. I felt embarrassed for them. They couldn't compete.

This is a story, told the way you say stories should be told: Somebody grew up, fell in love, and spent a winter with her lover in the country. This, of course, is the barest outline, and futile to discuss. It's as pointless as throwing birdseed on the ground while snow still falls fast. Who expects small things to survive when even the largest get lost? People forget years and remember moments. Seconds and symbols are left to sum things up: the black shroud over the pool. Love, in its shortest form, becomes a word. What I remember about all that time is one winter. The snow. Even now, saying "snow," my lips move so that they kiss the air.

No mention has been made of the snowplow that seemed always to be there, scraping snow off our narrow road—an artery cleared, though neither of us could have said where the heart was.

Ann Beattie was born in 1947 in Washington, D.C. Her novels and short stories have won her critical acclaim and a wide audience.

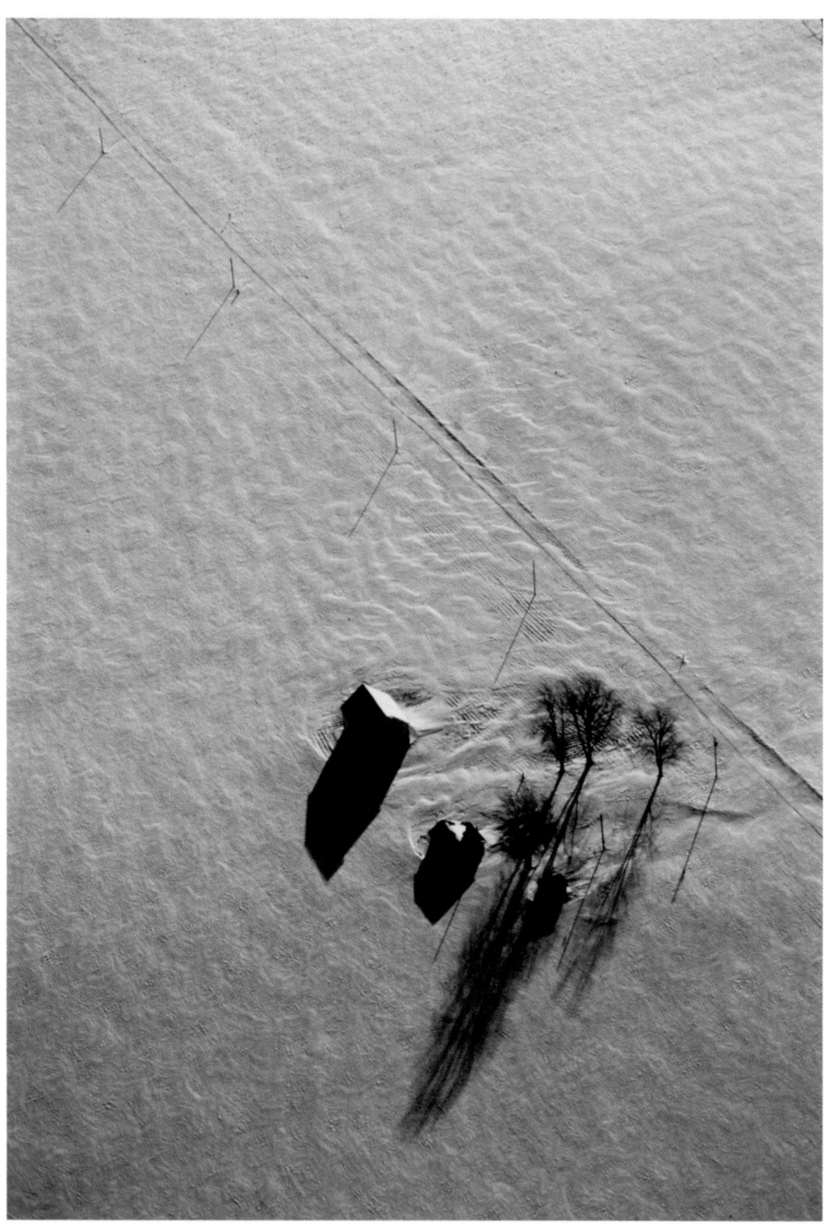

Illinois Farm, Richard Hamilton Smith.

From what position was this photograph taken? What ideas and emotions has this viewpoint helped the photographer to communicate?

1. ***Response***

   a. When you finished the story, did you feel you understood what the author was trying to accomplish? Express your ideas about the author's purpose in two or three statements. Do you have any questions about the work? Write those down, as well.

   b. In a group, try to answer each other's questions about "Snow."

2. ***Literature Studies*** *Short Story Elements* Create a list of the most important elements of a short story (for example, setting, mood). Which elements are strongest in "Snow," and which are weakest? Based on your analysis, would you classify "Snow" as a short story? Why or why not?

3. ***Writing*** *Storytelling* Using *free writing* (writing non-stop for about five minutes), explore the implications of the following statement:

   > "One night, giving me a lesson in storytelling, you said, 'Any life will seem dramatic if you omit mention of most of it.'"

4. ***Media*** *Visual Essay* Create a visual essay from any four consecutive sentences in this story and any combination of magazine illustrations and original artwork. The visuals you choose need not correspond literally to the words. Aim for metaphoric and symbolic correspondences between text and visuals.

"Much later, I discovered that my father was famous in the region because of what the people called his 'gift'..." But it seems that some gifts are impossible to preserve.

A Secret Lost in the Water

By Roch Carrier

Translated from the French by Sheila Fischman

After I started going to school my father scarcely talked any more. I was very intoxicated by the new game of spelling; my father had little skill for it (it was my mother who wrote our letters) and was convinced I was no longer interested in hearing him tell of his adventures during the long weeks when he was far away from the house.

One day, however, he said to me:

"The time's come to show you something."

He asked me to follow him. I walked behind him, not talking, as we had got in the habit of doing. He stopped in the field before a clump of leafy bushes.

"Those are called alders," he said.

"I know."

"You have to learn how to choose," my father pointed out.

I didn't understand. He touched each branch of the bush, one at a time, with religious care.

"You have to choose one that's very fine, a perfect one, like this."

I looked; it seemed exactly like the others.

My father opened his pocket knife and cut the branch he'd selected with pious care. He stripped off the leaves and showed me the branch, which formed a perfect Y.

"You see," he said, "the branch has two arms. Now take one in each hand. And squeeze them."

I did as he asked and took in each hand one fork of the Y, which was thinner than a pencil.

"Close your eyes," my father ordered, "and squeeze a little harder... Don't open your eyes! Do you feel anything?"

"The branch is moving!" I exclaimed, astonished.

Beneath my clenched fingers the alder was wriggling like a small, frightened snake. My father saw that I was about to drop it.

"Hang on to it!"

"The branch is squirming," I repeated. "And I hear something that sounds like a river!"

"Open your eyes," my father ordered.

I was stunned, as though he'd awakened me while I was dreaming.

"What does it mean?" I asked my father.

"It means that underneath us, right here, there's a little fresh-water spring. If we dig, we could drink from it. I've just taught you how to find a spring. It's something my own father taught me. It isn't something you learn in school. And it isn't useless: a man can get along without writing and arithmetic, but he can never get along without water."

Much later, I discovered that my father was famous in the region because of what the people called his 'gift': before digging a well they always consulted him; they would watch him prospecting the fields or the hills, eyes closed, hands clenched on the fork of an alder bough. Wherever my father stopped, they marked the ground; there they would dig; and from there water would gush forth.

Years passed; I went to other schools, saw other countries, I had children, I wrote some books and my poor father is lying in the earth where so many times he had found fresh water.

One day someone began to make a film about my village and its inhabitants, from whom I've stolen so many of the stories that I tell. With the film crew we went to see a farmer to capture the image of a sad man: his children didn't want to receive the inheritance he'd spent his whole life preparing for them—the finest farm in the area. While the technicians were getting cameras and microphones ready the farmer put his arm around my shoulders, saying:

"I knew your father well."

"Ah! I know. Everybody in the village knows each other ... No one feels like an outsider."

"You know what's under your feet?"

"Hell?" I asked, laughing.

"Under your feet there's a well. Before I dug I called in specialists from the Department of Agriculture; they did research, they analyzed shovelfuls of dirt; and they made a report where they said there wasn't any water on my land. With the family, the animals, the crops, I need water. When I saw that those specialists hadn't found any I thought of your father and I asked him to come over. He didn't want to; I think he

> There is creative reading as well as creative writing.
>
> Ralph Waldo Emerson

was pretty fed up with me because I'd asked those specialists instead of him. But finally he came; he went and cut off a little branch, then he walked around for a while with his eyes shut; he stopped, he listened to something we couldn't hear and then he said to me: 'Dig right here, there's enough water to get your whole flock drunk and drown your specialists besides.' We dug and found water. Fine water that's never heard of pollution."

The film people were ready; they called to me to take my place.

"I'm gonna show you something," said the farmer, keeping me back. "You wait right here."

He disappeared into a shack which he must have used to store things, then came back with a branch which he held out to me.

"I never throw nothing away; I kept the alder branch your father cut to find my water. I don't understand, it hasn't dried out."

Moved as I touched the branch, kept out of I don't know what sense of piety—and which really wasn't dry—I had the feeling that my father was watching me over my shoulder; I closed my eyes and, standing above the spring my father had discovered, I waited for the branch to writhe, I hoped the sound of gushing water would rise to my ears.

The alder stayed motionless in my hands and the water beneath the earth refused to sing.

Somewhere along the roads I'd taken since the village of my childhood I had forgotten my father's knowledge.

"Don't feel sorry," said the man, thinking no doubt of his farm and his childhood; "nowadays fathers can't pass on anything to the next generation."

And he took the alder branch from my hands.

French-Canadian writer **Roch Carrier** was born in Québec in 1937. His novels, plays, and short stories are popular with readers and critics alike. "A Secret Lost in the Water" first appeared in Carrier's *The Hockey Sweater and Other Stories* (1979). In 1999, he was appointed to the prestigious position of Canada's National Librarian.

1. ***Response***

   a. Describe the relationship the narrator has with his father. Use a chart to show how the narrator and his father are similar, but also different.

   b. What point do you think the author, Roch Carrier, is making about the connections between fathers and sons? Do you agree or disagree with Carrier? Explain.

   c. Find at least three pieces of evidence to suggest that the narrator regrets that he has lost the secret his father gave him. Now find three details that suggest the narrator is happy with the decision he made about becoming a writer. What do you think Carrier might be saying in his short story?

   d. Suggest reasons why the first person point of view can help to make a work of fiction read like a true story. Have you ever used that technique in your own writing to make a story seem authentic?

2. ***Oral Language*** *Opening Statement* Prepare an opening statement for a debate on whether or not the son should have been more careful about preserving the secret his father imparted to him. In your statement, you should indicate where your sympathies lie: with the father and the farmer, or with the narrator. Be prepared to present your statement to the class.

3. ***Making Connections*** In a small group, explore the meaning of the term *self-discovery*. In what ways are "Mirror Image" and "A Secret Lost in the Water" both about self-discovery? Discuss whether the two stories have much in common. Create a list of other works (stories, novels, movies, and so on) that deal with self-discovery. Do these works feature similar conflicts or story lines? Explain.

Sometimes a new perspective on life is only an impulse away...

The Pose

By Anwer Khan

Translated by Muhammad Umar Memon

Who knows what got into her head. She abruptly broke her stride and slipped into Shandar Cloth Store. Then she opened the door of the show window and, deftly, removing the lovely mannequin, stood herself in the plastic dummy's place and assumed its pose.

It was evening. The street was packed with people, but they were so preoccupied as they went their way that none of them noticed what she had just done.

Why did she do it? She probably didn't know that herself. True, she was something of a daredevil in her childhood. But now she was a grown young woman, a college student, smart, sophisticated, urbane. Even the most daring boys at the college got cold feet walking with her. What she'd just done, well, it just happened. It was entirely unpremeditated.

Standing in the show window she felt a strange sense of comfort wash upon her. She was now, after all, a part of this bustling marketplace. She could also look closely at the place, the whole of it, standing in just one spot, without having to move. Walking as one of the crowd or while shopping, she never felt herself a part of the life around her—the buoyant, strident life, full of vigour and excitement.

Her tense body gradually became unstrung, and an unprovoked smile came to her lips. She quite liked it—standing with one foot slightly forward, the hem of her sari going over her head and then dropping down to wrap itself around the joint of her right elbow. She looked positively ravishing. She could stand in her new posture forever, she thought, overcome by a sudden impulse, although her knees had already begun to ache from the pressure.

She was just considering easing up on her heels a little when her eyes caught sight of a peasant who suddenly cut through the crowd on the sidewalk and came over to the show window and began gawking at her with eyes at once full of lust and wonder. His eyes seemed to say: Incredible! These craftsmen can be so skilful! How they make statues that look like real people!

It was good the glass panel stood between them, otherwise the country bumpkin would certainly have ventured to touch her.

The peasant perhaps wanted to linger on for a while, but the scouring glances of the passersby forced him to move on. As soon as he had moved away, she relaxed her feet a little. Even shook them a bit. But now her lips began to feel dry. "Just a little while longer," she told her lips under her breath, "and then I'll take you to a restaurant and treat you to a glass of ice water, followed by a steaming cup of some finely brewed tea." Her thirst let up a bit and she slipped back into her former pose.

She certainly had no wish to exhibit herself like this to the pedestrians. Perhaps the thought had never even entered her mind. Rather, it pleased her to think that she was now a full participant in the teeming life around her. It was a strange feeling. She had never experienced it before.

"Oh!"—the expression came from the lips of two college girls—"how lifelike!"

Their voices, travelling along the glass panels and filtering through the holes in the steel strips holding the frame, came upon her softly, as if from a great distance.

The two girls gawked at her with admiration as they exchanged a few words among themselves, while she looked at them with tenderness. She was happy. Incredibly happy. No one had looked at her so appreciatively before. At least not in her presence. Like a kind and caring queen receiving the adulation of her subjects, she sustained her regal pose until the girls had once again melted into the crowd and disappeared from view.

"Let's see who comes next?" she thought to herself.

Her feet had again started to protest. This time around, though, she sent them a warning, a rather stern one: Scoundrels, stay put! Can't you wait even a little? She wouldn't care a hoot about their protest, she decided.

She was still congratulating herself on her firmness when she caught sight of a cop who had just separated from the crowd and after taking a pinch of chewing tobacco from a box he held was rubbing it with his thumb. The moment he saw her, his hand stopped dead, his mouth fell open, and his eyes widened. She stared at the cop sweetly. The cop's eyelashes began to flap frantically; he rubbed the tobacco hastily and stuffing it between his lower lip and tooth practically stuck his eyes against the glass of the show window.

She was overcome by a powerful urge to laugh, but managed to stop herself with the greatest difficulty. Suddenly her feet began to itch uncontrollably. There was even a slight, involuntary tremble. But the cop thought it was a mere illusion, or the effect of the tobacco.

The cop stared at her for a long time. He would withdraw a little, then come back and inspect her closely. This went on for so long that she began to tire. Is the idiot going to leave the place at all?—she wondered. She was feeling uncomfortable. She knew she couldn't go on standing in that pose. All the same, she also knew that she was safe inside the show window. Where would she find such protection outside?

Thank God the cop finally decided to leave, and she drew a breath of relief, loosened her hands and feet, straightened up her tense back, indeed even massaged it a bit. Night was approaching and the crowd had thinned down to a few swift-footed pedestrians.

Soon it will grow dark, she thought. She'd better get out of here while there was still some light. The cloth store must be emptying out. Somebody might see her getting out of the show window. She'd have to be very careful ... and fast. And yet there was such comfort inside the show window! How she wallowed in that pleasure! Another ten minutes? Why not ...

She was still mulling over this when she spotted her girlfriend Sheyama on the sidewalk. Right away she sprang into her former pose and held her breath. Sheyama threw an inattentive look in her direction and because her thoughts were elsewhere, the danger, luckily, was averted. The thought that some of her acquaintances might spot her here had not occurred to her until Sheyama came along. This was precisely the time when her older brother returned from work, she recalled with horror. He's already suffering from a heart ailment. What if he saw the family's honour exposed so shamelessly out on the street? Wouldn't he drop dead?

Two boys appeared in her field of vision. They were returning from school, their satchels glued to their backs. They looked with zesty curiosity and pasted their faces—eyes and all—flat against the glass.

"Hey, she's real," the voice of one of the boys entered her ear faintly. Once again she wanted to laugh.

"Punk—it's plastic," the other boy said. "Whoever uses a live model?"

"But she looks so real. Seems she'd open her mouth and start speaking any moment."

"That's because of the evening. In proper light, you'd see."

"Hi!" the boy said as he winked at her mischievously.

The other one broke into a gale of laughter. Then he too waved at her and said "Bye!" and the two walked out of her field of vision.

As soon as they were gone, she suddenly began to laugh, but just as suddenly, became very nervous.

A young man was looking at her with perplexed eyes from across the glass. When their eyes met, he smiled. She smiled back, if only to hide her trepidation. She quickly grabbed the plastic dummy, and tried to install it, pretending to be one of the store attendants.

The youth's eyes were still riveted on her.

Arranging the sari around the mannequin she looked at the youth from the corner of her eye to see who he was looking at. His eyes lingered briefly at the plastic figure, then bounced off it and became glued to her.

She backed up, supremely confident, opened the door to the show window and walked out.

None of the store attendants saw her go out, or if they did, she was so agile and so fast that they couldn't figure out what had happened. The doorman didn't notice as he was busy talking to one of the sales clerks.

Confidently she strode away, briskly but lightly, happy and satisfied. As though she'd just unloaded the entire pestering weight of her body and soul. After she had walked away some distance, she turned around and looked back. The youth was still staring at her, perhaps with wonder.

She quickly turned down another street.

Anwer Khan, born in Bombay, India, holds M.A. degrees in Urdu and Persian. Writing since the 1960s, he has published three collections of short stories and a novel. "The Pose" was taken from his collection, *Yad Basere* (1990).

1. ***Response***

a. Though the exact setting of "The Pose" is never mentioned, there are some references within the story that can help readers make an educated guess. Where and when do you think the story might take place? Explain your reasoning.

b. What does the protagonist seem to gain from her impulsive decision to pose in the store window? Speculate on why she might have those reactions.

c. Suggest reasons why the author chose to have the young woman remain nameless in this story.

d. Would you describe yourself as the kind of person who acts impulsively? Do you think this affected the way you responded to "The Pose"? Explain.

2. ***Writing*** *Changing Points of View* Rewrite the first four paragraphs using the first person point of view. What effect does changing the point of view have on the telling of the story? Which narrative point of view is more effective for this particular story? Explain.

3. ***Language Conventions*** *Adjectives and Adverbs* Adjectives describe people, places, and things. Adverbs tell us how things are done. These words can suggest to readers how the author or protagonist feels about what is happening. Make a list of all the adjectives and adverbs used to describe the young woman. Next, create a similar list of words used to describe the various people who stare at her in the window. What conclusions can you draw based on these lists? Select a passage of your own writing and evaluate whether you have used adjectives and adverbs effectively.

4. ***Oral Language*** *Role Playing* If the protagonist later revealed her adventure to Sheyama, what would the two friends say to each other? With a partner, role-play the conversation that might unfold.

"Blowing up an elephant is not an everyday job."

The Elephant

By Slawomir Mrozek

Translated from the Polish by Konrad Syrop

THE DIRECTOR AT THE ZOOLOGICAL GARDENS HAD SHOWN himself to be an upstart. He regarded his animals simply as stepping stones on the road of his own career. He was indifferent to the educational importance of his establishment. In his zoo the giraffe had a short neck, the badger had no burrow and the whistlers, having lost all interest, whistled rarely and with some reluctance. These shortcomings should not have been allowed, especially as the zoo was often visited by parties of schoolchildren.

The zoo was in a provincial town, and it was short of some of the most important animals, among them the elephant. Three thousand rabbits were a poor substitute for the noble giant. However, as our country developed, the gaps were being filled in a well-planned manner. On the occasion of the anniversary of the liberation, on 22nd July, the zoo was notified that it had at long last been allocated an elephant. All the staff, who were devoted to their work, rejoiced at this news. All the greater was their surprise when they learned that the director had sent a letter to Warsaw, renouncing the allocation and putting forward a plan for obtaining an elephant by more economic means.

"I, and all the staff," he had written, "are fully aware how heavy a burden falls upon the shoulders of Polish miners and foundry men because of the elephant. Desirous of reducing our costs, I suggest that the elephant mentioned in your communication should be replaced by one of our own procurement. We can make an elephant out of rubber, of the correct size, fill it with air and place it behind railings. It will be carefully painted the correct color and even on close inspection will be indistinguishable from the real animal. It is well known that the elephant is a sluggish animal and it does not run and jump about. In the notice on the railings we can state that this particular elephant is particularly sluggish. The money saved in this way can be turned to the purchase of a jet plane or the conservation of some church monument.

"Kindly note that both the idea and its execution are my modest contribution to the common task and struggle.

"I am, etc."

This communication must have reached a soulless official, who regarded his duties in a purely bureaucratic manner and did not examine the heart of the matter but, following only the directive about reduction of expenditure, accepted the director's plan. On hearing the Ministry's approval, the director issued instructions for the making of the rubber elephant.

The carcass was to have been filled with air by two keepers blowing into it from opposite ends. To keep the operation secret the work was to be completed during the night because the people of the town, having heard that an elephant was joining the zoo, were anxious to see it. The director insisted on haste also because he expected a bonus, should his idea turn out to be a success.

The two keepers locked themselves in a shed normally housing a workshop, and began to blow. After two hours of hard blowing they discovered that the rubber skin had risen only a few inches above the floor and its bulge in no way resembled an elephant. The night progressed. Outside, human voices were stilled and only the cry of the jackass interrupted the silence. Exhausted, the keepers stopped blowing and made sure that the air already inside the elephant should not escape. They were not young and were unaccustomed to this kind of work.

"If we go on at this rate," said one of them, "we shan't finish by morning. And what am I to tell my missus? She'll never believe me if I say that I spent the night blowing up an elephant."

"Quite right," agreed the second keeper. "Blowing up an elephant is not an everyday job. And it's all because our director is a leftist."

They resumed their blowing, but after another half-hour they felt too tired to continue. The bulge on the floor was larger but still nothing like the shape of an elephant.

"It's getting harder all the time," said the first keeper.

"It's an uphill job, all right," agreed the second. "Let's have a little rest."

While they were resting, one of them noticed a gas pipe ending in a valve. Could they not fill the elephant with gas? He suggested it to his mate.

They decided to try. They connected the elephant to the gas pipe, turned the valve, and to their joy in a few minutes there was a full sized beast standing in the shed. It looked real: the enormous body, legs like columns, huge ears and the inevitable trunk. Driven by ambition the director had made sure of having in his zoo a very large elephant indeed.

"First class," declared the keeper who had the idea of using gas. "Now we can go home."

In the morning the elephant was moved to a special run in a central position, next to the monkey cage. Placed in front of a large real rock it looked fierce and magnificent. A big notice proclaimed: "Particularly sluggish. Hardly moves."

Among the first visitors that morning was a party of children from the local school. The teacher in charge of them was planning to give them an object-lesson about the elephant. He halted the group in front of the animal and began:

"The elephant is a herbivorous mammal. By means of its trunk it pulls out young trees and eats their leaves."

The children were looking at the elephant with enraptured admiration. They were waiting for it to pull out a young tree, but the beast stood still behind its railings.

"... The elephant is a direct descendant of the now-extinct mammoth. It's not surprising, therefore, that it's the largest living land animal."

The more conscientious pupils were making notes.

"... Only the whale is heavier than the elephant, but then the whale lives in the sea. We can safely say that on land the elephant reigns supreme."

A slight breeze moved the branches of the trees in the zoo.

"... The weight of a fully grown elephant is between nine and thirteen thousand pounds."

At that moment the elephant shuddered and rose in the air. For a few seconds it stayed just above the ground, but a gust of wind blew it upward until its mighty silhouette was against the sky. For a short while people on the ground could see the four circles of its feet, its bulging belly and the trunk, but soon, propelled by the wind, the elephant sailed above the fence and disappeared above the treetops. Astonished monkeys in the cage continued staring into the sky.

They found the elephant in the neighboring botanical gardens.

It had landed on a cactus and punctured its rubber hide.

The schoolchildren who had witnessed the scene in the zoo soon started neglecting their studies and turned into hooligans. It is reported that they drink liquor and break windows. And they no longer believe in elephants.

Slawomir Mrozek was born in Borzecin, Poland, in 1930. He studied architecture, oriental culture, and painting, and initially worked as a journalist. His writing established him as one of Poland's best-known playwrights and satirists. In 1968, Mrozek moved to Paris because his work was banned due to its controversial nature. However, by 1970, it was once again performed and published in Poland.

1. *Response*

a. What does the author achieve by including the line, "... only the cry of the jackass interrupted the silence"? Identify some other lines that create a similar effect.

b. Despite its absurdity, the story is quite realistic in a number of ways. What techniques does the author use to create a sense of realism in the telling of the tale?

c. What do you think is the purpose of the last paragraph in the story? What would be lost if it were omitted?

d. In what way might "The Elephant" be considered a *satire* (a work that criticizes something—for example, a person, a characteristic, an institution, or a government—by depicting it in a humorous, sarcastic, or scornful way)?

2. *Literature Studies* *Allegory* Read only on the literal level, an **allegory** can seem unrealistic, ridiculous, or trite. On the symbolic level, however, an allegory takes on special significance. What do you think the various elements and characters in "The Elephant" might symbolize? Present your interpretation of the moral lesson it presents.

An **allegory** is a simple story, such as a fable or parable, whose major purpose is to teach a moral lesson. An allegory can always be read on two levels—one literal, the other symbolic.

3. ***Making Connections*** In a brief comparison, identify the similarities between "The Elephant" and "He-y, Come On Ou-t!" Develop a chart to highlight their similarities and differences.

4. ***Language Conventions*** *Active and Passive Voice* The second-last sentence in the story is written in the **passive voice**: "It is reported that they drink liquor and break windows." Try to rewrite the sentence in the **active voice.** What difficulty did you encounter? Why do you think that the passive voice is often used in documents created by scientists, historians, and government officials?

In a sentence written in the **active voice**, the subject of the verb *performs* the action. In a sentence written in the **passive voice** the subject of the verb *receives* the action. In some passive constructions, the person or thing that performs the actions is unclear.

The Cask of Amontillado

By Edgar Allan Poe

The setting of this classic story is a nameless European city in an unspecified year—perhaps sometime during the eighteenth century. The action takes place during carnival, a public festival in which people wore elaborate costumes and participated in wild celebrations.

The thousand injuries of Fortunato I had borne as I best could, but when he ventured upon insult I vowed revenge. You, who so well know the nature of my soul, will not suppose, however, that I gave utterance to a threat. *At length* I would be avenged; this was a point definitely settled—but the very definitiveness with which it was resolved precluded the idea of risk. I must not only punish but punish with impunity. A wrong is unredressed when retribution overtakes its redresser. It is equally unredressed when the avenger fails to make himself felt as such to him who has done the wrong.

It must be understood that neither by word nor deed had I given Fortunato cause to doubt my good will. I continued, as was my wont, to smile in his face, and he did not perceive that my smile *now* was at the thought of his immolation.

He had a weak point—this Fortunato—although in other regards he was a man to be respected and even feared. He prided himself on his connoisseurship in wine. Few Italians have the true virtuoso spirit. For the most part their enthusiasm is adopted to suit the time and opportunity, to practise imposture upon the British and Austrian *millionaires*. In painting and gemmary,[1] Fortunato, like his countrymen, was a quack, but in the matter of old wines he was sincere. In this respect I did not differ from him materially;—I was skilful in the Italian vintages myself, and bought largely whenever I could.

[1] **gemmary:** gems, jewels

It was about dusk, one evening during the supreme madness of the carnival season, that I encountered my friend. He accosted me with excessive warmth, for he had been drinking much. The man wore motley. He had on a tight-fitting parti-striped dress, and his head was surmounted by the conical cap and bells. I was so pleased to see him that I thought I should never have done wringing his hand.

I said to him—"My dear Fortunato, you are luckily met. How remarkably well you are looking to-day. But I have received a pipe[2] of what passes for Amontillado,[3] and I have my doubts."

"How?" said he. "Amontillado? A pipe? Impossible! And in the middle of the carnival!"

"I have my doubts," I replied; "and I was silly enough to pay the full Amontillado price without consulting you in the matter. You were not to be found, and I was fearful of losing a bargain."

"Amontillado!"

"I have my doubts."

"Amontillado!"

"And I must satisfy them."

"Amontillado!"

"As you are engaged, I am on my way to Luchresi. If any one has a critical turn, it is he. He will tell me—"

"Luchresi cannot tell Amontillado from Sherry."

"And yet some fools will have it that his taste is a match for your own."

"Come, let us go."

"Whither?"

"To your vaults."

"My friend, no; I will not impose upon your good nature. I perceive you have an engagement. Luchresi—"

"I have no engagement;—come."

"My friend, no. It is not the engagement, but the severe cold with which I perceive you are afflicted. The vaults are insufferably damp. They are encrusted with nitre."

"Let us go, nevertheless. The cold is merely nothing. Amontillado! You have been imposed upon. And as for Luchresi, he cannot distinguish Sherry from Amontillado."

Thus speaking, Fortunato possessed himself of my arm; and putting on a mask of black silk and drawing a *roquelaire*[4] closely about my person, I suffered him to hurry me to my palazzo.

---

[2]**pipe:** a very large cask of wine [3]**Amontillado:** a particularly rare and valuable sherry wine
[4]***roquelaire:*** a knee-length cloak

There were no attendants at home; they had absconded to make merry in honour of the time. I had told them that I should not return until the morning, and had given them explicit orders not to stir from the house. These orders were sufficient, I well knew, to insure their immediate disappearance, one and all, as soon as my back was turned.

I took from their sconces two flambeaux, and giving one to Fortunato, bowed him through several suites of rooms to the archway that led into the vaults. I passed down a long and winding staircase, requesting him to be cautious as he followed. We came at length to the foot of the descent, and stood together on the damp ground of the catacombs of the Montresors.

The gait of my friend was unsteady, and the bells upon his cap jingled as he strode.

"The pipe?" said he.

"It is farther on," said I; "but observe the white web-work which gleams from these cavern walls."

He turned towards me, and looked into my eyes with two filmy orbs that distilled the rheum of intoxication.

"Nitre?" he asked, at length.

"Nitre," I replied. "How long have you had that cough?"

"Ugh! ugh! ugh!—ugh! ugh! ugh!—ugh! ugh! ugh! ugh! ugh! ugh! —ugh! ugh! ugh!"

My poor friend found it impossible to reply for many minutes.

"It is nothing," he said, at last.

"Come," I said, with decision, "we will go back; your health is precious. You are rich, respected, admired, beloved; you are happy, as once I was. You are a man to be missed. For me it is no matter. We will go back; you will be ill, and I cannot be responsible. Besides, there is Luchresi—"

"Enough," he said; "the cough is a mere nothing; it will not kill me. I shall not die of a cough."

"True—true," I replied; "and, indeed, I had no intention of alarming you unnecessarily—but you should use all proper caution. A draught of this Medoc will defend us from the damps."

Here I knocked off the neck of a bottle which I drew from a long row of its fellows that lay upon the mould.

"Drink," I said, presenting him the wine.

He raised it to his lips with a leer. He paused and nodded to me familiarly, while his bells jingled.

"I drink," he said, "to the buried that repose around us."

"And I to your long life."

He again took my arm, and we proceeded.

"These vaults," he said, "are extensive."

"The Montresors," I replied, "were a great and numerous family."

"I forget your arms."[5]

"A huge human foot d'or, in a field azure; the foot crushes a serpent rampant whose fangs are imbedded in the heel."

"And the motto?"

"*Nemo me impune lacessit.*"[6]

"Good!" he said.

The wine sparkled in his eyes and the bells jingled. My own fancy grew warm with the Medoc. We had passed through long walls of piled skeletons, with casks and puncheons intermingling, into the inmost recesses of the catacombs. I paused again, and this time I made bold to seize Fortunato by an arm above the elbow.

"The nitre!" I said; "see, it increases. It hangs like moss upon the vaults. We are below the river's bed. The drops of moisture trickle among the bones. Come, we will go back ere it is too late. Your cough—"

"It is nothing," he said; "let us go on. But first, another draught of the Medoc."

I broke and reached him a flagon of De Grâve. He emptied it at a breath. His eyes flashed with a fierce light. He laughed and threw the bottle upward with a gesticulation I did not understand.

I looked at him in surprise. He repeated the movement—a grotesque one.

"You do not comprehend?" he said.

"Not I," I replied.

"Then you are not of the brotherhood."

"How?"

"You are not of the masons."[7]

"Yes, yes," I said; "yes, yes."

"You? Impossible! A mason?"

"A mason," I replied.

"A sign," he said, "a sign."

"It is this," I answered, producing from beneath the folds of my *roquelaire* a trowel.

"You jest," he exclaimed, recoiling a few paces. "But let us proceed to the Amontillado."

"Be it so," I said, replacing the tool beneath the cloak and again offering him my arm. He leaned upon it heavily. We continued our

[5]**arms:** coat of arms
[6]***"Nemo me impune lacessit.":*** "No one attacks me with *impunity*." (without being punished)
[7]**masons:** Freemasons, an organization of men; once a secret society with its own signs and rituals

route in search of the Amontillado. We passed through a range of low arches, descended, passed on, and descending again, arrived at a deep crypt, in which the foulness of the air caused our flambeaux rather to glow than flame.

At the most remote end of the crypt there appeared another less spacious. Its walls had been lined with human remains, piled to the vault overhead, in the fashion of the great catacombs of Paris. Three sides of this interior crypt were still ornamented in this manner. From the fourth the bones had been thrown down, and lay promiscuously upon the earth, forming at one point a mound of some size. Within the wall thus exposed by the displacing of the bones, we perceived a still interior crypt or recess, in depth about four feet, in width three, in height six or seven. It seemed to have been constructed for no especial use within itself, but formed merely the interval between two of the colossal supports of the roof of the catacombs, and was backed by one of their circumscribing walls of solid granite.

It was in vain that Fortunato, uplifting his dull torch, endeavoured to pry into the depth of the recess. Its termination the feeble light did not enable us to see.

"Proceed," I said; "herein is the Amontillado. As for Luchresi—"

"He is an ignoramus," interrupted my friend, as he stepped unsteadily forward, while I followed immediately at his heels. In an instant he had reached the extremity of the niche, and finding his progress arrested by the rock, stood stupidly bewildered. A moment more and I had fettered him to the granite. In its surface were two iron staples, distant from each other about two feet, horizontally. From one of these depended a short chain, from the other a padlock. Throwing the links about his waist, it was but the work of a few seconds to secure it. He was too much astounded to resist. Withdrawing the key I stepped back from the recess.

"Pass your hand," I said, "over the wall; you cannot help feeling the nitre. Indeed it is *very* damp. Once more let me *implore* you to return. No? Then I must positively leave you. But I must first render you all the little attentions in my power."

"The Amontillado!" ejaculated my friend, not yet recovered from his astonishment.

"True," I replied; "the Amontillado."

As I said these words I busied myself among the pile of bones of which I have before spoken. Throwing them aside, I soon uncovered a quantity of building stone and mortar. With these materials and with the aid of my trowel, I began vigorously to wall up the entrance of the niche.

I had scarcely laid the first tier of the masonry when I discovered that the intoxication of Fortunato had in a great measure worn off. The earliest indication I had of this was a low moaning cry from the depth of the recess. It was *not* the cry of a drunken man. There was then a long and obstinate silence. I laid the second tier, and the third, and the fourth; and then I heard the furious vibrations of the chain. The noise lasted for several minutes, during which, that I might hearken to it with the more satisfaction, I ceased my labours and sat down upon the bones. When at last the clanking subsided, I resumed the trowel, and finished without interruption the fifth, the sixth, and the seventh tier. The wall was now nearly upon a level with my breast. I again paused, and holding the flambeaux over the mason-work, threw a few feeble rays upon the figure within.

A succession of loud and shrill screams, bursting suddenly from the throat of the chained form, seemed to thrust me violently back. For a brief moment I hesitated, I trembled. Unsheathing my rapier, I began to grope with it about the recess; but the thought of an instant reassured me. I placed my hand upon the solid fabric of the catacombs, and felt satisfied. I reapproached the wall. I replied to the yells of him who clamoured. I re-echoed, I aided, I surpassed them in volume and in strength. I did this, and the clamourer grew still.

It was now midnight, and my task was drawing to a close. I had completed the eighth, the ninth, and the tenth tier. I had finished a portion of the last and the eleventh; there remained but a single stone to be fitted and plastered in. I struggled with its weight; I placed it partially in its destined position. But now there came from out the niche a low laugh that erected the hairs upon my head. It was succeeded by a sad voice, which I had difficulty in recognizing as that of the noble Fortunato. The voice said—

"Ha! ha! ha!—he! he! he!—a very good joke, indeed—an excellent jest. We will have many a rich laugh about it at the palazzo—he! he! he!—over our wine—he! he! he!"

"The Amontillado!" I said.

"He! he! he!—he! he! he!—yes, the Amontillado. But is it not getting late? Will not they be awaiting us at the palazzo, the Lady Fortunato and the rest? Let us be gone."

"Yes," I said, "let us be gone."

"*For the love of God, Montresor!*"

"Yes," I said, "for the love of God!"

But to these words I hearkened in vain for a reply. I grew impatient. I called aloud—

"Fortunato!"

No answer. I called again—

"Fortunato!"

No answer still. I thrust a torch through the remaining aperture and let it fall within. There came forth in return only a jingling of the bells. My heart grew sick; it was the dampness of the catacombs that made it so. I hastened to make an end of my labour. I forced the last stone into its position; I plastered it up. Against the new masonry I re-erected the old rampart of bones. For the half of a century no mortal has disturbed them. *In pace requiescat!*[8]

---

[8] ***In pace requiescat!:*** Rest in peace!

Reproduction of original painting from John Hancock Mutual Life Insurance Company's art exhibit "Faces of Freedom."

This portrait of Edgar Allan Poe incorporates details from his most famous works, including "The Raven" and "The Tell-Tale Heart."

Edgar Allan Poe (1809–1849) is often referred to as the "father of the short story." Although he did not invent the form, Poe was among the first to define what a short story is and what it should do. According to Poe, "unity of effect or impression" is of utmost importance—all elements of a story, such as character, plot, setting, and mood, should work together to achieve one preconceived effect. Even the first sentence must aim at the purpose of the story."The Cask of Amontillado" was published in 1841.

1. ***Response***

   a. Edgar Allan Poe believed that the first sentence of a story should communicate the effect that the author is trying to create. Does Poe achieve that aim in this story? Explain.
   b. Describe the preparations and precautions Montresor undertook to achieve his goal. What do these tell us about Montresor's character?
   c. According to Montresor, what is necessary for the perfect revenge? By this standard, is Montresor's revenge perfect?
   d. An *unreliable narrator* is a narrator whose perspective is obviously biassed and whose views cannot be trusted by the reader. What elements of Montresor's story would you challenge? Explain why.

2. ***Literature Studies*** *Irony* Even though this story is about revenge and murder, there is a strong element of ironic humour. In a small group, find as many examples of **irony** as you can and categorize them as *verbal* (arising from what the characters say) or *situational* (arising from what the characters do). Which of the examples do you find the most ironic?

Irony is a method of expression in which the intended meaning is the opposite of, or is different from, the expressed meaning.

3. ***Critical Thinking*** Some works are written to enhance our understanding of human nature and the human condition. Other works are created mainly to entertain us, through the use of humour, horror, or suspense, for example. What do you think is the purpose of "The Cask of Amontillado"—to entertain or to comment significantly on life? Use examples from the story to support your viewpoint.

4. ***Making Connections*** What do "The Cask of Amontillado" and the story told by the bachelor in Saki's "The Storyteller" have in common? Would the aunt in "The Storyteller" consider Poe's story to be proper or improper? Why?

Brooms for Sale

By Thomas Raddall

"Greta's next step could be fatal, but standing still meant certain death."

This is a true story which happened many years ago. Greta was a young widow then, with a boy aged nine. They lived on a small farm in the woods west of the La Have River, near the coast of Nova Scotia. They were very poor.

Greta did all the farm work herself, tending the cattle, ploughing, seeding, and harvesting. In winter she got her own firewood with an axe in the woods. She was a tall Nova Scotia girl with the heart of a man. She had not the strength of a man, though, and no men lived near enough to help her. That was why the house and barn needed repair, and the fences were falling down. That was why each year the crops were smaller. But Greta would not give up.

One winter she thought of a way to get some extra money. There was a fishing village towards the mouth of the La Have, not many miles away. When the fishermen fitted out their vessels each spring, they needed all sorts of things. One thing was a supply of good brooms—but not the kind you buy in the shops. Fishermen must have a very stiff and strong broom, to sweep the deck after cutting and cleaning the day's catch.

Greta had grown up in a shore village and had seen such things made. You take a stick of birch wood about four feet long and three or four inches thick. Then you take a good sharp jack-knife. First, you must remove the birch bark. Then you start at one end of the stick, cutting a splint or shaving about half an inch wide and about as thick as the knife blade. You keep pushing the knife blade to within eight inches of the other end. There you stop. You go back and start another splint. You keep doing that, round and round the stick, until it is no more than an inch and a half thick. And there is your broom handle.

Now you take the bush of splints hanging near the other end, and bend them back over the eight inches of solid wood remaining there. You bind them together tightly in that position with strong cod-line, and with an axe you cut them off at about twelve inches below the cord. And there is your broom, all in one piece.

The Bank Fleet was very large in those days, and in the course of a season each vessel used a number of brooms. So each winter the outfitters bought a good supply.

Greta decided to make some brooms. The days were short and there were many chores to do in the house and barn, not to mention the wood-pile. She would have to do this extra chore after dark. The whittling made such a mess in her clean kitchen that she took part of the barn for a workshop.

Every evening after supper, when the little boy was asleep, she went to the barn, lit a fire in a rusty tin stove, and sat there hour after hour cutting splints by the light of a lantern. Her hands were used to hard work but after a time the grip on the knife made them sore. She tried wearing gloves, but that was awkward. So she tied a strip of linen over the blisters and went on. What pain she suffered, you can guess. But at last her palms were rough and hard, and she could work without a bandage. Sometimes she made four or five brooms before midnight.

By the end of January she had two hundred and forty brooms. It was time to sell them.

One chilly morning in February, she hitched the mare Judy to the sleigh, loaded her brooms, helped her child into the seat, and started for West La Have. She left the little boy in the care of her nearest neighbours, three miles down the road. It was pleasant driving through the woods, with the runners creaking on the snow and the harness bells ringing.

The village appeared, with its wharves and stores, and the wide frozen surface of the river. Greta got out of the sleigh happily. But in the first store she had disappointing news. The ship outfitters at West La Have had a full stock of brooms. They could buy no more.

"You might sell them down the river at East La Have," a store-keeper said, pointing over the ice. Greta looked. In the clear winter air the river did not seem very wide—half a mile, say. And three miles down the east shore was a chance to sell her precious brooms.

"The ice is good," the man said. "Several teams have been across to-day."

So Greta headed the mare across the river. It was pretty, she said afterwards—ice on the broad stream as far as you could see; the white banks and the dark woods; and blue smoke rising in small wisps from the houses by the shore.

When she reached East La Have she was stiff from her long drive in the cold, but she entered the store with a quick step and an eager face. The store-keeper looked out at her load and shook his head.

"Sorry, lady, but it seems everybody's been making brooms this winter. We've got too many now."

Half a dozen fishing captains sat by the stove, smoking and talking over the coming season on the Banks. They looked at the woman from up the river. Her coat was cheap and old, too thin for this sort of weather. They saw the worn overshoes, the home-knit woollen cap, the hands twisting anxiously inside the grey mittens. They looked at her tight mouth, and her eyes holding back the tears.

One of them said quietly, "Buy her brooms. If you don't, we will." The store-keeper called one of his clerks to carry the brooms inside. They made a great heap on the floor.

"Let's see, now. Two hundred and forty brooms at twenty-five cents ..."

"Forty cents," the fishing captain said. "Those are good brooms. I'd say you made them yourself, didn't you, ma'am?"

"Yes," Greta said.

The store-keeper counted out ninety-six dollars—nine tens, a five, and a one. Greta thanked him and the captains in a small, choked voice. As she went out the door one of them said, "You'd better drive home smart, ma'am. Looks like snow." She noticed then that the sunshine was gone, the sky was filled with a grey scud coming in very fast from the sea. A bleak, uneasy wind was blowing this way and that.

Greta had no purse. She stopped and fastened the bank notes to the inside hem of her skirt, using a big safety pin. She drove off, humming a tune to herself, and thinking of the things she could buy now for her boy and for the farm. Before she had gone far, the snow began to fly in small hard specks. When she reached the crossing place, a blizzard was blowing. She could not see across the river.

She turned off the road onto the ice, following the faint tracks of the other teams. After ten minutes the old tracks disappeared, buried in the new snow sweeping along the ice. She had to trust the horse to find the way. Greta was not afraid. After all, it was only half a mile or so.

The snow was now so thick that she could not see past Judy's ears. She let the reins go slack and crouched down in the seat, trying to find a little comfort in the storm. There was none. The snow whirled and stung; it seemed to come from every side. Sometimes it stopped her breath, like a cold white cloth laid over her mouth and nose. The little mare kept plunging her head and snorting in the blasts.

The way seemed strangely long. Greta noticed that the light was growing dim. The afternoon had gone. Soon now, surely, she must see the west shore looming through the storm. The horse went on and on, slipping here and there on patches of bare ice.

At last Judy came to a stop. Greta peered into the swirling snow and saw a dim, pale shape ahead. She shielded her eyes with her mittened hand for a better look. Through the snow-gusts she could see the thing was large, with three slim objects standing upon it and reaching up into the murk. Trees, of course! She cried thankfully, "Good girl, Judy! There's the shore. I knew you'd find it!"

She urged the horse on with a jerk at the reins. Judy went on a few steps and stopped again. The object stretched right across her path. It was close and clear now, and Greta gasped. Her very heart seemed to stop beating. For there, like a ghost risen out of the ice, lay a ship. A ship, of all things! A big schooner with three tall masts, all crusted with snow. What was it doing there? Slowly her mind filled with an awful suspicion. She tried to put it aside, but it came back. At last she faced the truth.

The little mare had been lost all this time. Instead of crossing the ice, they had been wandering down the river, towards the open sea. They were now somewhere near the mouth, where the ice was never safe. To prove it, here was the big three-master, frozen in where the crew had left it moored for the winter.

Poor Greta's heart was beating again in slow hard thumps. She was frightened. She did not know which way to turn. Were vessels anchored with their bows upstream or down? Or were they just moored any way at all? She could not remember.

It was quite dark now. Greta's arms and legs felt numb. One thing was certain, she was freezing there in the bitter wind and snow. So was the little horse. They must move or perish. Greta made up her mind. She got down and took hold of Judy's bridle, turned the sleigh carefully, and began to walk, leading the horse straight away from the long, pointing bow-sprit of the schooner.

The strongest blasts of the storm seemed to come from the right. Greta kept the wind on her right cheek. In that way at least she would avoid moving in a circle.

"Suppose the wind changes?" asked a small cold voice inside her. But that was the voice of fear, and she refused to listen.

The effort of walking took some of the cold ache out of her legs, but there was no feeling in her hands and feet, and her cheeks felt like wood. She kept changing her hold on Judy's bridle and rubbing her face with the other hand. The storm tore at her long full skirt and darted icy fingers through her thin coat. The world seemed full of snow, driving in a sharp slant on the wind, and sweeping along the ice with a hiss like escaping steam.

The mare was not shod for this sort of footing. She slipped and stumbled and seemed very tired. And Greta herself felt weary and empty. She had eaten nothing since the hasty breakfast at the farm.

Sometimes the wind lulled, and the cloud of fine snow drifted slowly about them. Its touch then was soft upon the cheek. Greta was tempted to let Judy go, to lie down on the ice and let that cold white powder go on brushing her face and soothing her fears and worries. Somehow the snow made her think of bed-sheets, clean and cool to the skin. How nice it would be, just to lie down and sleep away the night!

But whenever Greta's eyes closed, and the strength seemed to flow out of her limbs, there came into her mind a picture of the lonely boy at the neighbours' house, with his nose against the glass. She opened her eyes then, and stepped forward strongly in the darkness.

As the night went on, this happened many times. Greta became more and more drowsy with the cold, and more weary, and the little horse lagged and stumbled worse and worse. Finally, after one of those dreamy pauses, as Greta began to lead the horse again, she came upon a black patch in the ice ahead. It extended to the right and left as far as she could see. She moved closer—and stepped back in alarm. It was water—open water. She could hear it lapping against the edge of the ice.

She thought, "This is the end. We have come to the sea."

She closed her eyes, praying slowly and silently. She stood there a long time. At last she put her chin up. Aloud she said, "Judy, it's all or nothing now. Suppose it isn't the sea—suppose it's just the flooded ice along the shore! You know, where the ice sinks and buckles when the tide falls down the river. There's only one way to prove it, Judy. I must go to the edge and let my feet down into the water. Come, girl! Steady now! Come!"

Greta led the mare to the edge of the ice. The water looked very black. The snow was blowing harder than ever.

"If only I could see," she thought, "just for a minute. Just for a second. If only I could be sure." But there was only one way to be sure in this stormy blackness. She took a turn of the reins about her wrist, stooped, and lowered her left foot into the water. It came to her ankle, to her knee. The cold grip of the water sent a pain to her very bones. She gasped and lost her balance.

For one wild moment Greta thought she was gone. The sea! She was plunging into the sea! But her feet came upon something now, something slippery but solid. It was the sunken ice. She was standing over her knees in water. She paused to gather courage and her breath. She waded out to the length of the reins. The flooded ice held firm. It was tilted against hidden rocks, and now the water barely reached her trembling knees.

"Come, Judy," she cried, and pulled on the reins. The mare snorted and would not move. Greta threw her whole weight on the reins. Judy tried to draw back, but her worn iron shoes had no grip on the ice. Snorting with fear, she was dragged over the edge into the water. Greta found herself being dragged by the reins about her hand. The horse had floundered past her. She caught hold on the lurching sleigh. Dimly she saw a solid whiteness looming out of the windy dark. It was the shore—a pasture deep in snow.

Greta took the mare's head and led her up the bank. There was a low fence. The poles were rotten and she broke them down. She led Judy along inside the fence, wading through the drifts until she came to a gate and saw a light. Then she was standing at Judy's head outside a house and crying for help.

A man and a woman came to the door. She cried again, and they ran out to her. The man unhitched Judy quickly and took her off to the warmth and shelter of his barn. The woman half-led, half-carried Greta into her kitchen. Greta's clothes were crusted with snow, her wet skirts frozen stiff. But before she would let the good woman do anything for her, she stooped and turned up the icy hem of her skirt.

The precious packet was still there. She counted the notes with her numb white fingers. She laughed shakily. It was all there, the money she had made with her own hands, the money she had saved by her own courage in the storm.

Thomas Head Raddall (1913–1994) was an essayist, a short story writer and, most notably, an historical novelist. Much of his work was inspired by the stories and people of Nova Scotia, where he lived for most of his life.

1. *Response*

a. Describe in detail someone who takes action and fights the odds; either someone you know or someone you have read about or seen in a film. Why do we enjoy reading or hearing about such people?

b. Even though "Brooms for Sale" is a work of fiction, we are told in the opening sentence that it is "a true story which happened many years ago." Why do you think Thomas Raddall started his story with that statement? What does he gain and what does he lose as a result?

2. ***Literature Studies*** *Conflict* Conflict is an important element of most narratives; however, conflict does not always involve two or more characters who oppose one another. Identify the main conflict or conflicts in "Brooms for Sale." What other kinds of conflict have you encountered in narratives you have read or viewed?

3. ***Media*** *Real-life Heroes* People love true stories about individuals whose bravery and determination enable them to overcome great obstacles. Find an example of such a story from one of the popular media (TV, newspaper, magazine, or film). Write a brief summary that tells about the real-life hero and the challenge he or she faced. Did this story have any personal significance for you? Explain.

4. ***Making Connections*** In what ways are Greta and Walter Mitty ("The Secret Life of Walter Mitty") similar and different? Include examples from both stories in your comparison.

Today, a *vandal* is someone who commits an act of intentional destruction. But who were the first Vandals?

The Liberation of Rome

By Robin Hemley

A young woman named Amy Buleric sat in my office looking down at her feet. I figured someone had died, or maybe she was having emotional problems, or was sick. I bolstered myself for whatever horror or misfortune she might throw my way. A colleague of mine forces students to bring in obituaries when they claim a relative has died, but I think that's pathetic. I'd rather believe a student and risk being a fool than become power-crazed. So I was bolstering myself because I was afraid to hear what Amy Buleric was going to tell me about the reason for her absence for the last three weeks.

One time a student sent me a note, "Dr. Radlisch, I'm sorry I can't finish the paper on Hannibal for you." The next day I learned the boy had killed himself—not because of my paper, of course. He had problems I only found out about later. He must have sent me that note out of a pitiful sense of duty. Still, his words haunt me even today.

This young woman was fidgety, not looking at me, and so I sat there patiently, waiting for her to find the courage to tell me whatever it was that bothered her.

"Dr. Radlisch," she said finally, her voice almost a whisper.

"Take your time, Amy," I said, just as softly.

She looked past me to one of my bookshelves. "Why do you have that sign in your office?"

I sat up and turned around so quickly that a muscle popped in my neck. The sign was hand-lettered, done by a friend of my daughter, Claudia, who specializes in calligraphy for weddings. It reads, "If Rome be weak, where shall strength be found?"

"It's a quote from the poet Lucan," I said.

"Yes, I know," she said, a bangled arm sweeping aside her hair. She looked at me with what seemed suddenly like defiance and contempt. "But why is it here? It's . . . like . . . propaganda."

"I'm not sure I understand what you're saying, Amy," I said. I sat back in my chair. My thoughts, my voice became formal. "I thought we were here to discuss your absences, any problems you've been having."

I saw she was about to cry, so I stopped. "I mean," I said, softening my voice, "it's hard to find a solution unless I know what's wrong. Still, I'm glad you stopped in here to talk. I hate it when students simply disappear without a word."

It was too late. She started to cry, and I could see this was the last thing she wanted to do, that she was terribly embarrassed. The tears ran down her face and she didn't make any move to wipe them away.

"I wanted to disappear," she said, "but I couldn't. I had to confront you. That sign is my problem. Part of it anyway."

"Confront me?" I said. I scooted my chair back an inch or two.

"You've probably never had someone like me in one of your classes, and so there was no one to challenge your ideas."

"Ms. Buleric," I said. "I teach Roman history. I don't know what you're talking about. I have no ideas to be challenged. I voice the ideas of the ancients with my tongue, their accounts. I'm not sure where this is all leading, but I thought we were here to talk about your absences."

"I am here to talk about your lies," she said.

I stood up. Amy Buleric didn't rise from her chair and leave as I expected she would. Here I'd thought she needed my sympathy, my help, and she'd only come to accuse me of telling lies.

I sat on the edge of my desk and folded my arms. "How old are you, Amy? Nineteen. Twenty?"

"Twenty," she said.

"Why are you here?" I asked.

"Someone needs to stop you from telling lies."

I waved my hand at her. "Not that. I mean, why are you in college?" I smiled to show I wasn't her enemy. "Do you feel that you know everything already? Or do you think that college might just possibly, just on an outside chance, teach you something—something that might even challenge some of your old notions or the notions of your parents?"

Storytelling reveals meaning without committing the error of defining it.

Hannah Arendt

"What about you, Dr. Radlisch?" she said, sitting up straight in her chair. "Do you know everything already? What about your old notions? Can they be challenged?"

"People say I'm open-minded," I said, glancing at my watch.

"I'm here to better my people," she said, looking around the office as though her people had gathered around her.

"Your people? Are you a Mormon?"

"No."

"You're not . . . I mean, you don't look . . ."

"I'm a Vandal, Dr. Radlisch."

I put my chin in my hand. "A Vandal," was all I could manage to say.

"Part Vandal," she said. "Over half."

"You deface property?" I said.

"Another lie," she said. "Another stinking Roman lie." She spat on my carpet.

"You spat on my carpet," I told her and pointed to it.

"I'm a Vandal, Dr. Radlisch," she said. "If you only knew the truth about us."

"Amy," I said calmly. "I'm not doubting you, of course. But what you're telling me is that you're a Vandal. V-A-N-D-A-L. Vandal. Like the tribe? The one that disappeared from history in the sixth century A.D. when Belisarius defeated them and sold them into slavery?"

"Pig," she said. "Dog. Roman dung. Belisarius." And she spat again.

"Please stop spitting on my carpet," I asked her.

She nodded and folded her arms primly in her lap.

"And you're here in my office to set the record straight," I said.

"There isn't any record, Dr. Radlisch," she said. "That's the point. The Vandal tradition is entirely oral. We don't trust the written word. That was the way of the Romans. 'Lies are the province of Romans and writers.' That's an old Vandal proverb. The only record you have is the record of the Romans. They tell you that we were a war-like people who invaded Gaul at the beginning of the fifth century. But that was only because the Huns attacked us first. They drove us out of the Baltic. And we didn't attack the Gauls. We were just defending ourselves! Then the Franks defeated us in 409 and we fled into Spain. We were only there twenty years when a lying Roman governor invited us into North Africa to establish an independent homeland on the ashes of Carthage. We should have known better than to set up camp in Carthage. The only reason we captured Rome was to stop their oppression of us and other peoples who they had colonized or destroyed.

We didn't sack Rome. We liberated it."

She knew her history. Or at least a version, one that I had never heard before.

"And now you're coming forward."

"We've always been here," she said. "You've never noticed."

I wanted to believe her, but I was having a little difficulty. "So for the last fourteen hundred years . . ."

"That's right," she said. "Oh, we've intermarried some, but we've kept our traditions alive." She started to wail. Her eyes were closed and her mouth was stretched in an unnatural grimace. After a minute of this, she stopped, opened her eyes, and wiped her brow.

"Birth song," she announced.

"It's very different," I said. "Haunting."

She seemed pleased that I'd said this. She bowed her head. "For over a millennium our voices have been silenced. No one wanted to hear the Vandal songs. No one cared, though I suppose we were lucky. In some ways, we prefer the world's indifference to its attention. As soon as you're recognized, you're hunted and destroyed. So we waited. And now we're back."

My shoulders tensed and I rubbed my neck where the muscle had popped.

"Thank you for coming forward," I told her. "I know how hard it must be for you. I'm sure there are many things you could teach me."

She smiled at me again and all the anger seemed to be gone. "About the paper that's due?" she said.

"What?"

"Lies are the province of Romans and writers."

At first I didn't get it, but then I saw what she was telling me. "Oh, right," I said. "I guess you can't write it, can you?"

"No, I'm sorry," she said.

"No, don't be sorry," I said, reaching over and nearly touching her shoulder, but not quite. "I understand. I understand completely. It's part of your tradition."

"The Vandal tradition," she said. "Thanks, Dr. Radlisch. I knew you'd understand."

"That's my middle name."

"It is?"

"No, Amy. It's just a turn-of-phrase."

"Oh," she said, and she smiled. She liked me now. I could tell.

But I felt saddened. I was so used to teaching my subject a certain way. I had found a strange comfort in Lucan's quote, but now his question seemed unanswerable, at least by me. "Where shall strength be found?" How was I going to learn the new ways?

That night, I dreamed about my student who had killed himself. He was accusing me of something. He told me I was going to flunk out. I panicked and shot him. That was the dream. Ludicrous, but when I awoke, it felt so real that I nearly cried with relief. When I went to my office that day, I almost expected to see graffiti scrawled on the walls, "Death to All Vandals." But there was none. The walls were clean. No one had defaced them. What's more, Amy never showed up in class again. On the final transcript beside her name there was simply a blank, no "Withdrawn" as I'd hoped. It was up to me. I didn't know what to do. I couldn't give her an "A." But I couldn't flunk her. She knew her history. So I settled on a "B." But why had she stopped coming to class? Was it me? I thought we understood one another now. As I always told my students, they should come see me, no matter what the problem, before they just disappear.

American author **Robin Hemley** publishes both fiction and non-fiction. His short stories have won numerous awards. He teaches creative writing at Western Washington University in Bellingham, Washington.

1. ***Response***

a. When you first read the title of this story, what did you think it might be about? Now that you've completed the story, do you think the title is well chosen? Explain.

b. Imagine you are Amy Buleric. Instead of visiting Dr. Radlisch, you decide to give him a brief written note explaining why you can't complete the paper he has assigned. What does your note say?

c. Is Amy just a student who has invented a very clever excuse, or is she really a Vandal? And does the professor believe her story, or is he still a smug Roman "sympathizer" at the end? Did the conflict between them end decisively? Give reasons for your point of view.

2. ***Oral Language*** *Explore Ideas* In a group, discuss the following four quotations, drawing on your knowledge of history. To what extent do you agree with them? What are the implications of these statements? Present your conclusions to the class.

> "Those who cannot remember the past are condemned to repeat it."
> —George Santayana

> "History is written by the winners."
> —Alex Haley

> "History will be kind to me for I intend to write it."
> —Winston Churchill

> "It is sometimes very hard to tell the difference between history and the smell of skunk."
> —Rebecca West

3. ***Writing*** *Opinion Piece* "The Liberation of Rome" sketches what can happen when one culture dominates another. What are some of the outcomes of cultural domination suggested in the story? In a one-page opinion piece, state whether you feel yourself to be a member of a dominant or subordinate culture. Try to support your opinion with facts. What is your personal view about this situation?

Test

By Theodore Thomas

"His mother's scream rang steadily in his ears. As he strained at the wheel, he wondered how a scream could go on so long."

Robert Proctor was a good driver for so young a person. The turnpike curved gently ahead of him. Travel was light on this cool morning in May. He felt rested, but alert. He had been driving for two hours.

The sun was bright but not glaring. The air smelled fresh and clean. He breathed in deeply. It was a good day for driving.

He looked at the gray-haired woman sitting in the front seat with him. Her mouth was curved in a quiet smile. As she watched the trees and fields slip by on her side of the turnpike Robert Proctor looked back at the road. "Enjoying it, Mom?" he asked.

"Yes, Robert." Her voice was as cool as the morning.

He listened to the smooth purr of the engine. Up ahead he saw a big truck. It was spouting smoke as it sped along the turnpike. Behind it was a blue convertible, content to stay in line.

Robert Proctor noted this and put it in the back of his mind. He was slowly overtaking the car and the truck. He would reach them in another minute or two.

It was a good morning for driving. He pulled up and began to pass the blue convertible. Though his speed was a few miles an hour above the turnpike limit, his car was under perfect control.

The blue convertible suddenly swung out from behind the truck without warning. It struck his car near the right front fender. His car was knocked to the shoulder next to the turnpike median strip.

Robert Proctor was too wise to slam on the brakes. He fought the steering wheel to hold the car on a straight path. The left wheels sank into the soft left shoulder. The car seemed to pull toward the left. If it kept going that way, it might cross the island and enter the lane carrying cars coming from the other direction.

Robert held on to the steering wheel. Then the left front wheel struck a rock, and the tire blew out. The car turned sideways. It was then that his mother began to scream.

As the car turned, it skidded part way out into the oncoming lanes. Robert Proctor fought the steering wheel to right the car. But the drag of the blown tire was too much. His mother's scream rang steadily in his ears. As he strained at the wheel, he wondered how a scream could go on so long.

An oncoming car struck his car from the side, and spun him farther into the left-hand lanes.

He was thrown into his mother's lap. She was thrown against the right door. It was locked and it held. With his left hand he grabbed the steering wheel. He pulled himself up. He turned the wheel to try to stop the spin so he could get his car out of traffic. His mother could not right herself. She lay against the door, her cry rising and falling with the spin of the car.

The car began to slow down. In one of the spins, he twisted the wheel straight and headed down the left-hand lane. Before he could turn off the pike to safety, a car loomed ahead of him.

The man at the wheel of that other car seemed unable to move. His eyes were wide and filled with fear. Beside him sat a girl with her head against the back of the seat. Soft curls framed her lovely face. She was asleep.

It was not the fear in the man's face that reached Robert Proctor. It was the trust in the face of the sleeping girl. In a flash the two cars sped closer to each other. Robert Proctor had no time to change the direction of his car.

The driver of the other car remained frozen at the wheel. Robert Proctor stared into the face of the sleeping girl. His mother's cry still sounded in his ears.

He heard no crash when the two cars met head on at high speed. He only felt something push into his stomach. Then the world went gray. Just before darkness came, he heard the scream stop. He knew then that he had been hearing one single scream. It had only seemed to drag on and on.

Robert Proctor seemed to be at the bottom of a deep black well. There was a spot of faint light in the far distance. He could hear the rumble of a voice. He tried to pull himself toward the light and the sound. But the effort was too great. He lay still and gathered his strength to try again. The light grew brighter and the voice louder. When he tried again, he seemed to draw closer to the light and sound. He opened his eyes and looked at the man sitting in front of him.

"You all right, son?" asked the man. He wore a blue uniform. His round face was familiar.

Robert Proctor moved his head slowly. He discovered that he was lying back in a chair. He could move his arms and legs. He looked around the room. Then he remembered.

The man in the uniform saw the look in Robert's eyes. He said, "No harm done, son. You just took the last part of your driver's test."

Robert Proctor looked at the man. Though he saw the man clearly, he seemed to see the faint face of the sleeping girl in front of him.

The uniformed man went on talking. "We hypnotized you to make you think you were in an accident. We do it to everybody these days before they get their driver's license. Makes better drivers of them. Makes drivers more careful for the rest of their lives. Remember it now? Coming in here and all?"

Robert Proctor nodded, thinking of the sleeping girl. She never would have awakened. She would have gone from her light sleep to the dark sleep of death. Worst of all would have been his mother's death.

The uniformed man was still speaking. "So you think you're all set now. If you still want a driver's license, sign this application and we'll see."

Robert Proctor looked at the license application and signed it.

He looked up to find two men in long white coats. They were standing one on each side of him. Somehow the sight of them made him angry.

He started to speak but the uniformed man spoke first. "Sorry, son. You failed your license test. You're sick and need treatment."

The two men lifted Robert Proctor to his feet. He said, "Take your hands off me. What is this?"

The uniformed man said, "Nobody should want to drive a car after going through what you just went through. It should take months before you can even think of driving again. But you're ready to drive right now. Killing people doesn't seem to bother you. We can't let your kind run around loose any more. But don't you worry, son. They'll take good care of you. They'll fix you up." He nodded to the two men. They began to march Robert Proctor out.

At the door he spoke. His voice was so full of pleading the two men paused. "You can't really mean this," he said. "I must still be dreaming. This is all part of the test, isn't it?"

The uniformed man said, "No, son, but you can try again later." They dragged Robert out the door, knees stiff, feet dragging. As they pulled, his rubber heels slid along the two grooves worn in the floor.

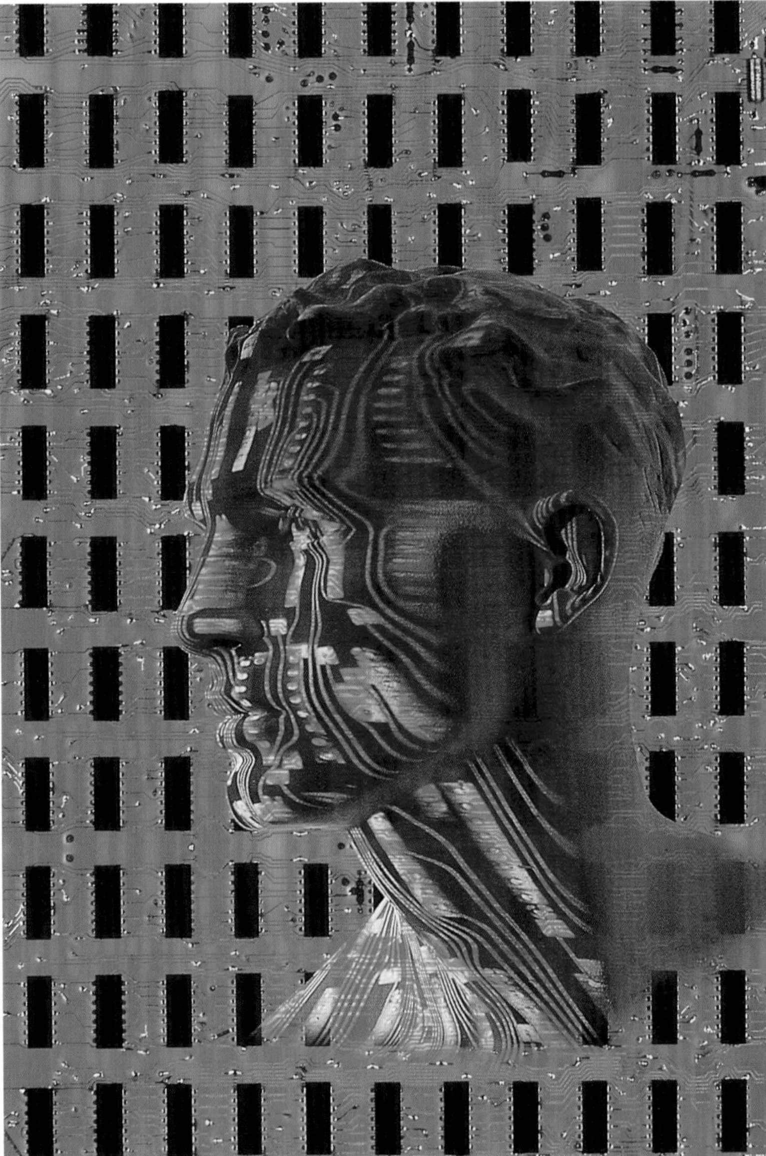

Wired Head, Chris Alan Wilton.

Examine this visual and describe its emotional effect. Show how that effect is created both by the subject matter and through artistic technique.

Theodore Thomas, American novelist, essayist, and short story writer, was born in 1920. He is best known for his science fiction writing, which has appeared in various magazines and anthologies.

1. ***Response***

   a. "Test" is carefully constructed to offer readers a series of unexpected twists and surprises. Identify these twists and explain how the author intentionally misleads the audience in each case. As a reader, do you often know what the surprise will be before you reach it? Explain what you like better: to be surprised, or to make a guess that turns out to be right.

   b. Is the test fair? Do you agree with the uniformed man's diagnosis of Robert at the end of the test? Give reasons for your point of view.

   c. Explain the significance of the "two grooves" that are described at the end of the story. What inference can you draw from this detail?

2. ***Literature Studies*** *Science Fiction* Much of what we call *science fiction* depends on extrapolation. The author chooses some aspect of the present as a starting point, then exaggerates it and projects it into the future. The results often serve as a warning about where current trends might take us. In "Test," what aspects of the present does Thomas extrapolate upon? What warnings are implied by the ending of the story?

3. ***Language Conventions*** *Sentence Length* Skim the story, noting the frequency with which the author employs short, simple sentences. Choose a three-paragraph passage in which short sentences predominate and rewrite it, combining sentences to create longer and more complex structures. Read the original passage aloud and then your rewrite. Do you prefer one version over the other? Explain. What have you learned about how sentence length can affect a reader?

Soul-Catcher

By Louis Owens

In the Mississippi swamps of the Yazoo River, a teenager learns about his Choctaw heritage—and the legend of *nalusachito* (the soul-catcher).

The old man held the rifle in one hand and walked bent over under the weight of the gunnysack on his back, as if studying the tangle of roots that was the trail. Behind him three lanky brown-and-black-and-white hounds crowded close to his thin legs and threw nervous glances at the wet forest all around. The only sound was that of the old man's boots and the occasional whine of one of the dogs. The sliver of moon had set, and the trail was very dark. The light from the carbide lamp on his hat cast a phosphorescent glow around the group, so that the old man, with his long silver hair, might have been one of the Choctaw shadows on the bright path home.

Out of the dark to the old man's right came a scream that cut through the swamp like jagged tin and sent the hounds trembling against his legs.

"Hah! Get back you!" he scolded, turning to shake his head at the cringing dogs. "That cat ain't going to eat you, not yet."

The dogs whined and pushed closer so that the old man stumbled and caught himself and the light from the headlamp splashed upon the trail. He shook his head again and chuckled, making shadows dance around them. He knew what it was that stalked him. The black *koi*[1] hadn't been seen in the swamps during the old man's lifetime, but as a child he'd heard the stories so often that he knew at once what the *koi* meant. It was an old and familiar story.

[1] ***koi:*** "panther" in Choctaw

He'd felt the black one out there in the swamps for a long time. The bird, *falachito*,[2] had called from the trees to warn him, and he had listened and gone on because what else was there to do? All of his life he had been prepared to recognize the soul-catcher when it should come.

The old man also knew that the screamer was probably the panther that the fool white man, Reeves, had wounded near Satartia a couple of weeks before. He could feel the animal's anger there in the darkness, feel the hatred like grit between his teeth. And he felt great pity for the injured cat.

The boar coon in the sack was heavy, and the old man thought that he should have brought the boy along to help, but then the forest opened and he was at the edge of his cabin clearing, seeing the thread of his garden trail between the stubble of the past year's corn and the dried husks of melon and squash vines. Behind him, this time to his left, the panther screamed again. The cat had been circling like that for the past hour, never getting any closer or any farther away.

He paused at the edge of the clearing and spoke a few words in a low voice, trying to communicate his understanding and sympathy to the wounded animal and his knowledge of what was there to the soul-catcher. For a moment he leaned the rifle against his leg and reached up to touch a small pouch that hung inside his shirt. All of his life the old man had balanced two realities, two worlds, a feat that had never struck him as particularly noteworthy or difficult. But as the cat called out once more, he felt a shadow fall over him. The animal's cry rose from the dark waters of the swamp to the stars and then fell away like one of the deep, bottomless places in the river.

When the old man pulled the leather thong to open the door, the hounds shot past and went to cower beneath the plank beds. He lowered the bag to the puncheon floor and pushed the door closed. After a moment's thought he dropped the bolt into place before reaching with one hand to hang the twenty-two on nails beneath a much larger rifle. Finally, he looked at the teenage boy sitting on the edge of one of the beds with a book in his lap. The lantern beside the boy left half of his upturned face in shadow, as if two faces met in one, but the old man could see one green eye and the fair skin, and he wondered once more how much Choctaw there was in the boy.

The boy looked up fully and stared at the old uncle. The distinct epicanthic fold of each eye giving the boy's face an oddly Oriental quality.

---

[2]***falachito:*** big crow

"*Koi*," the old man said. "A painter.[3] He followed me home."

After a moment's silence, the boy said, "You going to keep him?"

The old man grinned. The boy was getting better.

"Not this one," he replied. "He's no good. A fool shot him, and now he's mad." He studied the air to one side of the boy and seemed to make a decision. "Besides, this black one may be *nalusachito*,[4] the soul-catcher. He's best left alone, I think."

The boy's grin died quickly, and the old man saw fear and curiosity mingle in the pale eyes.

"Why do you think it's *nalusachito?*" The word was awkward on the boy's tongue.

"Sometimes you just know these things. He's been out there a while. The bird warned me, and now that fool white man has hurt him."

"*Nalusachito* is just a myth," the boy said.

The old man looked at the book in the boy's lap. "You reading that book again?"

The boy nodded.

"A teacher give that book to your dad one time, so's he could learn all about his people, the teacher said. He used to read that book, too, and tell me about us Choctaws." The old man grinned once more. "After he left, I read some of that book."

The old man reached a hand toward the boy. "Here, let me read you the part I like best about us people." He lifted a pair of wire-rimmed glasses from a shelf above the rifles and slipped them on.

The boy held the book out and the old man took it. Bending so that the lantern-light fell across the pages, he thumbed expertly through the volume.

"This is a good book, all right. Tells us all about ourselves. This writer was a smart man. Listen to this." He began to read, pronouncing each word with care, as though it were a foreign language.

> *The Choctaw warrior, as I knew him in his native Mississippi forest, was as fine a specimen of manly perfection as I have ever beheld.*

He looked up with a wink.

---

[3]**painter:** in the old man's dialect, he pronounces "panther" as "painter."

[4]***nalusachito:*** literally, "the big black thing" (na=thing, lusa=black, chito=big)

He seemed to be as perfect as the human form could be. Tall, beautiful in symmetry of form and face, graceful, active, straight, fleet, with lofty and independent bearing, he seemed worthy in saying, as he of Juan Fernández fame: "I am monarch of all I survey." His black piercing eye seemed to penetrate and read the very thoughts of the heart, while his firm step proclaimed a feeling sense of manly independence. Nor did their women fall behind in all that pertains to female beauty.

The old man looked at the boy. "Now there's a man that hit the nail on the head." He paused for a moment. "You ever heard of this Juan Fernández? Us Choctaws didn't get along too good with Spanish people in the old days. Remind me to tell you about Tuscaloosa sometime."

The boy shook his head. "Alabama?"

The old man nodded. "I read this next part to Old Lady Blue Wood that lives 'crost the river. She says this is the smartest white man she ever heard of." He adjusted the glasses and read again.

They were of such unnatural beauty that they literally appeared to light up everything around them. Their shoulders were broad and their carriage true to Nature, which has never been excelled by the hand of art, their long, black tresses hung in flowing waves, extending nearly to the ground; but the beauty of the countenances of many of those Choctaw and Chickasaw girls was so extraordinary that if such faces were seen today in one of the parlors of the fashionable world, they would be considered as a type of beauty hitherto unknown.

He handed the book back to the boy and removed the glasses, grinning all the while. "Now parts of that do sound like Old Lady Blue Wood. That unnatural part, and that part about broad shoulders. But she ain't never had a carriage that I know of, and she's more likely to light into anybody that's close than to light 'em up."

The boy looked down at the moldy book and then grinned weakly back at the old uncle. Beneath the floppy hat, surrounded by the acrid smell of the carbide headlamp, the old man seemed like one of the swamp shadows come into the cabin. The boy thought about his father, the old man's nephew, who had been only half Choctaw but looked nearly as dark and indestructible as the uncle. Then he looked down at his own hand in the light from the kerosene lantern. The pale skin embarrassed him, gave him away. The old man, his great-uncle, was Indian, and his father had been Indian, but he wasn't.

There was a thud on the wood shingles of the cabin's roof. Dust fell from each of the four corners of the cabin and onto the pages of the damp book.

"*Nalusachito* done climbed up on the roof," the old man said, gazing at the ceiling with amusement. "He moves pretty good for a cat that's hurt, don't he?"

The boy knew the uncle was watching for his reaction. He steeled himself, and then the panther screamed and he flinched.

The old man nodded. "Only a fool or a crazy man ain't scared when soul-catcher's walking around on his house," he said.

"You're not afraid," the boy replied, watching as the old man set the headlamp on a shelf and hung the wide hat on a nail beside the rifles.

The old man pulled a piece of canvas from beneath the table and spread it on the floor. As he dumped the coon out onto the canvas, he looked up with a chuckle. "That book says Choctaw boys always respected their elders. I'm scared alright, but I know about that cat, you see, and that's the difference. That cat ain't got no surprises for me because I'm old, and I done heard all the stories."

The boy glanced at the book.

"It don't work that way," the old man said. "You can't read them. A white man comes and he pokes around and pays somebody, or maybe somebody feels sorry for him and tells him stuff and he writes it down. But he don't understand, so he can't put it down right, you see."

How do you understand? the boy wanted to ask as he watched the uncle pull a knife from its sheath on his hip and begin to skin the coon, making cuts down each leg and up the belly so delicately that the boy could see no blood at all. The panther shrieked overhead, and the old man seemed not to notice.

"Why don't you shoot it?" the boy asked, looking at the big deer rifle on the wall, the thirty-forty Krag from the Spanish-American War.

The old man looked up in surprise.

"You could sell the skin to Mr. Wheeler for a lot of money, couldn't you?" Mr. Wheeler was the black man who came from across the river to buy the coonskins.

The old man squinted and studied the boy's face. "You can't hunt that cat," he said patiently. "*Nalusachito's* something you got to accept, something that's just there."

"You see," he continued, "what folks like that fool Reeves don't understand is that this painter has always been out there. We just ain't noticed him for a long time. He's always there, and that's what people forget. You can't kill him." He tapped his chest with the handle of the knife. "*Nalusachito* comes from in here."

The boy watched the old man in silence. He knew about the soul-catcher from the book in his lap. It was an old superstition, and the book didn't say anything about *nalusachito* being a panther. That was something the old man invented. This panther was very real and dangerous. He looked skeptically at the old man and then up at the rifle.

"No," the old man said. "We'll just let this painter be."

He pulled the skin off over the head of the raccoon like a sweater, leaving the naked body shining like a baby in the yellow light. Under the beds the dogs sniffed and whined, and overhead the whispers moved across the roof.

The old man held the skin up and admired it, then laid it fur-side down on the bench beside him. "I sure ain't going outside to nail this up right now," he said, the corners of his mouth suggesting a grin. He lifted the bolt and pushed the door open and swung the body of the coon out into the dark. When he closed the door there was a snarl and an impact on the ground. The dogs began to growl and whimper, and the old man said, "You, Yvonne! Hoyo!" and the dogs shivered in silence.

The boy watched the old man wash his hands in the bucket and sit on the edge of the other bed to pull off his boots. Each night and morning since he'd come it had been the same. The old uncle would go out at night and come back before daylight with something in the bag. Usually the boy would waken to find the old man in the other plank bed, sleeping like a small child, so lightly that the boy could not see or hear him breathe. But this night the boy had awakened in the very early morning, torn from sleep by a sound he wasn't conscious of hearing, and he had sat up with the lantern and book to await the old man's return. He read the book because there was nothing else to read. The myths reminded him of fairy tales he'd read as a child, and he tried to imagine his father reading them.

The old man was a real Choctaw—*Chahta okla*—a full-blood. Was the ability to believe the myths diluted with the blood, the boy wondered, so that his father could, when he had been alive, believe only half as strongly as the old man and he, his father's son, half as much yet? He thought of the soul-catcher, and he shivered, but he knew that he was just scaring himself the way kids always did. His mother had told him how they said that when his father was born the uncle had shown up at the sharecropper's cabin and announced that the boy would be his responsibility. That was the Choctaw way, he said, the right way. A man must accept responsibility for and teach his sister's children. Nobody had thought of that custom for a long time, and nobody had seen the uncle for years, and nobody knew how he'd even learned of the boy's birth, but there he was come out of the swamps across the river with his straight black hair hanging to his shoulders under the floppy hat and his face dark as night so that the mother, his sister, screamed when she saw him. And from that day onward the uncle had come often from the swamps to take the boy's father with him, to teach him.

The old man rolled into the bed, pulled the wool blanket to his chin, turned to the wall, and was asleep. The boy watched him and then turned down the lamp until only a dim glow outlined the objects in the room. He thought of Los Angeles, the bone-dry hills and yellow air, the home where he'd lived with his parents before the accident that killed both. It was difficult to be Choctaw, to be Indian there, and he'd seen his father working hard at it, growing his black hair long, going to urban powwows where the fancy dancers spun like beautiful birds. His father had taught him to hunt in the desert hills and to say a few phrases, like *Chahta isht ia*[5] and *Chahta yakni*,[6] in the old language. The words had remained only sounds, the powwow dancers only another Southern California spectacle for a green-eyed, fair-skinned boy. But the hunting had been real, a testing of desire and reflex he had felt all the way through.

Indians were hunters. Indians lived close to the land. His father had said those things often. He thought about the panther. The old man would not hunt the black cat, and had probably made up the story about *nalusachito* as an excuse. The panther was dangerous. For a month the boy had been at the cabin and had not ventured beyond the edges of the garden except to go out in the small rowboat onto the muddy Yazoo River that flanked one side of the clearing. The swampy forest around the cabin was like the river, a place in which nothing was ever clear: shadows, swirls, dark forms rising and disappearing again, nothing ever clearly seen. And each night he'd lain in the bed and listened to the booming and cracking of the swamp like something monstrously evil and thought of the old man killing things in the dark, picturing the old man as a solitary light cutting the darkness.

The panther might remain, its soft feet whispering maddeningly on the cabin roof each night while the old man hunted in the swamp. Or it might attack the old man who would not shoot it. For the first time the boy realized the advantage in not being really Choctaw. The old uncle could not hunt the panther, but he could, because he knew the cat for what it really was. It would not be any more difficult to kill than

[5] ***Chahta isht ia:*** I am Choctaw
[6] ***Chahta yakni:*** Choctaw land

the wild pigs he'd hunted with his father in the coastal range of California, and it was no different than the cougars that haunted those same mountains. The black one was only a freak of nature.

Moving softly, he lifted the heavy rifle from its nails. In a crate on the floor he found the cartridges and, slipping on his red-plaid mackinaw, he dropped the bullets into his pocket. Then he walked carefully to the door, lifted the bolt, stepped through, and silently pulled the door closed. Outside, it was getting close to dawn and the air had the clean, raw smell of that hour, tainted by the sharp odor of the river and swamp. The trees were unsure outlines protruding from the wall of black that surrounded the cabin on three sides. Over the river the fog hovered in a gray somewhat lighter than the air, and a kingfisher called in a shrill *kree* out across the water.

He pushed shells into the rifle's magazine and then stepped along the garden trail toward the trees, listening carefully for the sounds of the woods. Where even he knew there should have been the shouting of crickets, frogs, and a hundred other night creatures, there was only silence beating like the heartbeat drum at one of the powwows. At the edge of the clearing he paused.

In the cabin the old man sat up and looked toward the door. The boy had an hour before full daylight, and he would meet *nalusachito* in that transitional time. The old man fingered the medicine pouch on the cord around his neck and wondered about such a convergence. There was a meaning beyond his understanding, something that could not be avoided.

The boy brushed aside a muskedine vine and stepped into the woods, feeling his boots sink into the wet floor. It had all been a singular journey toward this, out of the light of California, across the burning earth of the Southwest, and into the darkness of this place. Beyond the garden, in the uncertain light, the trunks of trees, the brush and vines were like a curtain closing behind him. Then the panther cried in the damp woods somewhere in front of him, the sound insinuating itself into the night like one of the tendrils of fog that clung to the ground. The boy began to walk on the faint trail toward the sound, the air so thick he felt as though he were suspended in fluid, his movements like those of a man walking on the floor of the sea. His breathing became torturous and liquid, and his eyes adjusted to the darkness and strained to isolate the watery forms surrounding him.

When he had gone a hundred yards the panther called again, a strange, dreamlike, muted cry different from the earlier screams, and he hesitated a moment and then left the trail to follow the cry. A form slid from the trail beside his boot, and he moved carefully away, deeper into the woods beyond the trail. Now the light was graying, and the leaves and bark of the trees became delicately etched as the day broke.

The close scream of the panther jerked him into full consciousness, and he saw the cat. Twenty feet away, it crouched in a clutter of vines and brush, its yellow eyes burning at him. In front of the panther was the half-eaten carcass of the coon.

He raised the rifle slowly, bringing it to his shoulder and slipping the safety off in the same movement. With his action, the panther pushed itself upright until it sat on its haunches, facing him. It was then the boy saw that one of the front feet hung limp, a festering wound in the shoulder on that side. He lined the notched sight of the rifle against the cat's head, and he saw the burning go out of the eyes. The panther watched him calmly, waiting as he pulled the trigger. The animal toppled backward, kicked for an instant and was still.

He walked to the cat and nudged it with a boot. *Nalusachito* was dead. He leaned the rifle against a tree and lifted the cat by its four feet and swung it onto his back, surprised at how light it was and feeling the sharp edges of the ribs through the fur. He felt sorrow and pity for the hurt animal he could imagine hunting awkwardly in the swamps, and he knew that what he had done was right. He picked up the rifle and turned back toward the cabin.

When he opened the cabin door, with the cat on his shoulder, the old man was sitting in the chair facing him. The boy leaned the rifle against the bench and swung the panther carefully to the floor and looked up at the old man, but the old man's eyes were fixed on the open doorway. Beyond the doorway *nalusachito* crouched, ready to spring.

Louis Owens was born in Lompoc, California, of Choctaw, Cherokee, and Irish American heritage. He worked as a forest ranger and firefighter for the Forest Service, before obtaining his Ph.D. from the University of California. He has lectured in Italy, was Professor of Literature at the University of California, Santa Cruz, and Professor of English at the University of New Mexico, Albuquerque. His works include the novels *The Sharpest Sight* and *Wolfsong*, as well as several critical studies.

1. ***Response***

a. What atmosphere is created by the descriptive details in the opening four paragraphs? What specific details serve to create suspense?

b. Who do you think is the protagonist of the story—the old man or the boy? Explain.

c. In your view, why has the author refrained from naming the characters?

d. The conclusion of "Soul-Catcher" is *open-ended,* open to interpretation. What is your own interpretation of what happens? Do you enjoy stories that are open-ended, or do you prefer stories in which the message is clear and all the loose ends are tied up? Why?

2. ***Literature Studies*** *Conflict* In a small group, list the different kinds of conflict that occur in the story, both external and internal. For each one, discuss whether it was resolved, and if so, how. Try to reach a consensus about what is the most important or interesting conflict.

3. ***Language Conventions*** *Quotations* Examine the three quotations on pages 137 and 138 of the story, and identify how they have been specially treated to make them stand out from the rest of the story. Use a style guide or other reference work to find out the usual rules for presenting quotations. Following these rules, show an alternative way of presenting the first quotation. Find a piece of your own writing that includes quotations. Does your presentation of quotations fit the rules?

4. ***Making Connections*** In what ways is the boy similar to the narrator in "A Secret Lost in the Water"? What other similarities are there between the two stories?

Wilhelm

By Gabrielle Roy

"My mother at once forbade me to return to the O'Neills, so long, said she, as I had not got over the idea of Wilhelm."

My first suitor came from Holland. He was called Wilhelm and his teeth were too regular; he was much older than I; he had a long, sad face...at least thus it was that others made me see him when they had taught me to consider his defects. As for me, at first I found his face thoughtful rather than long and peaked. I did not yet know that his teeth—so straight and even—were false. I thought I loved Wilhelm. Here was the first man who, through me, could be made happy or unhappy; here was a very serious matter.

I had met him at our friends' the O'Neills', who still lived not far from us in their large gabled house on Rue Desmeurons. Wilhelm was their boarder; for life is full of strange things: thus this big, sad man was a chemist in the employ of a small paint factory then operating in our city, and—as I have said—lodged with equally uprooted people, the O'Neills, formerly of County Cork in Ireland. A far journey to have come merely to behave, in the end, like everyone else—earn your living, try to make friends, learn our language, and then, in Wilhelm's case, love someone who was not for him. Do adventures often turn out so tritely? Obviously enough, though, in those days I did not think so.

Evenings at the O'Neills' were musical. Kathleen played "Mother Machree," while her mother, seated on a sofa, wiped her eyes, trying the while to avert our attention, to direct it away from herself, for she did not like people to believe her so deeply stirred by Irish songs. Despite the music, Elizabeth kept right on digging away at her arithmetic; she still was utterly indifferent to men. But Kathleen and I cared a great deal. We feared dreadfully to be left on the shelf; we feared we should fail to be loved and to love with a great and absolutely unique passion.

When Mrs. O'Neill requested it of me—"to relieve the atmosphere," as she put it—I played Paderewski's "Minuet"; then Wilhelm would have us listen to Massenet on a violin of choice quality. Afterward he would show me in an album scenes of his country, as well as his father's house and the home of his uncle, his father's partner. I think he was anxious to convey to me that his family was better off than you might think if you judged by him—I mean by his having had to quit his native land and come live in our small city. Yet he need have had no fear that I should form an opinion on the basis of silly social appearances; I wanted to judge people in strict accordance with their noble personal qualities. Wilhelm would explain to me how Ruisdael had really most faithfully rendered the full, sad sky of the Low Countries; and he asked me whether I thought I should like Holland enough one day to visit it. Yes, I replied; I should much like to see the canals and the tulip fields.

Then he had had sent to me from Holland a box of chocolates, each one of which was a small vial containing a liqueur.

But one evening he had the ill-starred notion of accompanying me back home, as far as our front door, though it was only two steps away and darkness had not wholly fallen. He was chivalrous: he insisted that a man should not let a woman go home all alone, even if that woman only yesterday had still been playing with hoops or walking on stilts.

Alas! The moment his back was turned, Maman asked me about my young man. "Who is that great beanstalk?"

I told her it was Wilhelm of Holland, and all the rest of it: the box of chocolates, the tulip fields, the stirring sky of Wilhelm's country, the windmills.... Now all that was fine and honorable! But why, despite what I thought of appearances, did I believe myself obliged also to speak of the uncle and the father, partners in a small business which ... which ... made a lot of money?

My mother at once forbade me to return to the O'Neills, so long, said she, as I had not got over the idea of Wilhelm.

But Wilhelm was clever. One or two days each week he finished work early; on those days he waited for me at the convent door. He took over my great bundle of books—Lord, what homework the Sisters piled on us in those days!—my music sheets, my metronome, and he carried all these burdens to the corner of our street. There he would lower upon me his large and sad blue eyes and say to me, "When you are bigger, I'll take you to the opera, to the theater...."

I still had two years of the convent ahead of me; the opera, the theater seemed desperately far away. Wilhelm would tell me that he longed to see me in an evening gown; that then he would at last remove from its moth-proof bag his dress clothes and that we should go in style to hear symphonic music.

My mother ultimately learned that Wilhelm had the effrontery to carry my books, and it annoyed her very much. She forbade me to see him.

"Still," said I to Maman, "I can hardly prevent his walking next to me along the pavement."

My mother cut through that problem. "If he takes the same sidewalk as you, mind you cross right over to the other."

Now, she must have sent a message of rebuke to Wilhelm and told him, as she had me, precisely which sidewalk he should take, for I began seeing him only on the opposite side of the street, where he would stolidly await my passage. All the while I was going by, he held his hat in his hand. The other young girls must have been horribly envious of me; they laughed at Wilhelm's baring his head while I was passing. Yet I felt death in my soul at seeing Wilhelm so alone and exposed to ridicule. He was an immigrant, and Papa had told me a hundred times that you could not have too much sympathy, too much consideration for the uprooted, who have surely suffered enough from their expatriation without our adding to it through scorn or disdain. Why then had Papa so completely changed his views, and why was he more set even than Maman against Wilhelm of Holland? True enough, no one at home, since Georgianna's marriage, looked favorably upon love. Perhaps because as a whole we had already had too much to suffer from it. But I—presumably—I had not yet suffered enough at its hands....

And then, as I have said, Wilhelm was clever. Maman had forbidden him to speak to me on the street, but she had forgotten letters. Wilhelm had made great progress in English. He sent me very beautiful epistles which began with: "My own beloved child..." or else "Sweet little maid...." Not to be outdone, I replied: "My own dearest heart ...." One day my mother found in my room a scrawl on which I had been practising my handwriting and in which I expressed to Wilhelm a passion that neither time nor cruel obstacles could bend.... Had my mother glanced into the volume of Tennyson lying open upon my table, she would have recognized the whole passage in question, but she was far too angry to listen to reason. I was enjoined from writing to Wilhelm, from reading his letters, if, by a miracle, one of them succeeded in penetrating the defenses thrown up by Maman; I was even enjoined from thinking of him. I was allowed only to pray for him, if I insisted upon it.

Until then I had thought that love should be open and clear, cherished by all and making peace between beings. Yet what was happening? Maman was turned into something like a spy, busy with poking about in my wastebasket; and I then thought that she was certainly the last person in the world to understand me! So that was what love accomplished! And where was that fine frankness between Maman and me! Does there always arise a bad period between a mother and her daughter? Is it love that brings it on?... And what, what is love? One's neighbor? Or some person rich, beguiling?

During this interval Wilhelm, unable to do anything else for me, sent me many gifts; and at the time I knew nothing of them, for the moment they arrived, Maman would return them to him: music scores, tulip bulbs from Amsterdam, a small collar of Bruges lace, more liqueur-filled chocolates.

The only means left to us by which to communicate was the telephone. Maman had not thought of that. Obviously she could not think of everything; love is so crafty! Then, too, during her loving days the telephone did not exist, and this, I imagine, was why Maman forgot to ban it for me. Wilhelm often called our number. If it was not I who answered, he hung up gently. And many a time did Maman then protest, "What's going on?... I shall write the company a letter; I'm constantly being bothered for nothing. At the other end I can barely hear a sort of sighing sound." Naturally she could not foresee how far the tenacity of a Wilhelm would extend.

But when it was I who answered, Wilhelm was scarcely better off. There could be between us no real conversation without its exposing us to the discovery of our secret and consequent prohibition of the telephone. Moreover, we neither of us had any taste for ruses; Gervais employed them when he had on the wire the darling of his heart, to whom he spoke as though she were another schoolboy. But Wilhelm and I—without blaming Gervais, for love is love, and when it encounters obstacles, is even more worthy!—we strove to be noble in all things. Thus Wilhelm merely murmured to me, from afar, "Dear heart ..." after which he remained silent. And I listened to his silence for a minute or two, blushing to the roots of my hair.

One day, though, he discovered an admirable way to make me understand his heart. As I was saying "Allo!" his voice begged me to hold the wire; then I made out something like the sound of a violin being tuned, then the opening bars of "Thaïs."[1] Wilhelm played me the whole composition over the phone. Kathleen must have been accompanying him. I heard piano chords somewhere in the distance, and—I know not why—this put me out a trifle, perhaps at thinking that Kathleen was in on so lovely a secret. It was the first time, however, that Wilhelm put me out at all.

---

[1]**"Thaïs":** A mournful composition for violin and piano, from the opera *Thaïs,* by the French composer Jules Massenet (1842–1912). It is just under five minutes long.

Our phone was attached to the wall at the end of a dark little hallway. At first no one was surprised at seeing me spend hours there, motionless and in the most complete silence. Only little by little did the people at home begin to notice that at the telephone I uttered no word. And from then on, when I went to listen to "Thaïs" the hall door would open slightly; someone hid there to spy on me, motioning the others to advance one by one and watch me. Gervais was the worst, and it was very mean on his part, for I had respected his secret. He manufactured reasons for making use of the hall; as he went by he tried to hear what I could be listening to. At first, however, I held the receiver firmly glued to my ear. Then I must already have begun to find "Thaïs" very long to hear through. One evening I allowed Gervais to listen for a moment to Wilhelm's music; perhaps I hoped that he would have enough enthusiasm to make me myself admire the composition. But Gervais choked with mirth; later on I saw him playing the fool in front of the others, at the far end of the living room, bowing an imaginary violin. Even Maman laughed a little, although she tried to remain angry. With a long, sad countenance which—I knew not how—he superimposed upon his own features, Gervais was giving a fairly good imitation of Wilhelm in caricature. I was a little tempted to laugh. For it is a fact that there is something quite comic in seeing a sad person play the violin.

When you consider it, it is astonishing that all of them together should not have thought much sooner of parting me from Wilhelm by the means they so successfully employed from that night forward.

All day long, when I went by, someone was whistling the melody of "Thaïs."

My brother grossly exaggerated the Dutchman's slightly solemn gait, his habit of keeping his eyes lifted aloft. They discovered in him the mien of a Protestant minister, dry—said they—and in the process of preparing a sermon. Maman added that the "Netherlander" had a face as thin as a knife blade. This was the way they now referred to him: the "Netherlander" or the "Hollander." My sister Odette—I should say Sister Edouard—who had been informed and was taking a hand in the matter, even though she had renounced the world, my pious Odette herself told me to forget the "foreigner"… that a foreigner is a foreigner….

One evening as I listened to "Thaïs," I thought I must look silly, standing thus stock still, the receiver in my hand. I hung up before the end of the performance.

Thereafter, Wilhelm scarcely crossed my path again.

A year later, perhaps, we learned that he was returning to Holland.

My mother once more became the just and charitable pre-Wilhelm person I had loved so dearly. My father no longer harbored anything against Holland. Maman admitted that Mrs. O'Neill had told her concerning Wilhelm that he was the best man in the world, reliable, a worker, very gentle.... And Maman hoped that Wilhelm, in his own country, among his own people, would be loved... as, she said, he deserved to be.

Gabrielle Roy was born in Saint-Boniface, Manitoba in 1909. She held various teaching posts in Canada, then studied drama in Europe. On her return to Canada, she settled in Montréal, where she worked as a freelance reporter. She won three Governor General's Awards for her writing. All of her works were first written in French, then translated into English.

1. ***Response***
   a. Reread the opening two paragraphs and find details that foreshadow the doomed nature of the relationship between Wilhelm and the narrator. Why do you think the author included these hints about the ending?
   b. Why does the narrator's family disapprove of Wilhelm?
   c. What tactic ultimately succeeds in parting the narrator from Wilhelm? What advice might have helped the narrator resist this tactic?
   d. Identify specific attitudes and ideas expressed by the characters in "Wilhelm" that might be regarded as unacceptable in today's society. Which attitudes and ideas does the narrator reject, and which does she accept?

2. ***Oral Language*** Prepare a two-minute oral presentation in which you argue for or against the following statement:

   > It was the mother's responsibility to intervene in her daughter's life as she did.

   In your presentation, you should express your personal point of view and provide strong arguments to support it. Include specific references from the story.

3. ***Literature Studies*** *Theme* The main purpose of some literature is to present an important **theme** for the reader to ponder. In your own words, sum up the theme of this story in a single sentence. Reread the story to locate the three sentences or passages that, in your view, are most important in expressing the theme. Explain your choices. Conclude by telling whether the theme is important to you personally.

A **theme** is a central thesis or idea that is expressed directly or indirectly in a literary work.

4. ***Language Conventions*** *Ellipses* Using quotations from the story, show two different functions ellipses can serve. As well, explain how the author has used ellipses to reveal something important about the narrator's character.

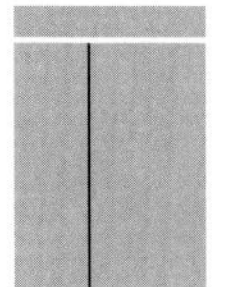

He-y, Come on Ou-t!

By Shinichi Hoshi

Translated from the Japanese by Stanleigh Jones

Who would have thought that something as simple as a hole in the ground could prove to be so useful?

The typhoon had passed and the sky was a gorgeous blue. Even a certain village not far from the city had suffered damage. A little distance from the village and near the mountains, a small shrine had been swept away by a landslide.

"I wonder how long that shrine's been here."

"Well, in any case, it must have been here since an awfully long time ago."

"We've got to rebuild it right away."

While the villagers exchanged views, several more of their number came over.

"It sure was wrecked."

"I think it used to be right here."

"No, looks like it was a little more over there."

Just then one of them raised his voice. "Hey what in the world is this hole?"

Where they had all gathered there was a hole about a meter in diameter. They peered in, but it was so dark nothing could be seen. However, it gave one the feeling that it was so deep it went clear through to the center of the earth.

There was even one person who said, "I wonder if it's a fox's hole."

"Hey-y, come on ou-t!" shouted a young man into the hole. There was no echo from the bottom. Next he picked up a pebble and was about to throw it in.

"You might bring down a curse on us. Lay off," warned an old man, but the younger one energetically threw the pebble in. As before, however, there was no answering response from the bottom. The villagers cut down some trees, tied them with rope and made a fence which they put around the hole. Then they repaired to the village.

"What do you suppose we ought to do?"

"Shouldn't we build the shrine up just as it was, over the hole?"

A day passed with no agreement. The news traveled fast, and a car from the newspaper company rushed over. In no time a scientist came out, and with an all-knowing expression on his face he went over to the hole. Next, a bunch of gawking curiosity seekers showed up; one could also pick out here and there men of shifty glances who appeared to be concessionaires. Concerned that someone might fall into the hole, a policeman from the local sub-station kept a careful watch.

One newspaper reporter tied a weight to the end of a long cord and lowered it into the hole. A long way down it went. The cord ran out, however, and he tried to pull it out, but it would not come back up. Two or three people helped out, but when they all pulled too hard, the cord parted at the edge of the hole. Another reporter, a camera in hand, who had been watching all of this, quietly untied a stout rope that had been wound around his waist.

The scientist contacted people at his laboratory and had them bring out a high-powered bull horn, with which he was going to check out the echo from the hole's bottom. He tried switching through various sounds, but there was no echo. The scientist was puzzled, but he could not very well give up with everyone watching him so intently. He put the bull horn right up to the hole, turned it to its highest volume, and let it sound continuously for a long time. It was a noise that would have carried several dozen kilometers above ground. But the hole just calmly swallowed up the sound.

In his own mind the scientist was at a loss, but with a look of apparent composure he cut off the sound and, in a manner suggesting that the whole thing had a perfectly plausible explanation, said simply, "Fill it in."

Safer to get rid of something one didn't understand.

The onlookers, disappointed that this was all that was going to happen, prepared to disperse. Just then one of the concessionaires, having broken through the throng and come forward, made a proposal.

"Let me have that hole. I'll fill it in for you."

"We'd be grateful to you for filling it in," replied the mayor of the village, "but we can't very well give you the hole. We have to build a shrine there."

"If it's a shrine you want, I'll build you a fine one later. Shall I make it with an attached meeting hall?"

Before the mayor could answer, the people of the village all shouted out.

"Really? Well, in that case, we ought to have it closer to the village."

"It's just an old hole. We'll give it to you!"

So it was settled. And the mayor, of course, had no objection.

The concessionaire was true to his promise. It was small, but closer to the village he did build for them a shrine with an attached meeting hall.

About the time the autumn festival was held at the new shrine, the hole-filling company established by the concessionaire hung out its small shingle at a shack near the hole.

The concessionaire had his cohorts mount a loud campaign in the city. "We've got a fabulously deep hole! Scientists say it's at least five thousand meters deep! Perfect for the disposal of such things as waste from nuclear reactors."

Government authorities granted permission. Nuclear power plants fought for contracts. The people of the village were a bit worried about this, but they consented when it was explained that there would be absolutely no above-ground contamination for several thousand years and that they would share in the profits. Into the bargain, very shortly a magnificent road was built from the city to the village.

Trucks rolled in over the road, transporting lead boxes. Above the hole the lids were opened, and the wastes from nuclear reactors tumbled away into the hole.

From the Foreign Ministry and the Defense Agency boxes of unnecessary classified documents were brought for disposal. Officials who came to supervise the disposal held discussions on golf. The lesser functionaries, as they threw in the papers, chatted about pinball.

The hole showed no signs of filling up. It was awfully deep, thought some; or else it might be very spacious at the bottom. Little by little the hole-filling company expanded its business.

> Reading makes immigrants of us all. It takes us away from home, but more important, it finds homes for us everywhere.
>
> Hazel Rochman

Bodies of animals used in contagious disease experiments at the universities were brought out, and to these were added the unclaimed corpses of vagrants. Better than dumping all of its garbage in the ocean, went the thinking in the city, and plans were made for a long pipe to carry it to the hole.

The hole gave peace of mind to the dwellers of the city. They concentrated solely on producing one thing after another. Everyone disliked thinking about the eventual consequences. People wanted only to work for production companies and sales corporations; they had no interest in becoming junk dealers. But, it was thought, these problems too would gradually be resolved by the hole.

Young girls discarded old diaries in the hole. There were also those who were inaugurating new love affairs and threw into the hole old photographs of themselves taken with former sweethearts. The police felt comforted as they used the hole to get rid of accumulations of expertly done counterfeit bills. Criminals breathed easier after throwing material evidence into the hole.

Whatever one wished to discard, the hole accepted it all. The hole cleansed the city of its filth; the sea and sky seemed to have become a bit clearer than before.

Aiming at the heavens, new buildings went on being constructed one after the other.

One day, atop the high steel frame of a new building under construction, a workman was taking a break. Above his head he heard a voice shout:

"He-y, come on ou-t!"

But, in the sky to which he lifted his gaze there was nothing at all. A clear blue sky merely spread over all. He thought it must be his imagination. Then, as he resumed his former position, from the direction where the voice had come, a small pebble skimmed by him and fell on past.

The man, however, was gazing in idle reverie at the city's skyline growing ever more beautiful, and he failed to notice.

Tokyo-born **Shinichi Hoshi** (1926–1997) was one of Japan's most prolific science fiction writers. During his career, he wrote well over a thousand short stories.

1. ***Response***

a. When the hole was first discovered, the villagers debated about what they should do with it. Why is it significant that their first plan involved rebuilding the shrine?

b. What obvious theme does this story present? What do you think the author, Shinichi Hoshi, might have been trying to achieve with this story?

c. Briefly describe your reaction to "He-y, Come on Ou-t!" Do you think the author would have been pleased with your reaction? Explain.

2. ***Literature Studies*** *Symbolism* This story is a fantasy. It invites readers to reach beyond the literal level and explore its **symbolic meaning.** With this in mind, work in a group to make a list of the important characters, details, and events of the story. Try to reach a consensus about what each item on the list might symbolize in the real world.

> The **symbolic meaning** of a work is developed through the symbols the author includes. A *symbol* is something that represents something else—for example, the lion can be a symbol of courage.

3. ***Media*** *Persuasion* The media are full of persuasive messages about the environment. With a partner, collect examples of these messages. Try to take examples from different media, and/or look for different viewpoints and approaches. For each example, summarize where you found it, who generated it, what its message is, and what audience you think it is trying to influence. State which message is most persuasive and explain how you reached that conclusion.

"He is loco, este hombre, a little crazy."

The Singing Silence

By Eva-Lis Wuorio

Old Vicente of Formentera was perhaps the happiest man I've ever known. And also, perhaps, the poorest.

He was a cadaverous, bent juniper of a man, brown and lined, and he owned not one piece of clothing that was not patched. He lived at Cala Pujol, in a lean-to made of stone and driftwood and brush, with a rusty iron brazier for his kitchen and a couple of cracked iron pots, discarded by the fishermen, from which to eat. But he owned also an excellent snorkel and a pair of rubber flippers and a diver's mask, and, as I say, I don't believe there was a happier man.

I had been coming to Formentera for several years before Vicente stood out in my eyes from the old fishermen who drew their boats up under the brush and the bamboo shelters at the end of the beach where the rocks begin. At last I realized he was not a fisherman. He had no time to fish.

I had some Ibicenco, his dialect, a language quite different from the Castilian Spanish, so I could tell, that day I first saw him, that he was asking with dignity, not pleading, for the loan of a fisherman's small boat. I could not understand, thinking him a fisherman, how he got along without a boat, but I offered to lend him the one I always rent in Formentera. I do not use it often anyhow. He thanked me, and again his dignity impressed me.

I watched him load the boat with the snorkel and the flippers and the face mask, an earthen jug of water, and a small parcel of provisions. There was no fishing gear, no underwater gun to go with his other equipment. I wondered what he intended to catch and how. I watched him row out, facing the horizon, a small man, intent.

I watched until he was but a speck on the horizon, and then I forgot about him. At Cala Pujol it is easy to forget. The turquoise waters are deep and clear to the bottom, the sand is untrodden, there is a long sweep of white-silver shore—the year I speak of, it was still that way—and the sun is a constant benediction. In peace, one forgets.

There came a day when the wind blew from Africa and the sea was sultry and the fishermen did not go out. They sat in the bamboo-roofed little bar on the beach and drank red wine and talked. "Vicente got in?"

"Not yet."

"He is *loco, este hombre*, a little crazy."

"Not at all, not so much. He has the good intention."

"You think so? You, too, are *loco*."

"Me? Not at all. I see the point. I understand very well."

"Vicente?" I asked. "He is the old man with the underwater equipment?"

"Ah," they said, "aha. Ah."

I asked for another bottle of the wine of the island, for only that is drunk there. We do not try to be smart by taking better-known wines.

And, so sitting there, with the wind from Africa blowing and stirring up the sea until it was muddy below and racing, sheep-white, above, I heard the story of Vicente.

He had been an ambitious boy 60 years ago, and he had left Formentera, the little island of the past. But 60 years ago there was not much for a Spaniard to do in his country of Spain. So Vicente went to sea in foreign ships, and after a time he came back. He walked the country, trying all sorts of jobs, but he ended where better men than he had ended, as a porter on the quays of Barcelona—a *mozo*.

He had had a dream, but dreams fail a man sometimes. So he carried the luggage of others: the rich Spaniards, the visitors, the tourists. Until ten years ago he stood there at the quay, a number on his hat, waving his hand at the passengers from the boats, pointing to himself and shouting, "Me? Me! Number Seventy-three!"

One day a rich American from a Palma boat saw his frantic wave and beckoned. Vicente got in line with the other porters and pushed his way up the gangplank to the white boat. There this rich American said to him, "Here are six suitcases, and that thing. Be careful with it; it's an antique."

Vicente recognized the earthen vessel. It was an amphora, a Phœnician one, a fine, rare specimen of the big jugs used for transporting wine or grain. In the old days fishermen sometimes caught them in their nets. They had often thrown them back into the sea, but this they did no longer, not since the *señores* from the town came to buy them for their museums.

Vicente hoisted the bags on his back, picked up the big, pinkish, sea-encrusted jug and started down the gangplank. The people were pushing and pulling, getting off the boat, coming on board, and he shouted as they shouted. He came to the quay, and another porter, stumbling on a mooring rope, fell against him and he dropped the amphora.

Two thousand years went down in a dusty sound of earth falling. Well.

Ten years before there were still amphorae and other relics of the Greeks and Phœnicians and Romans in the shallow coves of the islands of Ibiza, but now there were mostly only almost valueless objects of more recent times; valuable specimens were very rare. The American had paid $500 for this water jug of a Phœnician sailor, having had it verified as authentic by the authorities. Naturally he was angry.

But he was also a sensible man and knew that never in a lifetime could the porter Vicente make $500, so he was resigned and ready to forget his loss.

Not so Vicente. He knew the value men set now on these useless old jugs and pots; he had seen the disappointment on the face of the American. Vicente was an honorable man and he wanted to make amends.

He followed the American to his hotel, pleaded for his name and address, and promised to pay him back. A ragged piece of paper torn from a diary and scribbled with Abraham Lincoln Smith, 72 Hudson Avenue, Milwaukee, Wisconsin, U.S.A. became his most valuable possession. It was to him the ultimate milepost on the long road of his search.

I believe that somehow, in his dreams, Vicente saw himself at last arriving in Milwaukee, Wisconsin, U.S.A., with the ancient Phœnician amphora under his arm, receiving with joy the praise that would greet him there.

Vicente knew that he would never have the money to buy an amphora, but what was to prevent his finding one? Others had, dozens of them in the time of his boyhood. Why not he?

He had no family, so it did not take him long to bid farewell to his life in Barcelona, that bustling, busy city by the sea, where he had carried bags for the price of a small glass of wine in a smoky wineshop, and a windowless room to roof his nights.

When he had sold his few possessions he had the deck fare to Ibiza, and a little more. From the stern of the boat he looked back and saw the city sink into the sea, and for the first time he knew that his years there had been a prison of his own making. He had never, there, lifted up his eyes from the narrow streets to the wide sky.

And once again, as when he was a boy, the sea sang to him.

Back on the islands he set about the task he had chosen. He learned where the last amphora had been found, and he realized, as had others before him, that since the ancient pieces were valuable, all the inshore places must have been searched and emptied of their treasure.

Young Sandik, of Santa Eulalia del Rio, the carpenter's son, had made himself a reputation as an undersea swimmer. He had found a cannon at the bottom of the sea—but that's another story. To consult him, Vicente travelled by bus to Santa Eulalia del Rio, and Sandik's advice was brief. Get a mask, get flippers, go far out into the sea. There, way out, were still unknown shallows, no deeper than the height of a man, or twice or thrice the height of a man, and caught in the caves of the sea bottom, treasures might still be.

Now Vicente, like many of the island-born, had never learned to swim. But he spent the rest of his money, as Sandik advised, on a good snorkel and flippers and a mask. Then he took the little mail boat *Manolito* back to his island of Formentera. There, camping on the beach, scrounging his meals, intent as are all men with a singleness of purpose to urge them on, he set about teaching himself to swim.

He was over 60 then. An old man, as time makes men like Vicente old. Yet he was young in his urgency to learn and go on toward the far horizon of his purpose.

He learned to swim, and he learned to dive with the snorkel and the flippers and the mask, a froglike, crablike figure in the clear shallows about the beaches of Cala Pujol. He ventured farther and farther, to where the water turned purple, where the deeps began. This was the most talkative time of his life, after his first dives, for he could not contain his wonder at the unexpected beauty of the deep sea. The gardens of starfish, the varicolored, bug-eyed gentle fish that followed him, the slant of translucent sunlight on the mysterious caves and rocks—these he recounted to the fishermen who toiled upon the surface of the sea. And his tales were touched with wonder and awe. Never, he swore, had he known such freedom as at the bottom of the sea.

"But you can't breathe there!"

"One breathes with one's eyes, one's pores."

Never had he heard such music.

"But there is only silence under the sea?"

"It is a singing silence. Like many instruments sending their purest sounds up to the sky."

There is that to the Spanish language. The plowman often speaks the language of poetry. It is the way the words arrange themselves.

Day by day, week by week, month by month, and so into the years, Vicente, searching for the amphora which in honor he felt he must find to replace the one he had broken, grew happier. Each day was a new delight, a new adventure. No longer were his days imprisoned by the needs of the hours. Somehow there was always something for those needs, a fish to grill, a glass of wine, a piece of bread, a box of matches. To the fishermen his search had become a part of their life on the beach and the sea, and their generosity was quick, unthinking.

They told me the story of Vicente, that day the wind blew from Africa and stirred up the depths of the sea and sent the high green waves scurrying, and I, too, searched the horizon for the little boat. Then I turned to Father Pedro, the curé of San Fernando, who had joined us.

"What do you think, Father?" I said. "Will old Vicente find his amphora?"

The fat little priest joined his fingers. His eyes, too, were on the horizon, but he seemed undisturbed. The wind from Africa swayed the bamboo shelter over us.

"Well, now, you see," he said, "Vicente has the search. It is not what one finds, you know, but the search itself that is important. Only the search."

Last year, on another day, when the sea rose suddenly, stirred to tumult by the wind, the little boat Vicente had borrowed was tossed back to the beach.

No one saw the old man again.

The seas had been heavy.

But tied, securely, wrapped in seaweed at the bottom of the boat, was an amphora, an ancient Phœnician vessel salvaged from the centuries and the sea.

Father Pedro and the fishermen who had been Vicente's friends asked me, since I knew English, to write to Abraham Lincoln Smith of Milwaukee, Wisconsin, U.S.A. I did. I wrote a number of times to the address we had and finally to the mayor of the city.

No one had heard of him.

Annoyed by the foolish old man who had dropped his souvenir, the American had fabricated a name to get rid of him. Perhaps, however, he did come from Milwaukee. We do not know.

Eva-Lis Wuorio was born in 1918 in Finland, and immigrated to Canada at the age of 11. Her works include *To Fight in Silence, Escape If You Can, The Land of Right Up and Down,* and *The Woman With the Portuguese.* A number of her books have a World War II setting.

1. ***Response***

a. Create a list of adjectives that the narrator would (or did) use to capture Vicente's character. Was Vicente appealing or interesting to you? Why or why not?

b. In your view, how plausible is Vicente's decision to devote his life to finding a replacement for the amphora he broke? Explain.

c. Reread the final seven paragraphs of the story. What ideas do you think the author is communicating in these concluding passages?

d. What is your personal response to "The Singing Silence"? Comment both on the theme of the story and also on the way the theme is presented.

2. ***Vocabulary*** *Context Cues* Make a list of any unfamiliar words and expressions you encountered while reading the story. Were you able to infer their meaning from the context in which they were placed? Do you think the author anticipated some of the difficulties readers might face? Explain.

3. ***Writing*** *Eulogy* Using details and quotations from the story, write a **eulogy** for Vicente. Once you have revised your work, rehearse presenting the eulogy in front of a small group. What suggestions can the group make for improving the eulogy?

A **eulogy** is a tribute to someone who has just died, and is often delivered as a speech at a funeral.

4. ***Media*** *Inspirational Message* "The Singing Silence" offers an inspirational message on the importance of dreams and goals in life. Employing a medium other than writing, create a representation of the theme of the story. Your work should make a statement that Vicente would agree with. Your representation might take the form of a musical composition, video, digital image, poster, dance, dramatization, or collage.

Poetry

Poetry is life distilled.

Gwendolyn Brooks

Poets on Poetry

How can we as readers get the most out of poetry? William Shakespeare advises us to see poetry "feelingly."

Here is what some other poets say about poetry. Would you agree? What would you add?

"Poetry gives your most intimate self
the chance to talk to the most intimate
self of another. When these two meet
the sparks fly, the poem is charged with
light, and a new way of seeing and saying
enters the world."

—Lorna Crozier

"Literature is a state of culture,
poetry is a state of grace."

—Juan Ramon Jimenez

"Poetry is to prose
as dancing is to walking."

—John Wain

"If I read a book [and] it makes my whole body so cold no fire ever can warm me I know that is poetry. If I feel physically as if the top of my head were taken off, I know that is poetry."

—Emily Dickinson

"To read a poem is to hear it with our eyes;
to hear it is to see it with our ears."

—Octavio Paz

"Poetry is a string of words that parades
without a permit."

—Linda Hogan

Previous Page:
Rock Painting. Prehistoric Art, Zimbabwe

A Poet's Advice to Students

By E.E. Cummings

A poet is somebody who feels, and who expresses his feeling through words.

This may sound easy. It isn't.

A lot of people think or believe or know they feel—but that's thinking or believing or knowing; not feeling. And poetry is feeling—not knowing or believing or thinking.

Almost anybody can learn to think or believe or know, but not a single human being can be taught to feel. Why? Because whenever you think or you believe or you know, you're a lot of other people: but the moment you feel, you're nobody-but-yourself.

To be nobody-but-yourself—in a world which is doing its best, night and day, to make you everybody else—means to fight the hardest battle which any human being can fight; and never stop fighting.

As for expressing nobody-but-yourself in words, that means working just a little harder than anybody who isn't a poet can possibly imagine. Why? Because nothing is quite as easy as using words like somebody else. We all of us do exactly this nearly all of the time—and whenever we do it, we're not poets.

If, at the end of your first ten or fifteen years of fighting and working and feeling, you find you've written one line of one poem, you'll be very lucky indeed.

And so my advice to all young people who wish to become poets is: do something easy, like learning how to blow up the world—unless you're not only willing, but glad, to feel and work and fight till you die.

Does this sound dismal? It isn't.

It's the most wonderful life on earth.

Or so I feel.

I Carried With Me Poems

By Gail Dusenbery

I carried with me poems, poems which spewed out of
everything: I saw poems hanging from the clotheslines,
hanging from the streetlamps: I saw poems glowing
in the bushes, pushing out of the earth as tulips do;
I felt poems breathe in the dark March night like ghosts
which squared and wheeled through the air;
I felt poems brushing the tops of chimneys, brushing
by in the dark; I felt poems being born in the city,
Venuses breaking through a shattered sea of mirrors;
I felt all the poets of the city straining,
isolated poets, knowing none of the others, straining;
I felt that some gazed into the March night, looking,
and finding;
and others were running down the steep streets,
seeking, and seeking to embrace;
and others stood in empty bookstores turning over pages
of fellow poets whom they loved but didn't know;
and some pondered over coffee growing cold, in harshly
lit cafeterias, and gazed at the reflections of the eaters
in the wall-to-wall mirrors:
some dwelt on what it was to grow old;
some dwelled on love;
some had gone out of time;
some, going out of time, looked back into time, and
started;
I felt all these lives and existences, all with poems at
their center;

I knew none of these poets;
but I felt these intimations augured well, for me, and
for poetry:
and my steps grew big, giant steps, I bounded down
Park Street,
a tall, taciturn, fast-walking poets' accomplice.

Poetry Is . . .

By Betty Lies

Poetry is music, the tempos and tones of life, the beat of language enacted. It is the human voice singing its joys and griefs. It is movement. It is voice-dance.

Poetry is language, its deepest structures, grammar, syntax, etymologies, the origins of thought. It is metaphor and the rhythms of persuasion. It is precision and concision.

Poetry is pictures painted with words.

Poetry is seeing, noticing, close-ups of nature and its creatures. It's looking at the universe, the immense and the microscopic.

Poetry is a bridge between reason and the emotions; it helps us think and validates feeling. It calls to the imagination and demands an answer.

Poetry is the collective memory of the human race, the record of our experience through the ages. It gives flesh to dates and eras, and tells the lived reality of wars, cultural events, historical movements.

Poetry begins to ask the questions for our necessary spiritual quest.

Poetry is the universal voice, the human spirit calling across boundaries of time, geography, culture, age, race, gender, experience. Through it we learn about the other, and about ourselves.

We read and write poems and discover that we are not alone.

I Wrote a Poem

By Jennifer Takyi

I wrote a poem,
And nobody liked it,
So I threw it away,
But it won't let me go,
It's part of me.

What You Are Doing Now

By Gary Hyland

In grade eleven
you and this poem
meet for the first time
in an English classroom
when you would rather be
almost anywhere else
    gazing   lazing
    dancing   snoozing
    kissing   cruising
but all of history
from Cro-Magnon clans
to Puritans
to the Department of Education
was mobilized to get you
and this poem here/now

and you're thinking   *hey*
not so bad so far   *hey*
I understand most of this
At least it's not that gloopy
antique tombstone stuff/not

    O spirit soft of summer's breezes
    Who dwelleth in yon western reaches
    Where gulls conspire to form friezes
    With white waves on craggy beaches

at least it's not that snarly
strung-out lumpy stuff/not

my snow

stems

roses

till they

(petal

me)

Hey this is like football
he pins *I boot*
Hey it's basketball
he passes *I shoot*
Manoman I can do it!
Hey there's nothing to it!

Then your teacher announces
that you have thirty minutes
to write an analysis
of this poem
and when you look
the poem spits in your face
and stops.

How Beautifully Useless

By Raymond Souster

How beautifully useless,
how deliciously defiant
a poem is!

1. ***Response***
   a. Both Jennifer Takyi and Raymond Souster use few words to convey many meanings. Take either "I Wrote a Poem" or "How Beautifully Useless" and expand upon what you think the author is suggesting about the nature of poetry.
   b. Discuss what E.E. Cummings and Gail Dusenbery are saying about poetry, poets, and readers. Which sentiments or ideas do you agree with most? Which do you disagree with? Are there statements that you find difficult to understand? Suggest possible meanings for those statements. Summarize your conclusions for the class.
   c. Select one statement from "Poetry Is . . . " by Betty Lies and find a poem that you think exemplifies the statement. Explain your choice.
   d. Express your own view of poetry in a brief opinion piece. Try to support your opinion by referring to specific poems or personal experiences with poetry.

2. ***Oral Language*** *Dramatic Reading* Prepare a dramatized oral reading of "What You Are Doing Now." In a paragraph or two, describe the techniques you employed to make your reading more effective.

3. ***Writing*** *Poetry* Write your own version of "I Carried With Me Poems," starting with the same first line: "I carried with me poems, poems which spewed out of everything." Use images and details from your own experience or knowledge base.

4. ***Language Conventions*** *Run-on Sentences* As you read poetry you will notice that some poets use grammar or punctuation in unconventional ways for a particular effect. For example, in "I Wrote a Poem" on page 167, Takyi constructs a five-line poem using one run-on sentence. Think about the effect these lines would have if she had used end punctuation. Reread the other poems in this section, looking for run-on sentences. How have the poets used run-on sentences effectively?

Lyric Poetry

One way of classifying a poem is by the function it serves. A lyric poem is a poem whose primary function is to express a state of mind or a powerful emotion. The term *lyric* comes from *lyre*, a musical instrument similar to a harp. In ancient Greece, poets recited their verse to the accompaniment of music played on the lyre.

Lyric poetry can be intensely personal and is often written in the first person. Many popular forms, such as free verse and haiku, can be classified by their function as lyric poetry.

A lyric poem not only expresses emotion, it evokes emotion in the reader. Identify the powerful emotions expressed in each of the following short lyric poems. Which of the poems do you find most evocative? Explain your choice.

After a Heated Argument
By Kaneto Tota
Translated from the Japanese by Makoto Ueda

After a heated argument
I go out to the street
and become a motorcycle.

Love Is
By Ann Darr

a flock of birds, soaring, twisting, turning,
floating, lifting, swooping, landing, splitting into
pieces (individual birds) that can peck peck peck
before they once again unite in the flock that, rising,
goes reeling, shifting, flying (flying, that's the word
I was looking for) right out of sight.

Calgary 2 am

By Christopher Wiseman

In spite of the fact that it is twenty below
and the winter has lasted six months

in spite of being starved starved almost to death
for greenness and warmth flowers and birds

in spite of the deadness of endless classrooms
shopping centres television programmes

in spite of the pains in the gut the migraines
the wakings the palpitations

in spite of the sickening knowledge of laziness
of failure to meet obligations

in spite of all these things and more
I have to report that the moon tonight

is filling the house with a wild blueness
my children grow excel are healthy

my wife is gentle there are friends
and once in a while a poem will come

In spite of the fact that it is twenty below
tonight I smile Summer bursts inside me

Life in Our Village

By Matei Markwei

In our little village
When elders are around
Boys must not look at girls
And girls must not look at boys
Because the elders say
That is not good.

Even when night comes
Boys must play separately
Girls must play separately
But humanity is weak
So boys and girls meet.

The boys play hide and seek
And the girls play hide and seek.
The boys know where the girls hide
And the girls know where the boys hide
So in their hide and seek
Boys seek girls
Girls seek boys
And each to each sing
Songs of love.

God's World

By Edna St. Vincent Millay

O world, I cannot hold thee close enough!
    Thy winds, thy wide grey skies!
    Thy mists, that roll and rise!
Thy woods, this autumn day, that ache and sag
And all but cry with colour! That gaunt crag
To crush! To lift the lean of that black bluff!
World, World, I cannot get thee close enough!

Long have I known a glory in it all,
    But never knew I this:
    Here such a passion is
As stretcheth me apart,—Lord, I do fear
Thou'st made the world too beautiful this year;
My soul is all but out of me,—let fall
No burning leaf; prithee, let no bird call.

Spring Wind — Apollo Coast by Paul Grignon

Examine this image and discuss its use of colour, texture, space, light, and depth. How do these contribute to its mood? How does this painting affect the viewer?

A Red, Red Rose

By Robert Burns

O, my luve's like a red, red rose
That's newly sprung in June.
O, my luve is like the melodie
That's sweetly played in tune.

As fair art thou, my bonnie lass,
So deep in luve am I;
And I will luve thee still, my dear,
Till a' the seas gang dry.

gang: go

Till a' the seas gang dry, my dear,
And the rocks melt wi' the sun;
And I will luve thee still, my dear,
While the sands o' life shall run.

And fare thee weel, my only luve,
And fare thee weel a while!
And I will come again, my luve,
Though it were ten thousand mile.

weel: well

Canadian Sunrise

By Joan Besen of Prairie Oyster

Well, tired, bone-weary
Can't stand another day of rain
Go shout your troubles to the mountains
But the mountains echo back
It's the same old chain

Chorus:
Crying give me a sign, give me a sign.
However rough the road, however dark the skies,
Your frozen soul will melt like April ice
When a shot of gold hits your eyes.
Canadian sunrise, woa Canadian sunrise, woa.

Even smoking, dust choking.
When's it gonna rain again?
You had big dreams, now they've all gone flat.
Blown away to nothin' by the prairie rain.

Chorus

Between the rock and the raging sea,
Running till you're ragged and tossed.
Searching for something you think you'll never find
And you find out it was never lost.

Chorus

Demasduit's Dream

By Bob Hallett of Great Big Sea

I dreamt I saw a woman
Standing by the strand
Waiting for her people
To come in from the land

Waiting there for seven days
She built a fire in the sand
Waiting for her people
To come in from the land

"Demasduit's Dream" tells the story of a Beothuk woman, Demasduit (also known as Mary March). She was captured in March of 1819 by the English, at Red Indian Lake, Newfoundland and Labrador. Her husband, chief Nonosabasut, tried to rescue her, and was killed. She remained with her captives, learning English quickly, and provided them with a better understanding of her language.

She had the look of a refugee
Hiding in her eyes
And when I tried to talk to her
She answered with a cry

And pointed to the water
Out beyond the harbour line
Where a thousand ships lay waiting
They lay waiting for my sign
But . . .

Chorus:
I remember days of sunlight
With my father by my side
And the children, ran before us
Like the foam upon the tide

We ran like frightened partridge
When the strangers came to talk
Bringing sickness 'round them
And the thunder in their walk

We ran into the valleys
And we ran into the hills
They only ran before us,
Driven by the strangers' will

Chorus

I'm waiting by the landwash
Giant standing near
I see them coming always
Children in their fear

I'm waiting on my blanket
And the giant waits with me
And I will wait here always
As they fill the endless sea

Chorus

As in the Beginning

By Mary di Michele

A man has two hands and when one
gets caught on the belt and his fingers
are amputated and then patched
he cannot work. His hands are insured
however so he gets some money
for the work his hands have done before.
If he loses a finger he gets a flat sum
of $250 for each digit &/or $100 for a joint
missing for the rest of his stay on earth,
like an empty stool at a beggar's banquet.
When the hands are my father's hands
it makes me cry although my pen must keep scratching
its head across the page of another night.
To you my father is a stranger
and perhaps you think the insurance paid is enough.

Give me my father's hands when they are not broken
and swollen,
give me my father's hands, young again,
and holding the hands of my mother,
give me my father's hands still brown and uncallused,
beautiful hands that broke bread for us at table,
hands as smooth as marble and naked as the morning,
give me hands without a number tattooed at the wrist,
without the copper sweat of clinging change,
give my father's hands as they were in the beginning,
whole,
open,
warm
and without fear.

Do Not Stand at My Grave and Weep

By Mary E. Frye

Do not stand at my grave and weep.
I am not there, I do not sleep.
I am a thousand winds that blow,
I am the diamond glints on snow,
I am the sunlight on ripened grain,
I am the gentle autumn rain.
When you awaken in the morning's hush
I am the swift uplifting rush
Of quiet birds in circled flight.
I am the soft stars that shine at night.
Do not stand at my grave and cry,
I am not there. I did not die.

1. *Response*

a. For each poem in this section, write a brief phrase that sums up the emotion or state of mind the poet is expressing.
b. Which poem did you like best? Why?
c. The poems in this section have varying degrees of poetic structure, from the free verse of "As in the Beginning," to the patterned rhythm and rhyme of "God's World." What advantages and disadvantages come with a high degree of poetic structure? With less structure?
d. "Do Not Stand at My Grave and Weep" has become a favoured reading at funeral and memorial ceremonies. What do you think accounts for its popularity?
e. Write your own lyric poem. Choose an emotion or state of mind that is not represented by the poems in this section.

2. ***Literature Studies*** *Style* The style of "Life in Our Village" and "As in the Beginning" could be described as *understated.* In a group, explore the meaning of the term *understated.* What might be some characteristics of an understated style? Discuss whether "Life in Our Village" and "As in the Beginning" would be effective if the feelings expressed were more explicitly projected.

3. ***Critical Thinking*** Here is what Joan Besen says about her song "Canadian Sunrise": "I was trying to be descriptive about Canada, from one end to the other, trying to capture the experience of going back and forth across the country so much, as we do. In Canada you go to extremes: you go from ocean to mountain to rain forest and then it's absolutely flat as though the previous extreme never existed. Then it's rocks and trees for miles until you hit another ocean. If you go back and forth you really notice it." In a group, use Besen's statement to help you interpret "Canadian Sunrise." Make connections between the statement and specific lines in the song. If you wrote a song about Canada, what emotion would you want to express?

4. ***Media*** *Collage* Create a collage of visuals and text that evokes the feelings of a lyric poem of your choice. Your collage can be any combination of visuals, lines from the poem, and your own words.

5. ***Language Conventions*** *Parallel Structure* In the poem "As in the Beginning," the poet, Mary di Michele, has used **parallel structure**, with the repetition of the phrase "Give me my father's hands ..." Which other poets have used parallel structure in this section? Why do you think poets would choose to use this device?

Parallel structure is the repeated use of the same phrase or sentence, or the repeated use of a similar sentence structure. Parallel structure can be used to create balance or place emphasis on certain lines.

Painting was called silent poetry
and poetry speaking painting.
—*Ralph Waldo Emerson.*

Sonnet

The *sonnet* is a form of poetry that traditionally follows strict rules of metre, rhyme, structure, and length. It has fourteen lines, ten syllables per line, and a formal rhyme scheme. Most sonnets can also be classified as *lyric poems*.

Poets continue to be attracted to the creative challenge posed by the sonnet form. The best poets are able to fill the small and highly structured space of a sonnet with deep emotion and profound meaning.

Below is Elizabeth Barrett Browning's famous love poem, "How Do I Love Thee?" Speculate on why this sonnet gained the status of a classic. Do you think it still speaks to readers today?

Sonnet XLII
By Elizabeth Barrett Browning

How do I love thee? Let me count the ways.
I love thee to the depth and breadth and height
My soul can reach, when feeling out of sight
For the ends of Being and ideal Grace.
I love thee to the level of every day's
Most quiet need, by sun and candlelight.
I love thee freely, as men strive for Right;
I love thee purely, as they turn from Praise.
I love thee with the passion put to use
In my old griefs, and with my childhood's faith;
I love thee with a love I seemed to lose
With my lost saints,—I love thee with the breath,
Smiles, tears, of all my life!—and, if God choose,
I shall but love thee better after death.

Composed Upon Westminster Bridge

By William Wordsworth

Earth has not anything to show more fair:
Dull would he be of soul who could pass by
A sight so touching in its majesty:
This City now doth, like a garment wear
The beauty of the morning; silent, bare,
Ships, towers, domes, theatres, and temples lie
Open unto the fields, and to the sky;
All bright and glittering in the smokeless air.
Never did sun more beautifully steep
In his first splendour valley, rock, or hill;
Ne'er saw I, never felt, a calm so deep!
The river glideth at his own sweet will:
Dear God! the very houses seem asleep;
And all that mighty heart is lying still!

In the Crowd

By Ethelwyn Wertherald

Here in the crowded city's busy street,
Swayed by the eager, jostling, hasting throng,
Where Traffic's voice grows harsher and more strong,
I see within the stream of hurrying feet
A company of trees in their retreat,
Dew-bathed, dream-wrapped, and with a thrush's song
Emparadizing all the place, along
Whose paths I hear the pulse of Beauty beat.
'Twas yesterday I walked beneath the trees,
To-day I tread the city's stony ways;
And still the spell that o'er my spirit came
Turns harshest sounds to shy bird ecstasies,
Pours scent of pine through murky chimney haze,
And gives each careworn face a woodland frame.

Sonnet LV

By William Shakespeare

Not marble, nor the gilded monuments
Of princes, shall outlive this powerful rhyme;
But you shall shine more bright in these contents
Than unswept stone besmear'd with sluttish time.
When wasteful war shall statues overturn,
And broils root out the work of masonry,
Nor Mars his sword nor war's quick fire shall burn
The living record of your memory.
'Gainst death and all-oblivious enmity
Shall you pace forth; your praise shall still find room
Even in the eyes of all posterity
That wear this world out to the ending doom.
So, till the judgment that yourself arise,
You live in this, and dwell in lover's eyes.

"Not only marble, but the plastic toys"

By Wendy Cope

Not only marble, but the plastic toys
From cornflake packets will outlive this rhyme:
I can't immortalize you, love—our joys
Will lie unnoticed in the vault of time.
When Mrs Thatcher has been cast in bronze
And her administration is a page
In some O-level text-book, when the dons
Have analysed the story of our age,
When travel firms sell tours of outer space
And aeroplanes take off without a sound
And Tulse Hill has become a trendy place
And Upper Norwood's on the underground
Your beauty and my name will be forgotten—
My love is true, but all my verse is rotten.

Mrs Thatcher: Margaret Thatcher, former Prime Minister of the U.K.

O-level: General high school level in the U.K.

dons: professors

Tulse Hill, Upper Norwood: suburbs of London

Ozymandias

By Percy Bysshe Shelley

I met a traveller from an antique land
Who said: Two vast and trunkless legs of stone
Stand in the desert ... Near them, on the sand,
Half sunk, a shattered visage lies, whose frown,
And wrinkled lip, and sneer of cold command,
Tell that its sculptor well those passions read
Which yet survive, stamped on these lifeless things,
The hand that mock'd them and the heart that fed:
And on the pedestal these words appear:
'My name is Ozymandias, king of kings:
Look on my works, ye Mighty, and despair!'
Nothing beside remains. Round the decay
Of that colossal wreck, boundless and bare
The lone and level sands stretch far away.

1. *Response*

a. Several of the sonnets pose a challenge because they were written long ago, and the way English is spoken and written has changed since then. In a group, discuss how you responded to this challenge. Identify five reading strategies that contemporary readers can use to help them better understand poetry written in older varieties of English.

b. There are many sonnets that speculate on which endures longest—material objects or intangibles such as love or power. Shakespeare's "Sonnet LV," Cope's "Not only marble...," and Shelley's "Ozymandias" explore this question. In groups, analyse one of these sonnets. Come to a consensus on three statements that describe the position your poem is taking on the question described above. Write your sentences on poster paper and display them in your classroom.

c. Wordsworth's "Composed Upon Westminster Bridge" and Wertherald's "In the Crowd" look at the urban environment in unconventional ways. How are the poets' views similar and different? Did you prefer one poem over the other? Explain. What is your own perspective on city life?

2. ***Literature Studies*** *Sonnet Types* Carefully study the metre, rhyme scheme, and organization of Browning's Petrarchan sonnet ("Sonnet XLII") and Shakespeare's English sonnet ("Sonnet LV"). What are the distinguishing characteristics of each? Report your findings in a chart of your own design. When your chart is complete, use literary glossaries in the library or on the Internet to learn about the differences between the two forms of sonnet.

3. ***Writing*** *Parody* Wendy Cope's "Not only marble . . ." is a *parody* (a humorous imitation) of Shakespeare's "Sonnet LV." What specific features of Shakespeare's poem has Cope imitated? Are the messages of the poems similar or different? Select a serious poem and write your own parody of it.

4. ***Oral Language*** *In Conversation* Reread these sonnets, noting how the poets have used a first-person speaker. Each poem seems to be addressing a specific person, delivering a message using poetic language and structure. Use plain, non-poetic language to recreate one of these poems. Deliver your version to others.

The best and most beautiful things in the world
cannot be seen or even touched.
They must be felt with the heart.

—Helen Keller.

Light Verse

Light verse is the comedian of the poetic world. Its intention is to be humorous, clever, and sometimes rude. Though light verse often offers perceptive observations about human foibles and follies, there is always a whimsical or playful tone. More than anything, poets who indulge in light verse love to play and to pun with language.

Do you think these poems are clever? If so, how are they clever? How have the poets played with words?

The Limerick
Anonymous

The limerick packs laughs anatomical
Into space that is quite economical,
But the good ones, I've seen
So seldom are clean,
And the clean ones so seldom are comical.

To Make a Prairie
By Emily Dickinson

To make a prairie it takes a clover and one bee,
One clover, and a bee,
And revery.
The revery alone will do,
If bees are few.

World's Shortest Pessimistic Poem
By Robert Zend

Hope?
Nope.

Christmas Gift
By Victor Howes

Cashmere is a sweater
Mere cash, even better.

Writer's Block in the Computer Age

By Peggy Smith Krachun

Cursor, cursor, blinking cursor
Shade of iridescent green
Cursor in the "Home" position
On my new computer screen

Cursor at the starting gate
Chomping at the bit and byte
Pawing at the screen, impatient
Nagging me to start to write

Cursor poised for the race
In Position One, Line One
Waiting for a brilliant word
To set off the starting gun

Until now a plain old scribbler
Was the only thing I'd use
On it I would draw and doodle
While I waited for the Muse

Now I have a winking cursor
Mocking me in brilliant green
Have you ever tried to doodle
On a blank computer screen?

Nagging cursor, cursed cursor
Blinking on without a sound
Go away until I'm ready
I'll never write with you around.

from *Spellbound*

By Janet Minor

I have a spelling checker
It came with my PC;
It plainly marks four my revue
Mistakes I cannot sea.
I've run this poem threw it,
I'm sure your pleased too no,
Its letter perfect in it's weigh,
My checker tolled me sew.

A Spider Danced a Cosy Jig

By Irving Layton

A spider danced a cosy jig
Upon a frail trapeze;
And from a far-off clover field
An ant was heard to sneeze.

And kings that day were wise and just,
And stones began to bleed;
A dead man rose to tell a tale,
A bigot changed his creed.

The stableboy forgot his pride,
The queen confessed an itch;
And lo! more wonderful than all,
The poor man blessed the rich.

Crazy Times

By Miriam Waddington

When the birds riot
and the airplanes walk,
when the busy sit,
and the silent talk;

When the rains blow
and the winds pour,
when the sky is a land
and the sea its shore,

When shells grow snails
and worms eat toads,
when winters chase summers
on upside-down roads,

We'll sit by our fires
and warm our hands,
and tell old tales
of bygone lands.

Kidnap Poem

By Nikki Giovanni

ever been kidnapped
by a poet
if i were a poet
i'd kidnap you

put you in my phrases
and meter you to jones beach
or maybe coney island
or maybe just to my house

lyric you in lilacs
dash you in the rain
alliterate the beach
to complement my sea

play the lyre for you
ode you with my love song
anything to win you
wrap you in the red Black green
show you off to mama

yeah if i were
a poet i'd kid
nap you

from *Very Like a Whale*

By Ogden Nash

One thing that literature would be greatly the better
for
Would be a more restricted employment by authors
of simile and metaphor.
Authors of all races, be they Greeks, Romans, Teutons
or Celts,
Can't seem just to say that anything is the thing it is
but have to go out of their way to say that it is
like something else....

That's the kind of thing that's being done all the time
by poets, from Homer to Tennyson;
They're always comparing ladies to lilies and veal to
venison,
And they always say things like that the snow is a white
blanket after a winter storm.

Oh it is, is it, all right then, you sleep under a six-inch
blanket of snow and I'll sleep under a half-inch
blanket of unpoetical blanket material and we'll
see which one keeps warm,
And after that maybe you'll begin to comprehend
dimly
What I mean by too much metaphor and simile.

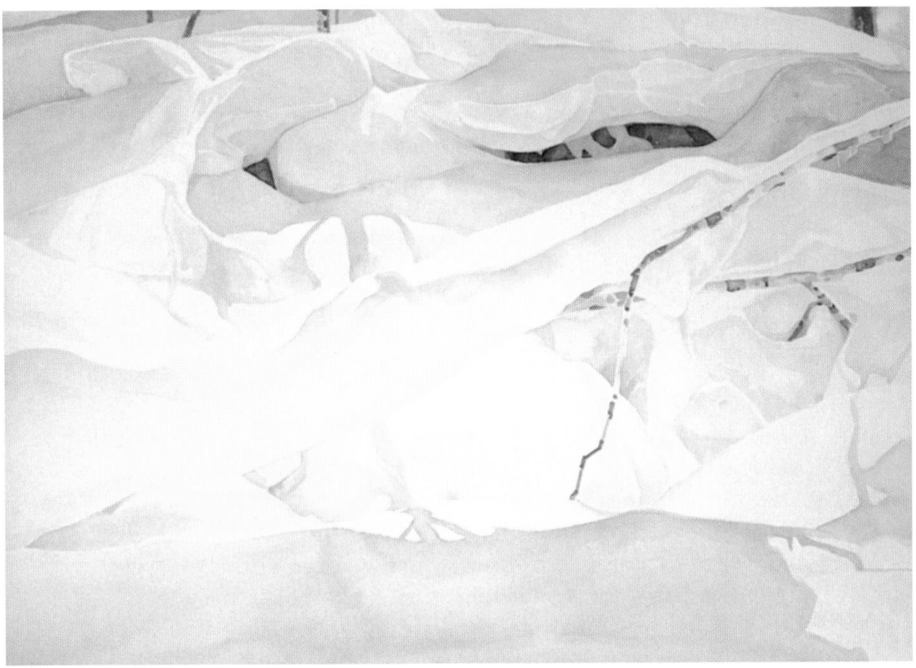

Winter's Blanket #1 by David McEown, watercolour

In your notebook, write a paragraph describing this painting. Try to make your description vivid without using similes or metaphors.

Poetry is the impish attempt
to paint the colour of the wind.
—*Maxwell Bodenheim*

1. ***Response***
a. "Writer's Block in the Computer Age" and "Spellbound" both deal humorously with the effect of computers on the writing process. Explain the techniques the poets use to generate the humour. Underneath their playful tone, these poems convey serious messages. What are they?
b. What do "A Spider Danced a Cosy Jig" and "Crazy Times" have in common? Which poem do you prefer? Why? Write an additional stanza or two for either (or both) of the poems.
c. Identify five specific examples of wordplay in "Kidnap Poem" and describe how the poet is playing with language in each case. Do you ever use wordplay in your own writing or speech? Explain.

2. ***Language Conventions*** *Spelling* Rewrite "Spellbound" making all the necessary corrections. On a different sheet of paper, write an additional two stanzas in the error-filled style of the original. Challenge a classmate to find and correct the errors. What type of error has the spell checker missed? How do you check for those types of errors in your own writing?

3. ***Writing*** *Limericks* Most limericks, like the one on page 186, are written to amuse, and many are written about interesting individuals—real or invented. For example:

    Limerick
    (Author unknown)

    There was a young woman named Bright
    Whose speed was much faster than light.
    She set out one day
    In a relative way,
    And returned on the previous night.

    Conventional limericks are five lines long and follow a definite pattern: lines one, two, and five contain eight syllables, and lines three and four contain six. The rhyme scheme is *aabba*. Write several limericks about the characters in a book you have studied or in a famous TV show or movie.

Satirical Poetry

Sometimes humour is used for the serious purpose of effecting positive change in people or in society. That kind of writing is known as *satire.* Poets were the first satirists, and the tradition of satirical poetry is alive and well today.

To fully appreciate satire, we must identify who or what is being ridiculed. Is it a specific person or society in general? Is it a behaviour, a belief, an attitude, or merely a minor human failing or weakness? All are legitimate targets for the satirical poet's wit.

In these poems, identify what exactly is being ridiculed. Discuss whether the attack or criticism is justified. What positive changes in attitude or behaviour do you think the poet is attempting to initiate?

Earth
By John Hall Wheelock

"A planet doesn't explode of itself," said drily
The Martian astronomer, gazing off into the air—
"That they were able to do it is proof that highly
Intelligent beings must have been living there."

Green Memory
By Langston Hughes

A wonderful time—the War:
when money rolled in
and blood rolled out.

But blood
was far away
from here—

Money was near.

St. George

By Nancy Senior

My dragon always loved walks
He used to go to the wall
where the golden chain hung
and take it in his mouth
laying his head on my lap
sideways, so the fire wouldn't burn my skirt

He looked so funny that way
with his legs dragging the floor
and his rear end high up
because he couldn't bend his hind legs
He was so well trained
always keeping his claws retracted
when he walked on the rug

With him on the leash, I could go anywhere
No band of robbers dared attack

This morning in the woods
we had stopped for a drink
where a spring gushes out of a cave

when suddenly, a man in armour
riding a white horse
leapt out of the bushes
crying "Have no fear, Maiden
I will save you"

And before I could say a word
he had stabbed my dragon in the throat
and leaping down from the horse
cut off his head
and held it up for me to see
the poor dead eyes still surprised
and mine filling with tears
He hadn't even had time to put out his claws

And the man said
"Don't cry, Maiden
You are safe now
But let me give you some good advice
Don't ever walk alone in the woods
for the next time you meet a dragon
there might not be a knight around to save you"

St. George and the Dragon by Uccello (Paolo di Dono), 1460. Oil on canvas

Nancy Senior, the author of "St. George," was inspired by this painting to write her poem. Would you interpret this painting in the same way? Explain.

The Unknown Citizen

By W. H. Auden

(To JS/07/M/378
This Marble Monument
Is Erected by the State)

He was found by the Bureau of Statistics to be
One against whom there was no official complaint,
And all the reports on his conduct agree
That, in the modern sense of an old-fashioned word, he was a saint,
For in everything he did he served the Greater Community.
Except for the War till the day he retired
He worked in a factory and never got fired,
But satisfied his employers, Fudge Motors Inc.
Yet he wasn't a scab or odd in his views,
For his Union reports that he paid his dues,
(Our report on his Union shows it was sound)
And our Social Psychology workers found
That he was popular with his mates and liked a drink.
The Press are convinced that he bought a paper every day
And that his reactions to advertisements were normal in every way.
Policies taken out in his name prove that he was fully insured,
And his Health-card shows he was once in hospital but left it cured.
Both Producers Research and High-Grade Living declare
He was fully sensible to the advantages of the Installment Plan
And had everything necessary to the Modern Man,
A phonograph, a radio, a car and a frigidaire.
Our researchers into Public Opinion are content
That he held the proper opinions for the time of year;
When there was peace, he was for peace; when there was war, he went.
He was married and added five children to the population,
Which our Eugenist says was the right number for a parent of his generation,
And our teachers report that he never interfered with their education.
Was he free? Was he happy? The question is absurd:
Had anything been wrong, we should certainly have heard.

#9

By Lawrence Ferlinghetti

'History is made
of the lies of the victors'
but you would never dream it
from the covers of the textbooks
nor from the way the victors are portrayed
as super-benevolent altruists
and lovers of the poor and downtrodden
who never had a chance to
rise up and write their own dubious stories
in the mystery we call history
(a river blurred with tears
or a running sea
whose fish change color
when cast upon the beach)
And the feelthy rich
get filthier or richer or whatever
because money really doesn't 'trickle down'
but rises like anything hot
And they keep getting more medals
for bad behavior and for agreeing that Yes
Justice has been done and
the stock market is open to everyone Long live usura[1]
and the jury system is the best ever for
preserving the status quota[2]
And in fact why not have historians who
leave blanks in their writings
to be filled in variously
depending on who's in power
and the computer makes changes easy
And anyway history isn't really history
until it's rewritten
or at least until
it repeats itself
And a lot of genocides and massacres

[1]**usura:** from the word *usury*, to rhyme with quota
[2]**status quota:** a play on the words *status quo* and *quota*

1. *Response*

a. Complete the following analysis for any of the poems in this section:

- Who or what do you think is being ridiculed?
- In your opinion, is the ridicule justified? Is the issue important? Explain.
- What is the tone of the attack?
- How is humour or ridicule created in the poem?
- Do you think the poem is an effective satire? Why?

b. Many song lyrics are satirical poems set to music. Find a song lyric that you consider to be satirical. Using the questions in part (a) above, complete an analysis of the lyrics. Present your analysis to the class after letting them hear the song.

2. *Literature Studies* *Allegory* To appreciate an **allegory**, it is necessary to go beyond the literal level of the work and come to terms with the deeper symbolic level. Read "St. George" carefully, then speculate on what each character or element on the literal level might symbolize. What belief, attitude, and/or behaviour do you think the poet wishes to change for the better? Compare your analysis with that of a classmate. Did you reach the same conclusions?

An **allegory** is a story with an underlying meaning parallel to but different from the surface meaning. An allegory presents ideas in a concrete, vivid way.

3. *Writing* *Satirical Poem* Write your own satirical poem directed at a human folly or foible that concerns or annoys you. Use any poem in this section as a model if you wish.

4. *Oral Language* *Discussion* As a group, choose one of the poems in this section and discuss its message. Half of your group can support the poet's point of view, while the rest of the group presents opposing points.

Poetry is .../a sort of answer I feel compelled to give/to my own life.

—*Furugh Farrukhzad*

Didactic Poetry

Some poets strive to produce positive changes, but prefer to avoid the satirical approach. Instead, their poetry offers explicit advice or moral lessons, and is known as *didactic verse.*

As readers, we rarely wish to be patronized or preached at by poets. For these reasons, didactic poetry works best when it has elements of craft and subtlety.

To what extent would you consider these to be good poems? Subtle poems? Which do you think is the most effective in influencing the reader's thoughts and feelings? Explain.

Heart
By Suniti Namjoshi

And then there was the woman who had no head,
all heart she was. She was even called Heart, and not
(as one might have expected) the Headless Woman.
Her function in life was to serve other people and this
she did with a willing heart. She cooked, she cleaned,
she baked, she scoured and she was always kind and
loving and gentle, and never once complained of feeling
tired. In the course of time her children grew up,
her husband grew old, eventually he died and then he
was buried. The Headless Woman was all alone. So
she went to the Government to ask for a pension. And
she didn't get it. Now I'm not suggesting that the
Government was brutal. The problem was that she
had no head and couldn't ask.

The Sunlight
By Chief Dan George

The sunlight does not leave its marks
on the grass.
So we, too, pass silently.

Universal Soldier

By Buffy Sainte-Marie

He's five foot two and he's six feet four
He fights with missiles and with spears
He's all of thirty-one and he's only seventeen
He's been a soldier for a thousand years.

He's a Catholic a Hindu an Atheist a Jain
A Buddhist and a Baptist and a Jew
And he knows he shouldn't kill and he knows he always will
Kill you for me my friend and me for you.

And he's fighting for Canada and he's fighting for France
He's fighting for the USA
And he's fighting for the Russians and he's fighting for Japan
And he thinks we'll put an end to war this way.

And he's fighting for democracy, he's fighting for the reds
He says it's for the peace of all
He's the one who must decide who's to live and who's to die
And he never sees the writing on the wall.

But without him how would Hitler have condemned them at Dachau
Without him Caesar would've stood alone
He's the one who gives his body as a weapon of the war
And without him all this can't go on.

He's the Universal Soldier and he really is to blame
His orders come from far away no more
They come from him and you and me
And brothers can't you see
This is not the way we put an end to war.

There Will Come Soft Rains

By Sara Teasdale

There will come soft rains and the smell of the ground,
And swallows circling with their shimmering sound;
And frogs in the pools singing at night,
And wild plum trees in tremulous white;
Robins will wear their feathery fire,
Whistling their whims on a low fence-wire;
And not one will know of the war, not one
Will care at last when it is done.
Not one would mind, neither bird nor tree,
If mankind perished utterly;
And Spring herself, when she woke at dawn
Would scarcely know that we were gone.

I Believe

By Robert Fulghum

I believe that imagination is stronger than knowledge—
That myth is more potent than history.
I believe that dreams are more powerful than facts—
That hope always triumphs over experience—
That laughter is the only cure for grief.
And I believe that love is stronger than death.

I have nothing to say, I am saying it,
and that is poetry.

—*John Cage*

the laughing heart

By Charles Bukowski

your life is your life.
don't let it be clubbed into dank
submission.
be on the watch.
there are ways out.
there is light somewhere.
it may not be much light but
it beats the
darkness.
be on the watch.
the gods will offer you
chances.
know them, take them.
you can't beat death but
you can beat death
in life,
sometimes.
and the more often you
learn to do it,
the more light there will
be.
your life is your life.
know it while you have
it.
you are marvelous
the gods wait to delight
in
you.

The Sun Witness

By Nurunnessa Choudhury
Translated from the Bengali by the author and Paul Joseph Thompson

Long ago a young girl
wearing a saffron coloured saree
walked gracefully
on her way—
She moved the square stone
from the white
near-dead grass.
By the lightning speed
of her black hand.

Silently, with her gaze,
she commanded the sun
to send its light
down upon everything,
even the white grass.

The sun accepted
her easy command
and came down with humility.

Days after,
she passed beggars in the street,
and tucked in her silk saree
to avoid their stains.

Seeing this,
The sun hid behind clouds,
and rain came,
unexpectedly, like tears.

Take Something Like a Star

By Robert Frost

O Star (the fairest one in sight),
We grant your loftiness the right
To some obscurity of cloud—
It will not do to say of night,
Since dark is what brings out your light.
Some mystery becomes the proud.
But to be wholly taciturn
In your reserve is not allowed.
Say something to us we can learn
By heart and when alone repeat.
Say something! And it says, "I burn."
But say with what degree of heat.
Talk Fahrenheit, talk Centigrade.
Use language we can comprehend.
Tell us what elements you blend.
It gives us strangely little aid,
But does tell something in the end.
And steadfast as Keats' Eremite,
Not even stooping from its sphere
It asks a little of us here.
It asks of us a certain height,
So when at times the mob is swayed
To carry praise or blame too far,
We may take something like a star
To stay our minds on and be staid.

Keats: John Keats, English poet (1795–1821)

Eremite: literally *hermit*, from a line by John Keats: "Like nature's patient, sleepless Eremite."

non-resident identity

By Mo Khan

east is east and west is west/ and never the twain shall meet// i'm running out of patience/ sense my situation/ tense, my ancient body burns/ i learn to bend and turn in self-defence/ self preservation/ cultural invasion/ ethnic mastication/ race-and-nation separation/ face it; nothing sates this age of information// second-generation asian rage/ engaged in recitation/ put my fate into rotation/ mired in contemplation/ tired of waiting for my compensation/ recompense/ i recommence/ i recommend you reconsider your attempts at reconciliation/ rehabilitation/ from your station you can catch the scent of rising incense/ thick, but not disguising my societal demise/ my culture's immolation/ it's immense, but then, are you surprised?// NRI[1]/ pardesi[2]/ made to see my race the way they see it/ day-to-day their prostrate grace/ is what i'm faced with/ hate is hastily replaced/ displaced by warm embraces/ great/ but what's it laced with?/ wait until i'm wasted/ seal my fate// exoticize/ eroticize me/ cauterize my conscious highs/ you're carbon-copying me down to size// my star is rising from the east/ my native tongue is unleashed/ scarred/ but each and every part of my speech/ hearkens to the drone of the sitar/ aur kitna beqaraar hai mera intezaar[3]/ it's hard// i'm yearning/ like a cut sardar[4] returning to his turban/ disregard this urban darkness/ i'm unhesitant to learn/ and unconcerned with/ near and far/ it's evident/ that home/ is more than where you are/ a global resident/ remembering the past but living in the present// embers of your pleasant trust/ combust and turn to conscious dust/ we must adjust/ there is/ no justice./ just us.//

---

[1]**NRI: non-resident Indian:** common term for South Asian immigrants

[2]**pardesi:** Hindi word meaning "stranger," especially to the country, that is, emigrant

[3]**"aur kitna . . .": Urdu:** "and how chaotic is my wait"

[4]**cut sardar:** a Sikh who shaves and chooses not to wear the turban

1. ***Response***

   a. For each poem in this section, write a brief summary (one or two sentences) of the moral lesson you think it presents. How explicit is the lesson in each poem? Does the explicitness of the lesson influence your appreciation of the poem? Explain.

   b. Which poem says something you strongly agree with? In a short composition, describe how society might change if many people truly took that lesson to heart.

   c. Poets who use the free verse form often use line breaks to emphasize certain words and ideas. Look at the line breaks in "the laughing heart" and "The Sun Witness." Identify one line break that effectively emphasizes something that is central to the poem's meaning, explaining how you came to that conclusion. Which poet do you think makes the most effective use of line breaks? Explain.

2. ***Language Focus*** *Gender* Study the pronouns used in "The Universal Soldier" and "There Will Come Soft Rains." What underlying assumptions do these pronouns suggest? Do you agree with those assumptions? Give reasons for your point of view.

3. ***Literature Studies*** *Interpretation* In a group, choose the one poem in this section that you feel is the most challenging to grasp. Work together to try to enhance your understanding. Pose questions about specific words and phrases and speculate on possible answers. Your goal is to present an interpretation of the poem to the rest of the class.

4. ***Media*** *Inspirational Poster* Choose a brief quotation from any of the poems in this section and create an inspirational poster to represent that quotation. You will need to find or create a visual that complements the message in the words. Display your poster in the classroom or around the school.

I would define the poetic effect as the capacity that a text displays for continuing to generate different readings, without ever being completely consumed.

—*Umberto Eco*

Descriptive Poetry

Descriptive poetry is notable for its vividness. Through memorable descriptions that appeal directly to our senses, descriptive poetry engages our minds, our hearts, and our imaginations.

For each of these poems, identify the specific senses that are being appealed to. Which poem do you think is most effective in painting a mental picture?

Waves
Anonymous (from the Arabic)

Waves
bow
before
the shore

courtiers
to their king

and then
withdraw.

Evening
By Claire Harris

the lift hums and stops
footsteps dim in the muffled corridor
a key struggles in the lock

the bright scent of onions opens and shuts

The Eagle
By Alfred, Lord Tennyson

He clasps the crag with crooked hands;
Close to the sun in lonely lands,
Ringed with the azure world he stands;
The wrinkled sea beneath him crawls;
He watches from the mountain walls,
And like a thunderbolt he falls.

Hockey

By Scott Blaine

The ice is smooth, smooth, smooth.
The air bites to the center
Of warmth and flesh, and I whirl.
It begins in a game ...
The puck swims, skims, veers,
Goes leading my vision
Beyond the chasing reach of my stick.

The air is sharp, steel-sharp.
I suck needles of breathing,
And feel the players converge.
It grows to a science ...
We clot, break, drive,
Electrons in motion
In the magnetic pull of the puck.

The play is fast, fierce, tense.
Sticks click and snap like teeth
Of wolves on the scent of a prey.
It ends in the kill ...
I am one of the pack in a mad,
Taut leap of desperation
In the wild, slashing drive for the goal.

A poem is like a wine glass in which you can hold up a little bit of reality and taste it.

—*Gwen Harwood*

The Rain Hammers

By Michael Wade

The rain hammers at my window
with fists abandoned by the wind
my curtains billow with delight
at the curious black waters bludgeoning

inside
a semi-precious bumblebee
mysteriously hums above
a plastic flower

eternity becomes
the sound of the sea in the night
the pound of the tide in the black
the flood of the shore in the dark
the cry of the gull in the dawn

the sun comes out of the sea
covered with weed
surrounded with sound
cornered by clouds
and breathes on the world.

Twilight Entered My Room

By Pandelis Prevelakis

Twilight entered my room
like a red lion.
Its reflected light fell in the mirror
and I felt its soft paws
touching my naked feet.
I stooped under the table
which the day's work had blessed
and saw the sun kissing my feet
with its red tongue.

Big Ben, Parliament & River Thames—London, England by Harald Sund

How do you think the effects in this photo were achieved? What effect does the photo have on the viewer? Write a descriptive poem about this image.

Prelude #1

By T. S. Eliot

The winter evening settles down
With smells of steaks in passageways.
Six o'clock.
The burnt-out ends of smoky days.
And now a gusty shower wraps
The grimy scraps
Of withered leaves about your feet
And newspapers from vacant lots;
The showers beat
On broken blinds and chimney-pots,
And at the corner of the street
A lonely cab-horse steams and stamps.
And then the lighting of the lamps.

The Spider Holds a Silver Ball

By Emily Dickinson

The Spider holds a Silver Ball
In unperceived Hands—
And dancing softly to Himself
His Yarn of Pearl—unwinds—

He plies from Nought to Nought—
In unsubstantial Trade—
Supplants our Tapestries with His—
In half the period—

An Hour to rear supreme
His Continents of Light—
Then dangle from the Housewife's Broom—
His Boundaries—forgot—

1. ***Response***
a. Descriptive poetry often seeks to suggest a particular mood. What is the dominant mood of each poem in this section? Identify specific words or phrases that are instrumental in creating that mood.
b. Look closely at the poem "Hockey." What patterns can you detect that help to build a structure for the poem? Do you prefer to write highly structured or less structured poems? Explain.
c. Description can capture the experience of hearing, seeing, smelling, tasting, and touching. Based on your reading of the poems in this section, including those on page 207, which of the five kinds of sensory experiences are most often described? Why? Write your own descriptive poem, focussing on one or more of the five senses.

2. ***Language Conventions*** *Vivid Language* There are several keys to good description: forceful verbs, specific nouns, colourful adjectives, lively adverbs. Create a four-column chart with those four headings. Drawing from all the poems in this section, find examples to complete your chart. Add some of your own examples to each column.

3. ***Media*** *Multimedia Presentation* Create a multimedia presentation based on one or more of the poems in this section. Your presentation may incorporate computers, video or audio tape, CDs, magazine illustrations, original artwork, oral commentary, live music, movement, or dance, in any combination. The entire poem must be included somehow in your work.

As honey sweetens/the mouth
readily/a poem should
make sense/right away.

—*Atakuri Molla*

Narrative Poetry

Narrative poetry tells a story. It is concerned with characters, contexts (time, place, and situation), and conflict. Often the poet maintains a tight focus on the thoughts and feelings of the protagonist, and the details of the story are only suggested. This obliges the reader to participate in the creative process to fill in the gaps.

As you read the poems below, use your imagination to see beyond the few details the poets provide. What stories suggest themselves to you?

My Hands
By Takeo Nakano

My hands tremble
As I sign my naturalization
papers
Making me a Canadian
citizen
And Canada my final resting
place.

Day After Day . . .
By Wang Hung Kung
Translated by Kenneth Rexroth

Day after day the rain falls.
Week after week the grass grows.
Year after year the river flows.
Seventy years, seventy years,
The wheel of dreams revolves.

Meeting at Night
By Robert Browning

The gray sea and the long black land;
And the yellow half-moon large and low;
And the startled little waves that leap
In fiery ringlets from their sleep,
As I gain the cove with pushing prow,
And quench its speed i' the slushy sand.

Then a mile of warm sea-scented beach;
Three fields to cross till a farm appears;
A tap at the pane, the quick sharp scratch
And blue spurt of a lighted match,
And a voice less loud, through its joys and fears,
Than the two hearts beating each to each!

Gaining Yardage

By Leo Dangel

The word *friend* never came up
between Arlo and me—we're farm neighbors
who hang around together, walk beans,
pick rocks, and sit on the bench
at football games, weighing the assets
of the other side's cheerleaders.
Tonight we lead 48 to 6, so the coach
figures sending us both in is safe.
I intercept an underthrown pass
only because I'm playing the wrong position,
and Arlo is right there to block for me
because he's in the wrong place,
so we gallop up the field, in the clear
until their second-string quarterback
meets us at the five-yard line,
determined to make up for his bad throw.
Arlo misses the block, the guy has me
by the leg and jersey, and going down,
I flip the ball back to Arlo, getting up,
who fumbles, and their quarterback
almost recovers, then bobbles the ball
across the goal line, and our coach,
who told even the guys with good hands
never to mess around with laterals,
must feel his head exploding,
when Arlo and I dive on the ball together
in the end zone and dance and slap
each other on the back.
They give Arlo the touchdown, which rightly
should be mine, but I don't mind,
and I suppose we are friends, and will be,
unless my old man or his decides to move
to another part of the country.

Snake

By D. H. Lawrence

A snake came to my water-trough
On a hot, hot day, and I in pyjamas for the heat,
To drink there.

In the deep, strange-scented shade of the great dark carob-tree
I came down the steps with my pitcher
And must wait, must stand and wait, for there he was at the trough
before me.

He reached down from a fissure in the earth-wall in the gloom
And trailed his yellow-brown slackness soft-bellied down, over the
edge of the stone trough
And rested his throat upon the stone bottom,
And where the water had dripped from the tap, in a small clearness,
He sipped with his straight mouth,
Softly drank through his straight gums, into his slack long body,
Silently.

Someone was before me at my water-trough,
And I, like a second comer, waiting.

He lifted his head from his drinking, as cattle do,
And looked at me vaguely, as drinking cattle do,
And flickered his two-forked tongue from his lips, and mused a
moment,
And stooped and drank a little more,
Being earth-bronze, earth-golden from the burning bowels of the
earth
On the day of Sicilian July, with Etna[1] smoking.

The voice of my education said to me
He must be killed,
For in Sicily the black, black snakes are innocent, the gold are
venomous.

[1]**Etna:** Situated in Sicily, Italy, Mount Etna is the highest active volcano in Europe.

And voices in me said, If you were a man
You would take a stick and break him now, and finish him off.

But must I confess how I liked him,
How glad I was he had come like a guest in quiet, to drink at my water-trough
And depart peaceful, pacified, and thankless,
Into the burning bowels of this earth?

Was it cowardice, that I dared not kill him?
Was it perversity, that I longed to talk to him?
Was it humility, to feel so honoured?
I felt so honoured.

And yet those voices:
If you were not afraid, you would kill him!

And truly I was afraid, I was most afraid,
But even so, honoured still more
That he should seek my hospitality
From out the dark door of the secret earth.

He drank enough
And lifted his head, dreamily, as one who has drunken,
And flickered his tongue like a forked night on the air, so black,
Seeming to lick his lips,
And looked around like a god, unseeing, into the air,
And slowly turned his head,
And slowly, very slowly, as if thrice adream,
Proceeded to draw his slow length curving round
And climb again the broken bank of my wall-face.

And as he put his head into that dreadful hole,
And as he slowly drew up, snake-easing his shoulders, and entered farther,
A sort of horror, a sort of protest against his withdrawing into that horrid black hole,
Deliberately going into the blackness, and slowly drawing himself after,
Overcame me now his back was turned.

I looked around, I put down my pitcher,
I picked up a clumsy log
And threw it at the water-trough with a clatter.

I think it did not hit him,
But suddenly that part of him that was left behind convulsed in
undignified haste,
Writhed like lightning, and was gone
Into the black hole, the earth-lipped fissure in the wall-front,
At which, in the intense still noon, I stared with fascination.

And immediately I regretted it.
I thought how paltry, how vulgar, what a mean act!
I despised myself and the voices of my accursed human education.

And I thought of the albatross,
And I wished he would come back, my snake.

For he seemed to me again like a king,
Like a king in exile, uncrowned in the underworld,
Now due to be crowned again.

And so, I missed my chance with one of the lords
Of life.
And I have something to expiate;
A pettiness.

Carolyn Walking, N.M. by Marilyn Conway

Use one of the poems in this section as a model and write a narrative poem that tells a story inspired by this photo. You could use first person, third person, objective, or omniscient point of view.

Legend

By Judith Wright

The blacksmith's boy went out with a rifle
and a black dog running behind.
Cobwebs snatched at his feet,
rivers hindered him,
thorn-branches caught at his eyes to make him blind
and the sky turned into an unlucky opal,
but he didn't mind.
I can break branches, I can swim rivers, I can stare out
any spider I meet,
said he to his dog and his rifle.

The blacksmith's boy went over the paddocks
with his old black hat on his head.
Mountains jumped in his way,
rocks rolled down on him,
and the old crow cried, You'll soon be dead;
and the rain came down like mattocks.
But he only said
I can climb mountains, I can dodge rocks, I can shoot
an old crow any day.
And he went on over the paddocks.

When he came to the end of the day the sun began falling.
Up came the night ready to swallow him,
like the barrel of a gun,
like an old black hat,
like a black dog hungry to follow him.
Then the pigeon, the magpie and the dove began wailing,
and the grass lay down to pillow him.
His rifle broke, his hat blew away and his dog was gone,
and the sun was falling.

But in front of the night the rainbow stood on a mountain
just as his heart foretold.
He ran like a hare,
he climbed like a fox,
he caught it in his hands, the colours and the cold—

like a bar of ice, like the columns of a fountain,
like a ring of gold.
The pigeon, the magpie and the dove flew up to stare,
and the grass stood up again on the mountain.

The blacksmith's boy hung the rainbow on his shoulder,
instead of his broken gun.
Lizards ran out to see,
snakes made way for him,
and the rainbow shone as brightly as the sun.
All the world said, Nobody is braver, nobody is bolder,
nobody else has done
anything to equal it. He went home as easy as could be
with the swinging rainbow on his shoulder.

The Child Who Walks Backwards

By Lorna Crozier

My next-door neighbour tells me
her child runs into things.
Cupboard corners and doorknobs
have pounded their shapes
into his face. She says
he is bothered by dreams,
rises in sleep from his bed
to steal through the halls
and plummet like a wounded bird
down the flight of stairs.

This child who climbed my maple
with the sureness of a cat,
trips in his room, cracks
his skull on the bedpost,
smacks his cheeks on the floor.
When I ask about the burns

on the back of his knee,
his mother tells me
he walks backwards
into fireplace grates
or sits and stares at flames
while sparks burn stars in his skin.

Other children write their names
on the casts that hold
his small bones.
His mother tells me
he runs into things,
walks backwards,
breaks his leg
while she lies
sleeping.

Subway Exit: Spring

By Jane Poston

a green world of pigeons.
into
ator
cal-
es-
way
sub-
St.
ton
ing-
Arl-
the
via
born
re-
I am
ing
Each morn-

1. ***Response***

a. For any two poems in this section, complete the following analysis:

- What is your best estimate of when and where the narrative takes place?
- What are the characteristics of the narrator or protagonist?
- What conflict, if any, does the narrative describe?
- What do you think is the main purpose of the poem?

b. Discuss the advantages and disadvantages of telling a story through verse rather than prose. Come to a consensus on at least three advantages and three disadvantages. Provide support for your positions, using specific references to the poems in this section, where possible.

c. In your opinion, which poem in this unit tells the most powerful and/or engaging story? Explore your response in a brief piece of writing, supplying the reasons for your preference. How does your opinion compare with the responses of your classmates?

2. ***Oral Language*** *Poetry Performance* In groups, prepare a dramatic performance of either Judith Wright's "Legend" or D. H. Lawrence's "Snake." What special techniques can your group use to enhance the impact of your performance? After your presentation, reflect in writing on which techniques were most successful. Include suggestions that will help you prepare future oral presentations.

3. ***Media*** *Storyboard* Assume you were going to create a video to represent one of the poems in this section. In preparation for the filming, create a storyboard outlining the various shots your video camera would record. Your storyboard should contain at least ten frames. Accompany each frame with one or two sentences that specify details such as the camera angle, lighting requirements, and positioning of characters and so on.

Listen, real poetry doesn't say anything,
it just ticks off the possibilities.
Opens all doors.
You can walk through any one that suits you.

—*Jim Morrison*

Reflective Poetry

Poems that search for deep truths and pose the essential questions of existence are classified as *reflective poetry*. Here the poets contemplate life and what it means to be human. They invite us to reflect on matters of identity and purpose: Who am I? Why am I here? Is there an ultimate purpose to life? What is the nature of happiness?

Once you have read the following two poems, write down the essential questions that the poems imply. Are any answers suggested in these lines? Explain. How would you answer the questions?

from *Auguries of Innocence*
By William Blake

To see a World in a Grain of Sand,
And a Heaven in a Wild Flower,
Hold Infinity in the palm of your hand,
And Eternity in an hour.

from *I Have Had to Learn to Live With My Face*
By Diane Wakoski

I look at pictures of myself as a child.
I looked lumpy, unformed, like a piece of dough,
and it has been my task as a human being
to carve out a mind, carve out a face,
carve out a shape with arms & legs, to put a voice inside,
and to make a person from a presence.
And I don't think I'm unique.
I think a thousand of you, at least, can look at those old photos,
reflect on your life
and see your own sculpture at work.

This Morning I Sat

By Rosalie Fowler

This morning I sat
indolent and limp
against a window pane
and watched a frantic sparrow
defying my lean cat.

The cat was taut
with leap and speed
and stealth and strength.
The bird had only poetry to wield
and lost.

Cats eat up grace with relish.
But they are poets too
and can create cunning
and flights of terror
with their eyes.

A small shudder
rippled down my flesh.

Do I have wings or claws?

Poetry ... is another way to
be hurled straight into
the heart of God.

—*Marjorie Holmes*

The Real Math

By Oscar Peñaranda

Here's a clue
if you take what I did
and to that add my dreams
divide by what I didn't do
and said I would do
multiply that by what I didn't say
yet did just the same
then subtract what I could have done
but said to myself impossible

Then you have something
on me
yet after all this
you can find it in your heart

to erase everything
take nothing before and beyond
erase all
and gather the answer of who I am
cradled in your hands
only at that moment

then you can begin
to call me by a
name

if not
let me slide and remain

—anonymous

Nothing Is Like Nothing Else

By Elizabeth Brewster

When I was young and knew no better
I was always wanting to compare this to that:
Hearts might be cold as ice cream cones:
Water shone like flashlights;
Autumn leaves were mustard
On the sky's blue china plate.

But now I know different.
Now I know that nothing is like nothing else.
A white plate is a white plate, smooth, glossy;
Snow is another whiteness: not powdery,
Not like wool or silk or feathers,
But like itself, cold, dense, soft,
And yet sometimes hard, sometimes pointed,
Reflecting the sky, which is not like blue nylon,
But has its own special colour, texture, absence of texture.
And there are so many objects,
So many whites, blues, transparencies,
That the eye and the mind must be careful,
Must work very hard not to be confused by them.

And when I get beyond objects
(Seashells, mirrors, bottles of ginger ale,
Daisy petals, and all the rest)
And try to consider minds and motives
And poetry and politics
And work and friendship—
Then language is difficult indeed,
Since minds are never alike
And never like snow.

The New House

By Maya Angelou

What words
have smashed against
these walls,
crashed up and down these
halls,
lain mute and then drained
their meanings out and into
these floors?

What feelings, long since
dead,
streamed vague yearnings
below this ceiling
light?
In some dimension,
which I cannot know,
the shadows of
another still exist. I bring my
memories, held too long in check,
to let them here shoulder
space and place to be.

And when I leave to
find another house,
I wonder, what among
these shades will be
left of me.

Death of a Young Son by Drowning

By Margaret Atwood

He, who navigated with success
the dangerous river of his own birth
once more set forth

on a voyage of discovery
into the land I floated on
but could not touch to claim.

His feet slid on the bank,
the currents took him;
he swirled with ice and trees in the swollen water

and plunged into distant regions,
his head a bathysphere;
through his eyes' thin glass bubbles

he looked out, reckless adventurer
on a landscape stranger than Uranus
we have all been to and some remember.

There was an accident; the air locked,
he was hung in the river like a heart.
They retrieved the swamped body,

cairn of my plans and future charts,
with poles and hooks
from among the nudging logs.

It was spring, the sun kept shining, the new grass
lept to solidity;
my hands glistened with details.

After the long trip I was tired of waves.
My foot hit rock. The dreamed sails
collapsed, ragged.

I planted him in this country
like a flag.

My Father Is a Simple Man

By Luis Omar Salinas

I walk to town with my father
to buy a newspaper. He walks slower
than I do so I must slow up.
The street is filled with children.
We argue about the price
of pomegranates, I convince
him it is the fruit of scholars.
He has taken me on this journey
and it's been lifelong.
He's sure I'll be healthy
so long as I eat more oranges,
and tells me the orange
has seeds and so is perpetual;
and we too will come back
like the orange trees.
I ask him what he thinks
about death and he says
he will gladly face it when
it comes but won't jump
out in front of a car.
I'd gladly give my life
for this man with a sixth
grade education, whose kindness
and patience are true ...
The truth of it is, he's the scholar,
and when the bitter-hard reality
comes at me like a punishing
evil stranger, I can always
remember that here was a man
who was a worker and provider,
who learned the simple facts
in life and lived by them,
who held no pretense.
And when he leaves without
benefit of fanfare or applause
I shall have learned what little
there is about greatness.

Ethics

By Linda Pastan

In ethics class so many years ago
our teacher asked this question every fall:
if there were a fire in a museum
which would you save, a Rembrandt painting
or an old woman who hadn't many
years left anyhow? Restless on hard chairs
caring little for pictures or old age
we'd opt one year for life, the next for art
and always half-heartedly. Sometimes
the woman borrowed my grandmother's face
leaving her usual kitchen to wander
some drafty, half-imagined museum.
One year, feeling clever, I replied
why not let the woman decide herself?
Linda, the teacher would report, eschews
the burdens of responsibility.
This fall in a real museum I stand
before a real Rembrandt, old woman,
or nearly so, myself. The colors
within this frame are darker than autumn,
darker even than winter—the browns of earth,
though earth's most radiant elements burn
through the canvas. I know now that woman
and painting and season are almost one
and all beyond saving by children.

Rembrandt: Rembrandt Harmenszoon van Rijn (1606–1669), a Dutch painter.

Poetry is the opening and closing of a door,
leaving those who look through to guess
about what is seen during a moment.
—*Carl Sandburg*

Philosophy and Meditation by Rembrandt. 1632. Oil on wood. Musée du Louvre, Paris

Consider this painting and the teacher's question in "Ethics." How would you respond to that question?

1. ***Response***

a. "This Morning I Sat" and "The New Math" both explore the issue of identity, asking the question, "Who and what am I?" Which poem do you prefer? Why?
b. The speaker in Linda Pastan's "Ethics" concludes by suggesting an answer to the ethical question posed at the beginning of the poem. Express the answer in your own words. Do you agree with that answer? Explain.
c. Which of the poems in this section ends on a note of uncertainty? Why do you think uncertainty might be a quality of many reflective poems?
d. Choose one poem in this section and compose your own poetic answer to the question it poses.

2. ***Critical Thinking*** Reflective poetry deals with essential questions about people and about life. In a group, brainstorm a list of essential questions that could become the starting point for a reflective poem. Your list should contain ten questions. Compare lists in a class discussion. Generally speaking, can the questions you framed be answered definitively? What does this suggest about the process of seeking answers to such questions?

3. ***Language Conventions*** *Rhetorical Questions* To create a reflective poem, a poet could use **rhetorical questions**, as Maya Angelou does in "The New House." Reread her poem to see how she has used rhetorical questions. How many of the essential questions you developed in activity 2 were rhetorical? Use one of them as a starting point for a new poem.

Rhetorical questions are questions asked for effect, rather than in a search for information.

4. ***Writing*** *Celebratory Poem* In "My Father Is a Simple Man," the narrator describes and celebrates the essence of a father. Using the poem as a model, write your own poem in which you reflect on the life of a loved one and celebrate what that person means to you. As Salinas does, include specific details that bring the person to life.

The Test of Time

Some poems defy time. Instead of fading as the years pass, they flourish and grow richer. We read them and reread them, study them and appreciate them. All the following poems have transcended the moment at which they were written and have been woven into the fabric of our culture.

There are some important questions to consider as you read these poems. What qualities make a poem a *classic?* Who decides which poems do and do not receive this honour? What are the benefits and the dangers of valuing some works far more than others?

"A good poem is a contribution to reality.

The world is never the same once a good poem has been added to it. A good poem helps to change the shape and significance of the universe, helps to extend [people]'s knowledge of [themselves] and the world around [them]."

—Dylan Thomas

"Poetry fosters a passionate interest in language, its rhythm and emotional power. It inspires a willingness to write and revise until a poem is the closest you can get to what you want to say."

—Barbara Sapergia

"In Inuit, the word to make poetry is the word to breathe; both are derivatives of *amerca*, the soul, that which is eternal: the breath of life."

—Edmund Carpenter

"A poem is a watch designed
To tick forever in the mind."

—Fred Cogswell

"Since flesh can't stay,
we pass the words along."

—Erica Jong

La Belle Dame Sans Merci

By John Keats

O what can ail thee, knight-at-arms,
Alone and palely loitering?
The sedge has withered from the lake,
And no birds sing.

O what can ail thee, knight-at-arms,
So haggard and so woe-begone?
The squirrel's granary is full,
And the harvest's done.

I see a lily on thy brow,
With anguish moist and fever dew,
And on thy cheeks a fading rose
Fast withereth too.

I met a lady in the meads,
Full beautiful—a faery's child,
Her hair was long, her foot was light,
And her eyes were wild.

I made a garland for her head,
And bracelets too, and fragrant zone;
She looked at me as she did love,
And made sweet moan.

I set her on my pacing steed,
And nothing else saw all day long,
For sidelong would she bend, and sing
A faery's song.

She found me roots of relish sweet,
And honey wild, and manna dew,
And sure in language strange she said,
"I love thee true."

La Belle Dame Sans Merci: the beautiful woman without mercy

She took me to her elfin grot,
And there she wept, and sighed full sore,
And there I shut her wild wild eyes
With kisses four.

And there she lulléd me asleep,
And there I dreamed—Ah! woe betide!
The latest dream I ever dreamed
On the cold hill side.

I saw pale kings and princes too,
Pale warriors, death-pale were they all;
They cried—"La Belle Dame sans Merci
Hath thee in thrall!"

I saw their starved lips in the gloam,
With horrid warning gapéd wide,
And I awoke and found me here,
On the cold hill's side.

And this is why I sojourn here,
Alone and palely loitering,
Though the sedge has withered from the lake,
And no birds sing.

Ulysses

By Alfred, Lord Tennyson

It little profits that an idle king,
By this still hearth, among these barren crags,
Matched with an agéd wife, I mete and dole
Unequal laws unto a savage race,
That hoard, and sleep, and feed, and know not me.

I cannot rest from travel; I will drink
Life to the lees. All times I have enjoyed
Greatly, have suffered greatly, both with those
That loved me, and alone; on shore, and when

Through scudding drifts the rainy Hyades
Vexed the dim sea. I am become a name;
For always roaming with a hungry heart
Much have I seen and known—cities of men
And manners, climates, councils, governments,
Myself not least, but honored of them all—
And drunk delight of battle with my peers,
Far on the ringing plains of windy Troy.
I am a part of all that I have met;
Yet all experience is an arch wherethrough
Gleams that untraveled world, whose margin fades
For ever and for ever when I move.
How dull it is to pause, to make an end,
To rust unburnished, not to shine in use!
As though to breathe were life. Life piled on life
Were all too little, and of one to me
Little remains; but every hour is saved
From that eternal silence, something more,
A bringer of new things; and vile it were
For some three suns to store and hoard myself,
And this gray spirit yearning in desire
To follow knowledge like a sinking star,
Beyond the utmost bound of human thought.

Hyades: a group of stars that, in ancient times, was believed to be a messenger of spring rain

This is my son, mine own Telemachus,
To whom I leave the scepter and the isle—
Well-loved of me, discerning to fulfill
This labour by slow prudence to make mild
A rugged people, and through soft degrees
Subdue them to the useful and the good.
Most blameless is he, centered in the sphere
Of common duties, decent not to fail
In offices of tenderness, and pay
Meet adoration to my household gods,
When I am gone. He works his work, I mine.

Telemachus: In Greek mythology, and in Homer's *The Odyssey*, Telemachus was the son of Ulysses and Penelope.

There lies the port; the vessel puffs her sail:
There gloom the dark, broad seas. My mariners,
Souls that have toiled, and wrought, and thought with me—
That ever with a frolic welcome took
The thunder and the sunshine, and opposed

Free hearts, free foreheads—you and I are old;
Old age hath yet his honor and his toil.
Death closes all; but something ere the end,
Some work of noble note, may yet be done,
Not unbecoming men that strove with Gods.
The lights begin to twinkle from the rocks;
The long day wanes; the slow moon climbs; the deep
Moans round with many voices. Come, my friends.
'Tis not too late to seek a newer world.
Push off, and sitting well in order smite
The sounding furrows; for my purpose holds
To sail beyond the sunset, and the baths
Of all the western stars, until I die.
It may be that the gulfs will wash us down;
It may be we shall touch the Happy Isles,
And see the great Achilles, whom we knew.
Though much is taken, much abides; and though
We are not now that strength which in old days
Moved earth and heaven, that which we are, we are:
One equal temper of heroic hearts,
Made weak by time and fate, but strong in will
To strive, to seek, to find, and not to yield.

A Bird Came Down

By Emily Dickinson

A Bird came down the Walk—
He did not know I saw—
He bit an Angleworm in halves
And ate the fellow, raw,

And then he drank a Dew
From a convenient Grass—
And then hopped sidewise to the Wall
To let a Beetle pass—

He glanced with rapid eyes
That hurried all around—
They looked like frightened Beads, I thought—
He stirred his Velvet Head

Like one in danger, Cautious,
I offered him a Crumb
And he unrolled his feathers
And rowed him softer home—

Than Oars divide the Ocean,
Too silver for a seam—
Or Butterflies, off Banks of Noon
Leap, plashless as they swim.

The Song My Paddle Sings

By Pauline Johnson

West wind, blow from your prairie nest
Blow from the mountains, blow from the west.
The sail is idle, the sailor too;
O! wind of the west, we wait for you.
Blow, blow!
I have wooed you so,
But never a favour you bestow.
You rock your cradle the hills between,
But scorn to notice my white lateen.

I stow the sail, unship the mast:
I wooed you long but my wooing's past;
My paddle will lull you into rest.
O! drowsy wind of the drowsy west,
Sleep, sleep,
By your mountain steep,
Or down where the prairie grasses sweep!
Now fold in slumber your laggard wings,
For soft is the song my paddle sings.

August is laughing across the sky,
Laughing while paddle, canoe and I,
Drift, drift,
Where the hills uplift
On either side of the current swift.

The river rolls in its rocky bed;
My paddle is plying its way ahead;
Dip, dip,
While the waters flip
In foam as over their breast we slip.

And oh, the river runs swifter now;
The eddies circle about my bow.
Swirl, swirl!
How the ripples curl
In many a dangerous pool awhirl!

And forward far the rapids roar,
Fretting their margin for evermore.
Dash, dash,
With a mighty crash,
They seethe, and boil, and bound, and splash.

Be strong, O paddle! be brave, canoe!
The reckless waves you must plunge into.
Reel, reel.
On your trembling keel,
But never a fear my craft will feel.

We've raced the rapid, we're far ahead!
The river slips through its silent bed.
Sway, sway,
As the bubbles spray
And fall in tinkling tunes away.

And up on the hills against the sky,
A fir tree rocking its lullaby,
Swings, swings,
Its emerald wings,
Swelling the song that my paddle sings.

Dulce Et Decorum Est

By Wilfred Owen

Bent double, like old beggars under sacks,
Knock-kneed, coughing like hags, we cursed through sludge,
Till on the haunting flares we turned our backs,
And towards our distant rest began to trudge.
Men marched asleep. Many had lost their boots,
But limped on, blood-shod. All went lame, all blind;
Drunk with fatigue; deaf even to the hoots
Of gas-shells dropping softly behind.
Gas! GAS! Quick, boys!—An ecstasy of fumbling,
Fitting the clumsy helmets just in time,
But someone still was yelling out and stumbling
And flound'ring like a man in fire or lime.—
Dim through the misty panes and thick green light,
As under a green sea, I saw him drowning.

In all my dreams, before my helpless sight,
He plunges at me, guttering, choking, drowning.

If in some smothering dreams, you too could pace
Behind the wagon that we flung him in,
And watch the white eyes writhing in his face,
His hanging face, like a devil's sick of sin,
If you could hear, at every jolt, the blood
Come gargling from the froth-corrupted lungs
Obscene as cancer, bitter as the cud
Of vile, incurable sores on innocent tongues,—
My friend, you would not tell with such high zest
To children ardent for some desperate glory,
The old lie: *Dulce et decorum est*
Pro patria mori.[1]

[1] ***Dulce et decorum est pro patria mori:*** It is sweet and proper to die for your country. (A Latin quotation from the Roman poet, Horace)

Harlem

By Langston Hughes

What happens to a dream deferred?

Does it dry up
like a raisin in the sun?
Or fester like a sore—
And then run?
Does it stink like rotten meat?
Or crust and sugar over—
like a syrupy sweet?

Maybe it just sags
like a heavy load.

Or does it explode?

If not poetry, then what?
—*Rosario Castellanos*

With me poetry has not been
a purpose, but a passion.
—*Edgar Allan Poe*

1. ***Response***
   a. Describe some of the challenges you faced as a reader, as you read the poems in this section.
   b. Why do you think people continue to study these and other challenging poems despite the obstacles?

2. ***Literature Studies*** *Interpretation and Appreciation* Interpretation involves understanding a poem's theme and/or message—its literal and symbolic meanings. Appreciation involves enjoying the artistry of a poem—the creative manipulation of language and poetic form. In a sustained piece of writing (at least two pages long), offer your own interpretation and appreciation of one poem in this section. You should explain what you think the poem is about, provide examples of the author's poetic skill, and suggest why you think the poem has stood the test of time.

3. ***Research and Inquiry*** Use your research skills to compile essential background information on one of the poets who is featured in this section. You might give an overview of the poet's career, list his or her major poetic works, summarize characteristic themes, and comment on the poet's reputation and accomplishments. Include any other details or material that you think would help a reader discover the context for the poet's work. Present the background information in an engaging way, incorporating visuals if possible.

4. ***Making Connections*** Using library resources or the Internet, find one additional classic poem that you particularly like. Read the poem aloud to a group or the class, and explain why you selected that particular poem. How is it like or unlike the poems in this section?

Biographies

MAYA ANGELOU has worked as an actor, teacher, and activist. The first of her autobiographical books, *I Know Why the Caged Bird Sings*, gained universal recognition. She has published many poems, and wrote poetry for Clinton's inauguration, and the UN's 50th birthday.

MARGARET ATWOOD'S poetic reputation was established in 1966 when *The Circle Game* won the Governor General's Award. She has published numerous books of poetry, including the well-known collection, *The Journals of Susanna Moodie: Poems*. She is also an award-winning novelist, winning the Governor General's Award in 1985 for *The Handmaid's Tale*, and the Booker Prize in 2000 for her novel, *The Blind Assassin*.

WYSTAN HUGH AUDEN was born in 1907. In 1930, his collection, *Poems*, established him as an important and influential poet in England. He also wrote plays and librettos, and was a noted editor and essayist. He died in Vienna in 1973.

ELIZABETH BARRETT BROWNING was born in England in 1806. Her first poetry collection, *An Essay on Mind and Other Poems*, was published anonymously. In 1844, her collection, *Poems*, gained the attention of the poet Robert Browning. They eloped in 1846. Barrett's *Sonnets from the Portuguese*, dedicated to her husband, was published in 1850, and her verse novel, *Aurora Leigh*, in 1857. She died in Florence in 1861.

ELIZABETH BREWSTER was born in New Brunswick in 1922. She has won numerous awards for her poetry, including the President's Silver Medal for Poetry in 1979, and the Saskatchewan Arts Boards, Lifetime Award for Excellence in the Arts, in 1995.

CHARLES BUKOWSKI'S poetry was first published in the 1940s, and then he allegedly gave up writing for the next 20 years. However, his poetry did continue to appear in many small literary publications during that time. Although he wasn't associated with the major Beat writers, his informal style and non-conforming literary approach appeal to readers of Beat poetry.

ROBERT "ROBBIE" BURNS was born in Scotland in 1759. Although poverty limited his formal education, he read widely. His first poetry collection, published in 1786, was an immediate success, and his later literary works—consisting almost entirely of songs—included the well-known New Year's Eve song, "Auld Lang Syne." He died in 1796.

NURUNNESSA CHOUDHURY has published a collection called *The Sun Witness*. She also translated the anthology *I See Cleopatra and Other Poems* with Paul Joseph Thompson.

WENDY COPE was born in 1945 in the south of England. Her collection, *Making Cocoa for Kingsley Amis*, contains literary jokes and parodies in the style of some well-known poets.

LORNA CROZIER grew up in Swift Current, Saskatchewan. Along with other Saskatchewan writers, she has founded a monthly writing workshop jokingly named *The Moose Jaw Movement*. In 1992, her poetry collection, *Inventing the Hawk*, won the Governor General's Award.

EDWARD ESTLIN CUMMINGS became known as an experimental poet, due to his unconventional use of form, punctuation, spelling, and syntax. Although his name often appears without capitalization, this was never at the legal request, or even wish, of Cummings himself. It was one publisher's style decision, which was adopted by subsequent publishers as the "correct" style.

LEO DANGEL'S collections of poetry include *Home From the Field*, *Hogs and Personals: Poems*, and *Old Man Brunner Country*.

EMILY DICKINSON was born in Massachusetts in 1830. Although she remained in almost total physical isolation from the outside world most of her life, she maintained many correspondences and read widely. She was an extremely prolific poet, but was not publicly recognized during her lifetime. Her first volume of poetry was published posthumously in 1890, and the last in 1955. She died in 1886.

MARY DI MICHELE was born in Italy in 1949, and immigrated to Canada in 1955. She has worked as poetry editor for *Poetry Toronto*, and for *Toronto Life*. She has won a number of awards for her poetry.

GAIL DUSENBERY'S poems have appeared in *Wild Dog, Cow, Poetry* (Chicago), *Poems Read in the Spirit of Peace and Gladness*, and *Free Poems Among Friends*. Her collection of poems, *The Mark*, was published in 1967.

THOMAS STEARNS ELIOT was born in Missouri in 1888, but settled in England in 1914. His first book of poems—*Prufrock and Other Observations*—immediately established him as a leading poet after its publication in 1917. Eliot remains an important figure in poetry and literary criticism throughout the English-speaking world. He received the Nobel Prize for Literature in 1948, and died in London in 1965.

LAWRENCE FERLINGHETTI was born in Yonkers, New York in 1919. He is recognized as one of the most important and influential poets of the "Beat" movement. By 1952, he had established himself as a writer, artist, and political activist. Along with a friend, he opened the City Lights bookstore in San Francisco, which became a mecca for writers and artists.

ROBERT FROST was born in San Francisco in 1874. His first two poetry collections—*A Boy's Will* and *North of Boston*—established his reputation as a poet. His later poetry collections won him more fame and honours, including four Pulitzer Prizes. He died in Boston in 1963.

MARY E. FRYE. Although the poem "Do Not Stand at My Grave and Weep" is attributed to Mary E. Frye, it was "formerly attributed to Native American sources."

ROBERT FULGHUM'S first published essay, "All I Really Need to Know I Learned in Kindergarten," evolved over seven years into 14 million books in 93 countries, a syndicated newspaper column, and a theatre piece.

NIKKI GIOVANNI is a writer of prose and of adult and children's poetry, and is also well-known for her poetry recitals. She has received many awards for her written and performed poetry.

LANGSTON HUGHES was born in Missouri in 1902. He wrote novels, short stories, poetry, and plays, and his work was influenced greatly by jazz. He was part of the Harlem Renaissance of the 1920s. He died in 1967.

GARY HYLAND lectures at the University of Regina, and is an award-winning poet and editor. His books include *Just off Main, Street of Dreams*, and *After Atlantis*.

PAULINE JOHNSON was one of Canada's most popular and successful entertainers in the early 1900s, giving hundreds of recitals of her poetry countrywide. She was the first Aboriginal poet to have had her work published in Canada.

JOHN KEATS was an English Romantic poet, born in London, England, in 1795. Although he studied medicine, he never practised his profession, preferring to write poetry instead. His first volume of poetry, published in 1817, received negative reviews. In 1820, he published his third and best volume of poetry, *Lamia, Isabella, The Eve of St. Agnes and Other Poems*.

PEGGY SMITH KRACHUN grew up in Placentia, the former French capital of Newfoundland. She is a freelance writer, but also sings and writes songs. Krachun co-edited the short story collection *Doors Held Ajar* with Isobel Brown and Nellie P. Strowbridge.

DAVID HERBERT LAWRENCE was a novelist, poet, short story writer, and essayist. His radical views were a continual source of controversy and his novel, *Lady Chatterley's Lover*, involved him in a much-publicized censorship case.

IRVING LAYTON, poet, short story writer, essayist, and professor, was born in Romania in 1912. Since the early 1940s, he has been recognized in Canada as a versatile, revolutionary, and controversial poet of the "modern" school. He was nominated by Italy and Korea for the Nobel Prize in 1981 and received a Canada Council Award in 1967.

BETTY LIES is a poet in the schools for the New Jersey State Council on the Arts, and is working on a book temporarily entitled *Earth's Daughters: Stories of Women in Classical Mythology*.

GWENDOLYN MACEWEN was born in Toronto in 1941. She published her first poem at 17, and won the Governor General's Award at 27. During her writing career, she published 15 volumes of poetry, two novels, and a number of radio plays. MacEwen's work is included in most major Canadian anthologies. She died in 1987.

MATEI MARKWEI was born in Ghana. He is an ordained minister who attended Lincoln University, Pennsylvania, and Yale University. He contributed toward writing the play *The Griot*—which traditionally means a West African storyteller.

OGDEN NASH was born in New York in 1902. He published his first book for children, *The Cricket of Caradon*, in 1925, and his first poem appeared in *The New Yorker* in 1932. Nash published 19 books of poetry throughout his lifetime, and is probably best known for his limericks.

WILFRED OWEN was born in England in 1893. He taught English in France from 1913 to 1915. Then, in 1917, he enlisted in the army and fought in World War I as an officer in the Battle of Somme. While hospitalized for shell shock, Owen wrote about the horror of battle. He died one year after returning to fight, and one week before the war ended, in 1918. He was awarded the Military Cross for serving in the war with distinction.

LINDA PASTAN has published many poetry collections, including *The Five Stages of Grief* and *Waiting for My Life*. Much of her poetry deals with her own family life and, more recently, with issues of aging and mortality.

OSCAR PEÑARANDA was born in the Philippines in 1944. His first language is Waray, and his second and third, Tagalog (on the streets), and English (in classrooms). He has taught at San Francisco State University for 25 years, where he co-founded the first ethnic studies program in the U.S. His work is anthologized in many publications, including the earliest collections of Asian and Filipino American writing.

PANDELIS PREVELAKIS has written over 20 books of novels, criticism, plays, and poetry, many of which have been translated into English, French, and German.

BUFFY SAINTE-MARIE became known in the 1960s as a writer of protest songs and love songs, many of which were performed by artists such as Janis Joplin, Elvis Presley, Barbra Streisand, Neil Diamond, and Tracy Chapman. She was recently awarded the Award for Lifetime Musical Achievement by the First Americans in the Arts (U.S.), which award was also named after her, as a tribute to her legendary career.

LUIS OMAR SALINAS'S poems, which often relate the problems of Mexican Americans, have won a number of awards.

NANCY SENIOR was born in 1941, and emigrated from the U.S. to Saskatoon in 1967. Her poetry collections include *Poems* (1973), and *The Mushroom Jar* (1980).

WILLIAM SHAKESPEARE was born in 1564, in Stratford-on-Avon, England. He composed over a hundred sonnets between 1593 and 1601. These were written in the form of three quatrains and a rhyming couplet, now recognized as the Shakespearean sonnet. He died in 1616.

PERCY BYSSHE SHELLEY was born in 1792 in Sussex, England. He began writing poetry while at Eton, but his first publication was a Gothic novel, *Zastrozzi*. Shelley produced all his major works during the last four years of his life, including *Prometheus Unbound*. In 1822, just before his thirtieth birthday, he was drowned in a storm while sailing in his schooner.

RAYMOND SOUSTER was born in 1921 and won many awards for his poetry: including a Governor General's Award for Poetry, the President's Medal, the Centennial Medal, and the Silver Jubilee Medal.

EDNA ST. VINCENT MILLAY, born in 1892, was a poet and playwright. In 1923, her fourth volume of poems, *The Harp Weaver*, was awarded the Pulitzer Prize.

SARA TEASDALE was born in St. Louis, Missouri., U.S. in 1884, and published her first volume of poetry in 1907. Further volumes followed and, in 1918, she won the Columbia University Poetry Society prize (forerunner of the Pulitzer Prize for poetry), and the annual prize of the Poetry Society of America for *Love Songs*. Teasdale died in 1933.

ALFRED, LORD TENNYSON, English poet of the Victorian age, was born in 1809, and succeeded William Wordsworth as Poet Laureate in 1850. His reputation as a poet was established in 1842 with his revised volume of *Poems*. In 1850, he published one of his major poetic works, "In Memoriam;" an elegy mourning the death of his friend, Arthur Hallam.

DYLAN THOMAS was born in Wales in 1914. Although he excelled in English and reading, he dropped out of school at 16. His first book—*Eighteen Poems*—was published to great acclaim when he was 20. He died in 1953 at the age of 39.

MIRIAM WADDINGTON was born in Winnipeg in 1917. She was the Canada Council Exchange Poet to Wales in 1980, and has been poetry editor of *Poetry Toronto*, and writer-in-residence at both the Windsor Public Library and the University of Ottawa.

MICHAEL WADE is a creative writer and accomplished musician, who published his first poem in 1972 in *Voices Underground* magazine. He lives in Nova Scotia and is working on a novel.

AGNES ETHELWYN WERTHERALD was born of English-Quaker parents in Ontario in 1857. She began to write poetry later in life. Her first book of verse, *The House of the Trees and Other Poems*, was published in 1895. She died in 1940.

CHRISTOPHER WISEMAN has taught English and Creative Writing at the University of Calgary, and has been editor of *Dandelion* and *Ariel*. Wiseman received Alberta Poetry awards in both 1988 and 1989.

WILLIAM WORDSWORTH was born in 1770 in England. Wordsworth's earliest poetry collections—*An Evening Walk* and *Descriptive Sketches*—were published in 1793. He died in 1850, and his most famous poem, "The Prelude," was published posthumously by his wife.

JUDITH WRIGHT, an Australian, wrote poetry, children's books, non-fiction, and short stories, and also worked as a literary critic, editor, anthologist, active conservationist, and supporter of Aboriginal land rights. Wright received numerous awards for her writing, including the Human Rights Commission Award for Poetry, in 1994. She died in June, 2000.

Essays

But words are things, and a small drop of ink,
Falling like dew, upon a thought, produces
That which makes thousands, perhaps millions, think.

Lord Byron

It's Time to Think About Visors

After Bryan Berard's injury, it's not just an issue of athletes' personal choice

By Ken Dryden

I was at the March 11 game in Ottawa, sitting in the press box far from where it happened. I could see a Senators player near the Leafs' net spin quickly around to swing at a suddenly available puck. Then I saw Bryan Berard topple to the ice. The stick of Marion Hossa, the highly promising Senators left-winger, had struck Berard in the face with its full force. I looked at the TV monitor beside me. Berard was lying prone, his legs kicking at the ice. A dark spot formed beside him. Blood on ice is crimson; it splatters and streams. This was darker and thick.

I didn't think about his eye. I have seen so many pucks and sticks come threateningly close, then, with the tiniest reflexive twitch of a head, slam on the face's protective armature of cheekbones, eyebrows or nose. I wasn't ready for the news that came early the next morning. Bryan Berard, just a week after his 23rd birthday, was not likely to play again.

There is a sadness in Toronto that still hasn't lifted. And inevitably people are beginning to debate the mandatory use of face protectors in the NHL. The great majority of NHL players wore a full-face mask from the time they took their first strides on the ice at age 5 or 6 until they were 18. Most wore visors for a few more years until they reached the NHL and were given a choice. Then most decided to play as they never had before, with no facial protection at all.

In hockey's formative years, rules were created to protect what equipment didn't. Blows to the head were penalized; so were high-sticking and elbowing. In the past 20 years of minor hockey, with its helmets and masks, the head was as well protected as any other part of the body, and these penalties became obsolete even as they were still applied. Today's NHL players grew up knowing that a stick to the head might result in a penalty but not an injury. Sticks could be carried high or low and used with near impunity—it didn't matter.

Then, in the NHL, the players take their face masks off.

What Hossa did was an accident. That isn't the same, however, as saying it's merely an unfortunate part of the game. Some activities are riskier than others. Hockey's imaginable accidents are much more severe than those in basketball or soccer. It's not enough to find explanation in the inevitability of accident. We need to imagine accident as part of the game and generate plans to minimize it.

Would most available visors have saved Berard's eye? Not necessarily. Could a visor be designed that would have? Yes. Would wearing a visor have made most of today's eye injuries less likely? Yes.

Everything we do, sports included, is a compromise between safety and performance. Around the office we don't think of safety much. At the wheel of a car we do. Skiers can't ski down a hill fast until they learn how to control their speed and know they can stop if they have to. Hockey players will reach speeds of 40 km/h only when they know they can brake before the end boards. Safety doesn't need to straitjacket performance. Usually, it enhances it.

I know this from personal experience. When goalies first experimented with masks, they were distracted by all the differences they noticed. Masks are heavy; they're hot. When you try to see a puck at your feet, parts of them get in the way. I didn't wear a mask until an NCAA rule forced me to wear one. Then heavy and hot didn't matter, because you didn't have a choice. You learned to see through and past any obstructions. It was the same, years later, for skaters and helmets. It will be the same for visors.

Mandating visors will take more than a decree from the NHL. It will require the support of the players and the NHL Players' Association. It isn't the entire answer for a player to say, I don't want to wear a visor, and I shouldn't have to—it's my choice.

Knowledge is power.

Sir Francis Bacon

Sport depends on public acceptance. If it doesn't reflect the tastes and values of a time, players and spectators will seek out other activities. People are attracted to risk. Near misses are thrilling. Wipeouts at skiing or surfing; cars brushing a wall, turning broadside, sent catapulting into the air over other cars, that's exciting—when no one gets hurt, or really hurt.

But more hockey players are getting really hurt now. NHL players talk openly about a new lack of respect that players seem to have for one another. With this lack of respect, they are not only hurting one another, they are damaging the sport. This is what takes this beyond a matter of simple personal choice.

For the first 80 years of hockey's existence, no goalie wore a mask. It took nearly 40 more years before every skater was required to wear a helmet. From today's perspective, that doesn't seem possible, just as playing football without a helmet, then without a face mask, to us seems incredible lore. How could they do it? Ten years from now, maybe 20, but sometime, all hockey players will wear facial protection, and 20 years after that, it will seem just as incredible that they didn't always do it.

The question is not *if* but *when*. And the question for us is whether we drag out this time to its extreme or act sooner.

Hockey Hall-of-Famer **Ken Dryden** is president of the Toronto Maple Leafs. He was an NHL goaltender during the 70s, and during his career won the Calder Trophy, five Vezina Trophies, the Conn Smythe Trophy, six Stanley Cups, and was a five-time First Team All-Star.

1. ***Response***
   a. Drawing on your own knowledge and/or experience of hockey, generate your own list of the pros and cons of wearing a protective visor.
   b. What is Ken Dryden's thesis in this essay? Where does it first appear?
   c. Identify the places where Dryden inserted a personal element into the essay. What do you think he was trying to achieve? In your opinion, do the personal references make Dryden's essay stronger? Explain.

The **thesis** of an essay is the main idea or argument that the author is attempting to prove.

2. ***Literature Studies*** *Thesis and Supporting Details* In a persuasive essay, the writer wants the reader to accept a particular thesis. The writer does this by presenting supporting details (facts, statistics, examples, reasons, and so on) that help to prove the thesis. List the supporting details Dryden includes in his essay. Do you think Dryden proved his thesis convincingly? Explain. Based on the list you created in activity 1. a, what other details might Dryden have used to support his thesis?

3. ***Critical Thinking*** Should the wearing of visors be mandatory for professional hockey players? Give the reasons for your recommendation.

4. ***Media*** *Advertisement* Create an advertisement (a TV, radio, or magazine ad, or a poster or billboard) designed to convince a target audience to support the mandatory wearing of visors in the NHL. When you present your work to the class, describe the target audience and explain the specific techniques you would use to persuade that audience.

Where are all the funny Canadian writers?

The Importance of Being Earnest

By Lynn Coady

Every writer is familiar with the aggravation of rejection. And I'm not talking about photocopied slips initialed by an indifferent editor. I mean that really drawn out, knife-twisting kind of rejection where they've scrupulously tracked you down, solicited your work, thanked you profusely for your contribution, and then, at the last possible moment—sorry, we just don't think it's going to "fit" in with our "format." This has happened to me recently, as it probably has to every writer. But it got me thinking about why my work has been solicited and then rejected in the same sort of way by other editors. And when I say the same sort of way, I'm referring to the preface they always use: "It's hilarious, but…."

I would like to talk seriously about irreverence, and why, as a writer, I often find myself feeling like the class clown in a very dour religious boarding school. When you're a Canadian writer, people expect certain things from you. There are clichés that you feel expected, on some level, to live up to. Landscape, for example. You get the feeling people expect a hell of a lot of landscape in your work. Long, meandering descriptions of rivers and fields, as though our national prose must somehow reflect our geography.

True, many of the new generation of writers would seem to be sloughing off these traditional expectations. Urban-Canadian appears to be the new catch phrase. Readers can now enjoy gritty tales of the city, with all its attendant sordidness. Drug use, grimy alleyways, soulless, neurotic women and men having seedy Canadian sex in dingy boarding houses. It's all good. My only problem is that, as Canadians, we seem to be taking the urban landscape every bit as seriously as our pristine countryside. The one thing

Canadians can't seem to get out from under is this penchant for absolute earnestness in our writing. Rugged, noble country folk undergoing day-to-day hardships have been replaced by hip, dispassionate urbanites undergoing day-to-day hardships. It still doesn't make me laugh. If it weren't for Mordecai Richler's irony-rich novels, Canadian literature would have no equivalents to laugh-riots such as Roddy Doyle's *The Commitments*, or works of scathing, gleeful satire like *Catch-22* or *Breakfast of Champions*.

Maybe you think I'm frivolous, believing we should laugh at literature; perhaps you think this is somehow wrong of me. But I have a very legitimate reason for this: life makes me laugh, because life is stupid. If a work of literature is not able to get that sublime sense of stupidity across, at least in some degree, then I have to consider it a flawed work of literature. Because it simply doesn't represent, to me, a true picture of life in this world. Yes, even life in Canada.

It could be that I am more highly sensitized to this as a result of being from Atlantic Canada. The publication of my novel *Strange Heaven* came about, ironically, as a result of an editor's refusal to reproduce an excerpt of it in a Christmas anthology. It was a collection of Atlantic Canadian stories, the kind of book that seems part of an ongoing tradition of cloyingly sentimental renderings of life in the Maritimes. But should the sketches of your fictional little town become anything less than sunshiny, you're in trouble. You're breaking the rules. My story was about an ex-pregnant teenage girl with diarrhea sitting down to Christmas dinner with her senile, nonagenarian grandmother, her mentally handicapped uncle, her alcoholic other uncle, and her verbally abusive father. This may sound a little over-the-top to some, but to me it is nowhere near as outlandish and unbelievable as, say, an episode of *Road to Avonlea*. Basically, any time I see a depiction of a happy loving family enjoying a peaceful Christmas dinner—in the Maritimes or anywhere else—I call it bull.

So the editors were horrified, yet intrigued. They respectfully declined to include the excerpt in their anthology, but did ask to see the rest of the novel, and then published it. And weirdly, this particular story of Christmas dysfunction has become one of its most celebrated fragments.

The editor's words of rejection were that the story didn't "fit" with the rest of the collection. Why not? I'll tell you why not—because it wasn't hokey. To me, this implicit insistence that every story by every Maritime writer included in a Christmas anthology has to be hokey is nothing less than censorship. The smiley kind of censorship that hides behind a Pollyanna face of sentiment and dreary convention.

I had another experience of "not fitting" into an anthology recently. *Brick* magazine solicited contributions from authors across the country for a book called *Lost Classics*. Each author was asked to pen a short memory of some obscure book they remember from their past that ended up influencing them as adult writers. I came up with a book that had affected me profoundly right off the bat. The editors sent me some examples, however, and I knew at once that my excerpt would have to be nothing like the others. They were all very reverent and, yes, earnest.

My choice was actually a series of volumes, innocently titled *Uncle Arthur's Bedtime Stories*. These supposedly Christian morality tales had filled me with horror as a child, instilling the seeds of what developed into a distinctively warped relationship with God and religion. I couldn't think of any work of literature that had influenced me as deeply as that, so I set to work. Uncle Arthur's message was basically that God is out to get you, and it was reinforced with every story he told. Little Susie skips piano lessons to play hopscotch with her friends, and, *whammo!* From out of nowhere a brick falls, crushing her fingers so she can never play piano again. It's grotesque to think that somebody actually thought this was the way to raise good Christian children. It's *stupid*, and that's what I wanted to get across. People are stupid. We're all stupid. That's basically all I'm trying to get across in any of my writing. I don't think it's a particularly frivolous message, either.

Maybe it was naive to think I could get this past the editors of *Lost Classics*, but it boggled my mind that anyone would want to sit through page after page of absolutely humourless reminiscences of the cherished childhood tomes of Canadian writers. Surely, I thought, there are people like me out there, who would want to read the kind of thing I wanted to write.

But once again, the editors disagreed.

I have nothing against so-called "serious" writers who write "serious" books, essays, and articles. I just don't understand why I have to be one. Every nation boasting a mature literary tradition has its share of great ironists, so why are we permitted so few? Why are we consistently discouraged from poking fun at ourselves? Why does Mordecai Richler get to have all the fun?

A good essay must have this permanent quality about it; it must draw its curtain round us, but it must be a curtain that shuts us in, not out.

Virginia Woolf

Lynn Coady is a fiction writer and essayist. Born in Cape Breton, Nova Scotia, she received a BA from Carleton University, and an MFA from the University of British Columbia. Her novel *Strange Heaven* was published in 1998, and her collection of short stories, *Play the Monster Blind,* in 2000. Her second novel is due to be published in Spring 2002.

1. *Response*

a. Lynn Coady makes a number of controversial claims in this essay. What are they? For each one, explain your own position.
b. What approach does Coady use to convince readers that Canadian writers are too serious? Do you think that approach is convincing? Why or why not?
c. Give some examples of your favourite books and/or stories. Was humour an important component of any of them? Explain.

2. *Writing* *Humour* Try your own hand at writing something funny—a short story, anecdote, or skit, for example. When you've finished your first draft, reflect on the challenges of being humorous. What advice would you give to someone trying to write something funny?

3. *Vocabulary* *Unfamiliar Words* In the fifth paragraph of her essay, Coady uses the adjective *nonagenarian* to describe a character. Reread the sentence and speculate on what *nonagenarian* might mean. What strategies did you use to make your guesses? Consult a dictionary that contains etymologies to find out where the word comes from. Why would an author use a challenging word instead of one that most readers would know?

4. *Making Connections* Compare "The Importance of Being Earnest" with Drew Hayden Taylor's "What Colour Is a Rose?" Examine aspects such as intent, tone, and subject matter.

"Of course we have to be sure about the kinds of books we want our kids to read in school. Don't we?"

Whose Lathe?

By Ursula K. Le Guin

In a small town near Portland late this spring (1984), a novel, *The Lathe of Heaven*, was the subject of a hearing concerning its suitability for use in a senior high-school literature class. I took a lively interest in the outcome, because I wrote the novel.

The case against the book was presented first. The man who was asking that it be withdrawn stated his objections to the following elements in the book: fuzzy thinking and poor sentence structure; a mention of homosexuality; a character who keeps a flask of brandy in her purse, and who remarks that her mother did not love her. (It seemed curious to me that he did not mention the fact that this same character is a Black woman whose lover /husband is a White man. I had the feeling that this was really what he hated in the book, and that he was afraid to say so; but that was only my feeling.)

He also took exception to what he described as the author's advocacy of non-Christian religions and/or of non-separation of Church and State (his arguments on this point, or these points, were not clear to me).

Finally, during discussion, he compared the book to junk food, apparently because it was science fiction.

The English Department of the school then presented a carefully prepared, spirited defense of the book, including statements by students who had read it. Some liked it, some didn't like it, most objected to having it, or any other book, banned.

In discussion, teachers pointed out that since it is the policy of the Washougal School District to assign an alternative book to any student who objects on any grounds to reading an assigned one, the attempt to prevent a whole class from reading a book was an attempt to change policy, replacing free choice by censorship.

When the Instructional Materials Committee of the district voted on the motion to ban the book, the motion was defeated twenty votes to five. The hearing was public and was conducted in the most open and democratic fashion. I did not speak, as I felt the teachers and students had spoken eloquently for me.

Crankish attacks on the freedom to read are common at present. When backed and coordinated by organized groups, they become sinister. In this case, I saw something going on that worried me a good deal because it did not seem to be coming from an outside pressure group, but from elements of the educational establishment itself: this was the movement to change policy radically by instituting, or "clarifying," guidelines or criteria for the selection/elimination of books used in the schools. The motion on which this committee of the school district voted was actually that the book be withdrawn "*while guidelines and policies for the district are worked out.*" Those guidelines and policies were the real goal, I think, of the motion.

Guidelines? That sounds dull. Innocent. Useful. Of course we have to be sure about the kinds of books we want our kids to read in school. Don't we?

Well, do we? The dangerous vagueness of the term "guidelines and policies for the district" slides right past such questions as: Who are "we"? Who decides what the children read? Does "we" include you? Me? Teachers? Librarians? Students? Are fifteen-to-eighteen-year-olds ever "we," or are they always "they"?

And what are the guidelines to be? On what criteria or doctrines are they to be based?

The people concerned with schools in Oregon try, with ever-decreasing budgets, to provide good, sound food in the school cafeterias, knowing that for some students that's the only real meal they get.

> To know one's ignorance is the best part of knowledge.
>
> Lao-Tsze

They try, with ever-decreasing budgets, to provide beautiful, intelligent books in classes and school libraries, knowing that for many students those are the only books they read. To provide the best: everyone agrees on that (even the people who vote against school levies). But we don't and we can't agree on what books are the best. And therefore what is vital is that we provide variety, abundance, plenty—not books that reflect one body of opinion or doctrine, not books that one group or sect thinks good, but the broadest, richest range of intellectual and artistic material possible.

Nobody is forced to read any of it. There is that very important right to refuse and choose an alternative.

When a bad apple turns up, it can be taken out of the barrel on a case-by-case, book-by-book basis—investigated, defended, prosecuted, and judged, as in the hearing on my *Lathe of Heaven*. But this can't be done wholesale by using "guidelines," instructions for censorship. There is no such thing as a moral filter that lets good books through and keeps bad books out. Such criteria of "goodness" and "badness" are a moralist's dream but a democrat's nightmare.

Censorship, here or in Russia or wherever, is absolutely anti-democratic and elitist. The censor says: You don't know enough to choose, but we do, so you will read what we choose for you and nothing else. The democrat says: The process of learning is that of learning how to choose. Freedom isn't given, it's earned. Read, learn, and earn it.

I fear censorship in this Uriah Heepish[1] guise of "protecting our children," "stricter criteria," "moral guidance," "a more definite policy," and so on. I hope administrators, teachers, librarians, parents, and students will resist it. Its advocates are people willing to treat others not only as if they were not free but were not even worthy of freedom.

---

[1]***Uriah Heepish:*** Behaving in the manner of Uriah Heep, a servile character in *David Copperfield* by Charles Dickens

Ursula K. Le Guin, born in California, is a prolific writer best known for her science fiction and fantasy titles for young adults. She also writes poetry, children's books, novels, and short stories. A few of her over 30 titles include: *Going Out With Peacocks and Other Poems, Catwings, Always Coming Home, Rocannon's World,* and *The Wind's Twelve Quarters.*

1. ***Response***
   a. "Whose Lathe?" is divided into two distinct parts. What are they and how do they work together to develop the argument?
   b. What specific biases does Ursula K. Le Guin bring to her essay? How do you know? What counter-arguments might someone use in debating the issue of censorship with Le Guin?
   c. Have you seen any movies or listened to any recordings that you would not share with a nine-year-old? Validate your decision.
   d. Do you practise censorship on yourself, avoiding materials that you think are inappropriate? Explain your position, giving examples if possible.

2. ***Media*** *Censorship Survey* Conduct a survey on community attitudes toward censorship. You'll need to draft a questionnaire that asks specific questions about the appropriateness of censorship and the creation of guidelines. Find out which media (movies, computer games, CDs, Web sites, TV shows, and so on) people think should be subject to censorship. When your questionnaire is ready, distribute it to various grades in your school and to teachers and parents. Analyse the findings. What conclusions can you make? Report your findings to your class using PowerPoint or overheads.

3. ***Literature Studies*** *Organizational Patterns* There are several ways of organizing an essay. These organizational patterns help a writer construct a powerful argument. Here are some of the most commonly used patterns:

   - *Comparison and contrast:* investigation of the similarities and differences between two or more things
   - *Classification:* division of a complex topic into smaller categories
   - *Cause and effect:* exploration of why something happens and what the results will be
   - *Chronological order:* examination of a situation or event in the order in which it occurred
   - *Definition:* explanation of a series of key terms or concepts

   Select the pattern that best describes the way in which "Whose Lathe?" is organized. Explain your choice.

"This ship is going down ..."

Alarm Bells for Civilization

By Gwynne Dyer

It would have taken quite a hardy soul to see a bright side to the First World War at the time, but it may have served a useful purpose nevertheless. Like the alarm bells of a stricken ship, it still rings insistently across the decades: do something decisive right now, or this ship is going down with all hands. The ship is civilization.

It would be another two and a half decades before the first nuclear weapon was dropped on a city, another four decades before Dame Barbara Ward began talking about "spaceship earth," another six before Carl Sagan and his colleagues stumbled onto the ironically unifying concept of a "nuclear winter." But the First World War gave people their first glimpse of the abyss.

People began responding to the message right away. The war literature of the twenties and thirties was quite revolutionary in its style and its sensibility: ordinary men writing extraordinary things. Humble men like British infantryman Frank Richards would never before have had the temerity to write about their experiences; *Her Privates We*, Richards called his book about infantrymen in war. Or consider the League of Nations, that first, foredoomed attempt to bridge the abyss that the First World War revealed. Even governments realized that everything had changed.

The problem, as people in 1914 did not understand but people in 1918 were beginning to, was basically one of scale. Governments and states were still behaving in ways that had hardly changed since the eighteenth century, and (apart from the exacerbating effects of popular nationalism) the political causes and the initial strategic moves of the First World War differed little from those of the War of the Spanish Succession two centuries before. But if you quintuple the population, increase the per capita GNP tenfold, and replace single-shot muzzle-loading muskets with machine guns that fire six hundred bullets a minute, then you have changed the very nature of the game.

Conscript armies millions strong, supported by huge industrialized economies, fight very different wars from those that were waged by small armies of professional soldiers. It is not just that the butcher's bill is a lot higher; the political consequences of going to war are also different.

To be precise, the European empires went to war in 1914 believing that the conflict would serve the traditional purpose of adjusting the pecking order among the great powers. Instead, it ended up by destroying the losers utterly. Whole empires vanished, more than a dozen new countries appeared, and radical political movements like fascism and communism rose to power in great states—which was not what the initiators of the war had intended at all.

We have drunk quite deep of the horrors of the First World War over the years, so there is little point in going over them again here. Besides, the horrors suffered by the soldiers in the trenches were largely the same as those experienced by soldiers in any major nineteenth-century war (give or take a couple of novel weapons like poison gas and flamethrowers), except that they went on for much longer and affected many more people. It is the question of scale, in the war's physical and political aspects alike, that should hold our attention, as indeed it drew the attention of those who actually fought the war.

The shocking discovery that old institutions produce different and highly unwelcome results when you multiply the inputs tenfold or a hundredfold was what drove the many determined postwar attempts to change or replace those old institutions, from the creation of the League of Nations to Lenin's victory in the Soviet Union. The shock of the First World War also killed the smug confidence of the late nineteenth century that "history" knew what it was doing when it gave the Europeans such enormous power: one of the characteristics of twentieth-century European consciousness is a sense that history is in deep trouble and needs help.

But one can expand the argument quite a long way beyond that. There is nothing unique in the twentieth century's view of itself as the vital turning point of human history, of course—half the ages of humanity have believed that they lived in the final days. But the peculiar twentieth-century version of this apocalyptic vision relies on some quite tangible evidence, and the fact that people have cried wolf many times before does not disprove the existence of wolves.

I believe that our times, broadly defined—say, the nineteenth through the twenty-first centuries—really are a critical era that will make or break the experiment of human civilization. We have lived with one model of civilization for around five thousand years, but our powers over each other, over weapons, over the balance of the environment have grown so great that the transition to a different model has become a question of survival.

The model that has predominated in almost all civilized societies since early in the third millennium BCE is one in which war was actually the centrepiece. So-called "patriarchal" civilizations, typified in the ancient Middle Eastern tradition by god-kings, elaborate hierarchies, rigid class systems, slavery, armies, and the systematic depoliticization and suppression of women, were so efficient at warfare that they eliminated virtually all rival models.

There was once a variety of such rival models, and the earliest civilized societies were mostly a good deal less warlike, less autocratic, less brutal in almost every respect. Some, like those of Egypt and Crete, retained that character as late as 1500 BCE, but in the parts of the Middle East that were less isolated by geography, the patriarchal model had triumphed everywhere by the early part of the third millennium BCE. Moreover, there is strong reason to suspect that this transformation, however regrettable, may have been inevitable.

It is significant in this regard that the civilizations that grew more or less independently in east Asia and the New World appear to have undergone a similar collapse into "patriarchal" value systems and social structures at approximately similar points in their development. The fact that the same lurch into the patriarchal model occurred in so many societies, and that we have no examples of significant movement in the opposite direction until quite recently, suggests strongly that this may have been a highly functional adaptation—and I suspect that this may have been related, once again, to the question of scale.

Imagine an early urban society struggling to maintain social cohesion and political purpose through the traditional means of kinship ties and personal friendship. As it grows from a few thousand to tens and then hundreds of thousands of individuals, the old rough democracy is less and less able to cope. Just once let a militarized hierarchy gain sway over this society, and it will never lose control again, for it is simply more efficient at running things, both internally and in relations with other states.

War does not determine who is right—only who is left.

Bertrand Russell

It is more efficient, among other things, at conquering neighbours, so that soon there are no nonmilitarized states left in the region. Thenceforward, militarized kingdoms and empires predominate everywhere, and warfare is chronic. Gresham's Law applied to whole societies: bad social models drive out good.

The resulting international system flourished for five thousand years (despite a steady toll of casualties among the member states, not to mention their inhabitants) because it was functional. It answered a variety of needs, it rewarded those who collaborated and punished those who defied it, and the warfare that was its constant accompaniment did not do enough damage to threaten the survival of civilization itself.

Neither, to be frank, did the First World War. Eight million military dead (or thirteen million total fatalities, or whichever figure you favour) is an awesome toll, but it is not the end of civilization. However, it felt like the end of everything to the participants, and the perception is as important as the fact: it set the alarm bells off.

The political leaders no less than the soldiers who survived the First World War were frightened by the implications of industrialized warfare, and quite rightly so. People could not have identified the specific threat of nuclear weapons in 1919, but they were only twenty-five years away from the first nuclear test, and in a broader sense they already knew, or at least suspected, what was coming next. Thus the revolutionary conclusion that was born as a propaganda slogan in the war and has been a constant theme of public discourse ever since: that it is now necessary to end not just some particular war, but the whole institution of war.

I am not suggesting that this was an entirely original thought that occurred to people only after the assassination of Archduke Franz Ferdinand and the events that followed. The traditional moral and philosophical arguments about just and unjust wars had already developed, in the late nineteenth and early twentieth centuries, into a critique of the institution itself: Marxists flogged their simplistic nostrums, the Tsar of Russia called conferences on the subject, and early peace activists (with the suffragists prominent among them) struggled to gain the public's attention.

Moreover, one can argue with the benefit of hindsight that this was part of a considerably broader erosion of the patriarchal model. The democratic revolutions in America and France had swept away the divine right of (god-)kings even before the end of the eighteenth century, and the nineteenth century saw the abolition of slavery, the spread of democracy and even the first stirrings of the women's emancipation movement. Other aspects of the patriarchal model were coming into question, so it was only natural that the central institution of warfare would also come under attack sooner or later.

Why, after five thousand years without any serious challenge, should the patriarchal institutions have come into question in this period? If we admit the hypothesis that the rise of patriarchy, including the institution of warfare, filled a need for strong hierarchy and central direction in newly formed mass societies that had no other means of articulating themselves, then the advent of alternative, more democratic means for deciding a society's values and goals was bound to challenge patriarchy.

From the invention of printing to today's CNN, the modern mass media have begun to supply those means and thus have restored the possibility of democracy in mass societies. As a result, all the patriarchal institutions are under threat—and hardly before time, for the change in scale has made them potentially lethal.

The people who fretted about patriarchal institutions (though they didn't use that term) in the late nineteenth century did not know one tenth of it, of course. They had no idea of how destructive warfare could become, of how calamitous the environmental consequences of massive industrialization might be, even of the implications of unlimited childbearing. Yet without knowing any of the specific projections that have obsessed people in the late twentieth century, some of them knew enough to be worried anyway, and worried aloud for the benefit of everybody else.

It had virtually no effect: we are a species that responds better to crises than to predictions. Before all these well-founded fears could coalesce into an analysis of the problem and a prescription for dealing with it, there had to be some apocalyptic event to focus people's attention. The First World War was that event.

Although that war frightened millions of people into thinking seriously about the prospects for civilization itself for the first time, it solved nothing. Seventy-three years later, we are still in the midst of a struggle to alter the characteristic behaviours of civilized societies in ways that will give human civilization a better chance of survival.

It is a struggle that will probably continue long past our own lifetimes, and it is clearly not a foregone conclusion that we will win it. We have both the United Nations and nuclear weapons, the environmental movement and global warming, the rapid spread of democracy and the widening North-South economic gulf. We must continue to regard civilization as an experiment in progress.

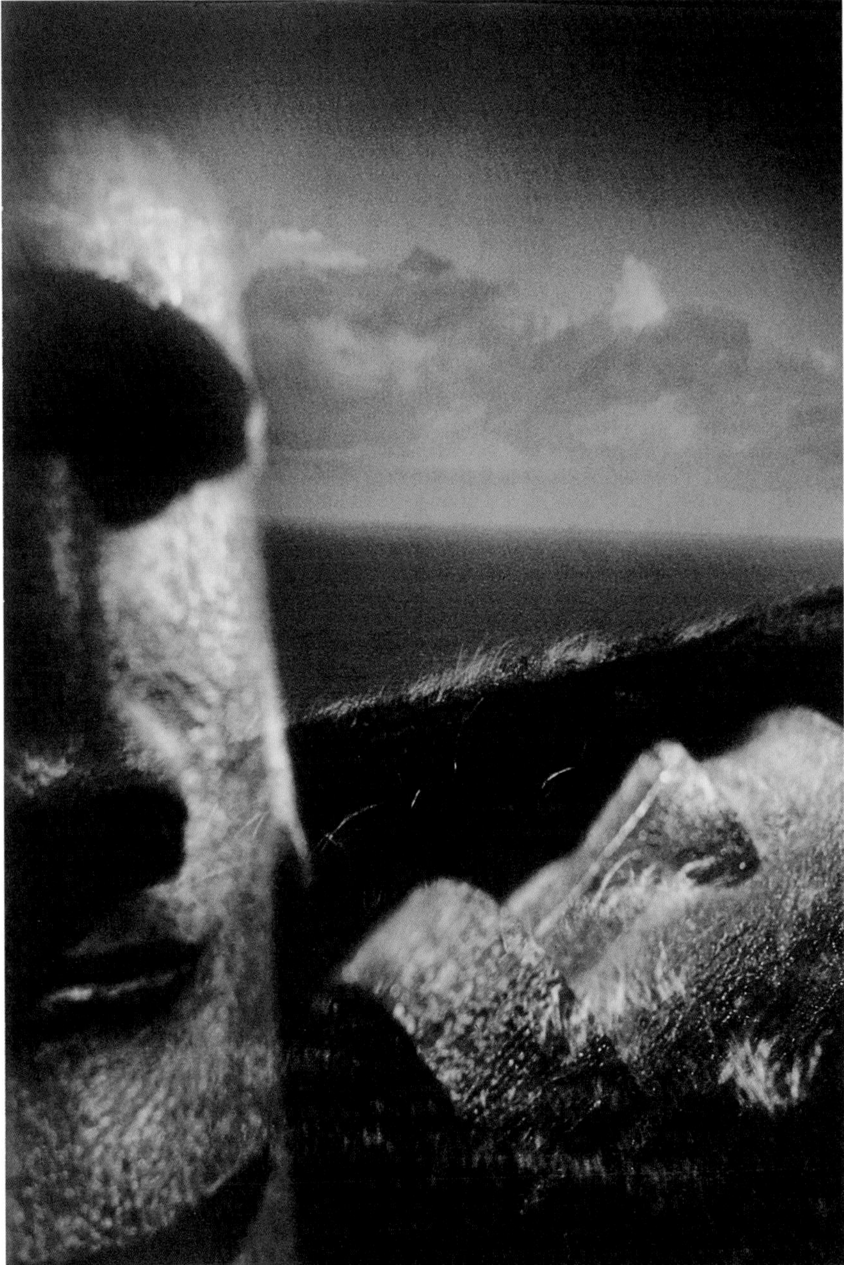

Easter Island by Abrams/Lacagnina. Photo

Research the Easter Island civilization that created these famous stone carvings. What are the parallels between the history of Easter Island and the history related in this essay?

But it is just as well that we had the First World War when we did. At a relatively modest cost, it gave us early warning of what kinds of perils we were about to encounter and caused us to start thinking about how to survive them a few decades earlier than we might otherwise have done. For all we know, that could be the margin between success and failure.

That is one of the speculations that can never be proved. But if you doubt that the margin is narrow, consider a twentieth century in which the old empires and the old complacency continued into the 1940s or 1950s, and acquired all the technology that accrued in the meantime, before they stumbled into their first fully industrialized war. We would probably be in a lot deeper trouble than we are—if, indeed, we were here at all.

Gwynne Dyer was born in 1945 in Newfoundland and Labrador. He is a journalist and historian now based in London, England, and writes a twice-weekly column that appears in over 150 newspapers in over 30 countries. He has worked in film and on radio, including the seven-part TV documentary series *War* in 1983. One episode of *War* was nominated for an Academy Award.

1. *Response*

a. In point form, summarize what you know about World War I. To help fill in the gaps in your knowledge, compare your summary with those of several classmates.
b. Gwynne Dyer says World War I "gave people their first glimpse of the abyss." In your own words, what is this abyss?
c. After you first read "Alarm Bells for Civilization," how well did you feel you understood it? What aspects of the essay were the most challenging for you as a reader?

2. *Writing* *Précis* Condense this essay into a **précis** of 150–200 words. Begin your précis with a brief statement of Dyer's thesis. Your précis should provide the most important evidence that Dyer presents to support his main argument. Why do you think creating a précis might be a useful skill?

A **précis** is a concise summary of a text. It is written in full sentences, but contains only the most important information.

3. ***Literature Studies*** *Essay Structure* Many formal essays follow a traditional structure:

   An *introduction* (usually the first paragraph) clearly states the thesis or controlling idea, engages reader interest, and previews organization or content.

   The *body* (at least three paragraphs following the introduction) develops arguments and ideas to support the thesis, provides supporting evidence, mentions counter-arguments and disproves them.

   The *conclusion* (usually the last paragraph of the essay) provides a logical follow-up to the thesis and arguments offered in the essay, summarizes key points, and includes an insightful conclusion related to the thesis.

   Examine "Alarm Bells for Civilization," and identify each of the above components. Does this selection follow the above structure exactly? Would you consider it an example of a traditional essay? Explain.

4. ***Language Conventions*** *Sentence Structure* Skim "Alarm Bells for Civilization" to find two sentences that are three or more lines long. For each sentence, identify what punctuation is used and explain the function of each punctuation mark. Rewrite each sample sentence as two or more shorter sentences. Would you recommend that Dyer edit his essay to decrease the complexity of his sentences? Explain.

5. ***Research and Inquiry*** Using the Internet and other reference resources, research and prepare a brief written report on one of the following: Dame Barbara Ward, Carl Sagan, Frank Richards, the League of Nations, Archduke Franz Ferdinand, or the GNP.

Reading makes a person complete. Would you agree?

Of Studies

By Sir Francis Bacon

Studies serve for delight, for ornament, and for ability. Their chief use for delight is in privateness and retiring; for ornament, is in discourse; and for ability, is in the judgment and disposition of business. For expert men can execute, and perhaps judge of particulars, one by one; but the general counsels, and the plots and marshalling of affairs come best from those that are learned. To spend too much time in studies is sloth; to use them too much for ornament is affectation; to make judgment wholly by their rules is the humor of a scholar. They perfect nature, and are perfected by experience: for natural abilities are like natural plants, that need pruning by study; and studies themselves do give forth directions too much at large, except they be bounded in by experience. Crafty[1] men contemn studies, simple men admire them, and wise men use them; for they teach not their own use; but that is a wisdom without them and above them, won by observation. Read not to contradict and confute, nor to believe and take for granted, nor to find talk and discourse, but to weigh and consider. Some books are to be tasted, others to be swallowed, and some few to be chewed and digested; that is, some books are to be read only in parts; others to be read, but not curiously;[2] and some few to be read wholly, and with diligence and attention. Some books also may be read by deputy, and extracts made of them by others; but that would[3] be only in the less important arguments and the meaner sort of books; else distilled books are, like common distilled waters, flashy[4] things. Reading maketh a full man; conference a ready man; and writing an exact man. And, therefore, if a man write little, he had need have a great memory;

The above image is the title page from *Instauratio Magna* by Bacon. The viewer sees a ship heading toward two pillars—the pillars of Hercules. These pillars represented the limits of human exploration for the ancients—and so Bacon uses this image of exploration by sea to symbolize human exploration into learning—learning that will surpass what the ancients taught. The Latin phrase at the bottom of the image means "Many will pass through and knowledge will be increased."

if he confer little, he had need have a present wit; and if he read little, he had need have much cunning, to seem to know that he doth not. Histories make men wise; poets, witty; the mathematics, subtile; natural philosophy, deep; moral, grave; logic and rhetoric, able to contend. *Abeunt studia in mores.*[5] Nay, there is no stond or impediment in the wit but may be wrought out by fit studies, like as diseases of the body may have appropriate exercises. Bowling is good for the stone[6] and reins, shooting for the lungs and breast, gentle walking for the stomach, riding for the head, and the like. So if a man's wit be wandering, let him study the mathematics; for in demonstrations, if his wit be called away never so little, he must begin again. If his wit be not apt to distinguish or find differences, let him study the schoolmen; for they are *Cymini sectores.*[7] If he be not apt to beat over matters, and to call up one thing to prove and illustrate another, let him study the lawyer's cases. So every defect of the mind may have a special receipt.

Notes

1. By *crafty* Bacon presumably means *sly*.
2. carefully
3. should
4. flat, or showy
5. Studies pass into (that is, form) manners.
6. Of the bladder or reins (kidneys)
7. Dividers of cuminseed; that is, hairsplitters. See St. Matthew 23:23.

Sir Francis Bacon (1551–1626) studied law and entered the House of Commons at the age of 23. In 1597 he published *Essays*, the first essays to be written in English. (The French writer Montaigne had originated the form in 1580.) Bacon is therefore often called the "father" of the English essay. Each of his essays was a concise exploration of a single topic, such as travel, truth, or friendship. Though the essay form has changed greatly since Bacon's time, his works are still admired for their brevity and cleverness, and as examples of Elizabethan values.

1. ***Response***

a. Francis Bacon makes many claims in "Of Studies." Choose one of those claims and express it in your own words.
b. What "defect" of your own mind could you improve through study? Identify one specific book or other resource that would help you to increase your knowledge in that area.
c. "Some books are to be tasted, others to be swallowed, and some few to be chewed and digested …" Make a personal list of books that fit each of the conditions described by Bacon in the preceding quotation.

2. ***Language Conventions*** *Parallelism* Identify the **parallelism** in the opening two sentences in "Of Studies." Find other examples of parallelism in the essay, and suggest at least two reasons why parallelism is a useful writing technique.

Parallelism is the intentional use of identical or similar grammatical structure within one sentence or in two or more sentences.

3. ***Writing*** *Persuasive Essay* Write a persuasive essay in which you consider three main functions or purposes of an activity you know about from personal experience. Sample titles are:

- Of Sport
- Of Extracurricular Activities
- Of Part-time Jobs

In your essay, be sure to express a clear point of view about your topic.

Is Lightman the "last holdout against the onslaught of unbridled technology," or just afraid of e-mail?

Progress

By Alan Lightman

Over the past several years, friends and colleagues have become increasingly irritated with me for not being on the electronic network. Scientists want to send me their data on E-mail. Secretaries for distant committees, forced to resort to the telephone, hound me for my E-mail address and lapse into stunned silence when I allow that I don't have one. University administrators, who organize meetings and send messages across campus at the push of a button, grumble about hand-carrying information to me or, even worse, putting paper in an envelope and sending it through the interdepartmental-mail system. I admit I'm a nuisance. But I resist getting on the Internet as a matter of principle, as a last holdout against the onslaught of unbridled technology galloping almost blindly into the twenty-first century.

For at least the past two hundred years, human society has operated under the assumption that all developments in science and technology constitute progress. According to that view, if a new metal alloy can increase the transmission of data from 10 million bits per second to 20 million, we should create it. If a new plastic has twice the strength-to-weight ratio as the older variety, we should produce it. If a new automobile can accelerate at twice the rate of the current model, we should build it. Whatever is technologically possible will find an application and improve us....

Today, at the end of the twentieth century, a crucial question before us is whether developments in technology inevitably improve the quality of life. And if not, we must ask how our society can employ some selectivity and restraint, given the enormous capitalistic forces at work. That is a terribly difficult problem for several reasons, not the least of which is the subjective nature of progress and quality of life. Is progress greater human happiness? Greater comfort? Greater speed in personal transportation and communication? The reduction of human suffering? Longer life span? Even with a definition of progress, its measurements and technological requirements are not straightforward. If progress is human happiness, has anyone shown that twentieth-century people are happier than nineteenth-century people? If progress is comfort, how do we weigh the short-term comfort of air-conditioning against the long-term comfort of a pollution-free environment? If progress is longer life span, can we ever discontinue life support for a dying patient in pain?

Only a fool would claim that new technology rarely improves the quality of life. The electric light has expanded innumerable human activities, from reading to nighttime athletic events. Advances in medicine—particularly the germ theory of disease, public-health programs, and the development of good antiseptics—have obviously reduced physical suffering and substantially extended the healthy human life span.

But one can also argue that advances in technology do not always improve life. I will skip over such obvious environmental problems as global warming, ozone depletion, and nuclear-waste disposal, and consider something more subtle: high-speed communications. We are already seeing people at restaurants talking into cellular phones as they dine. Others take modems on vacations, so they can stay in touch with their offices at all times. Or consider E-mail, the example I began with. E-mail has undeniable benefits. It is faster than regular mail and cheaper and less obtrusive than the telephone. It can promote conversations among far-flung communities of people, and it can encourage otherwise reticent talkers to speak up, via computer terminals. But E-mail, in my view, also contributes to the haste, the thoughtlessness, and the artificial urgency that increasingly characterize our world. The daily volume of E-mail communications is inflating without limit. A lawyer friend says he spends 50 percent of his time at work sifting through unimportant E-mail messages to arrive at the few that count. Some communications are invariably of the form "Please ignore my last message." Evidently, it has become so easy and fast to communicate that we often do so without reflection. When messages come in so quickly and effortlessly, we irresistibly and immediately respond in kind. Although I cannot document it, I suspect that bad decisions are being made because of the haste of transmitting and responding to E-mail messages.

> Progress lies not in enhancing what is, but in advancing toward what will be.
>
> Kahlil Gibran

But more to the point is the overall fast-food mentality at work in the rapid conveyance of our thoughts and responses. We are suffocating ourselves. We are undercutting our contemplative powers. We could even be, ironically, impeding progress.

E-mail, of course, is only one example. Its use or abuse is up to the individual. But E-mail is representative of other technological developments, such as genetic engineering, throw-away plastics, advanced life-support systems, and computer networks. Certainly, many of those developments will have good consequences. But that is not the point. Modern technology is racing forward with little examination or control. To be sure, a number of thinkers and writers have for some time expressed alarm over where unchecked science and technology might be taking us. Mary Shelley, in *Frankenstein* (1818), was certainly concerned about the ethical dilemmas of artificial life. So was H. G. Wells in *The Island of Dr. Moreau* (1896), wherein the evil surgeon, Dr. Moreau, synthesizes creatures that are half man and half beast. In *Walden* (1854), Thoreau wrote, "We do not ride on the railroad; it rides upon us." A more recent example is Don DeLillo's *White Noise* (1985), in which the hero is exposed to a cloud of poisonous industrial chemicals, and then suffers a far worse mental ailment because of a computerized medical system that constantly announces his fate. But those countervailing voices have, for the most part, been ignored. That is not just because of the considerable economic forces that are propelling today's ravenous technological engine. Rather, we seem to believe—perhaps at some subconscious level—that technology is our sacred future.

I am not in favor of squashing new developments in pure science, in any form. The act of understanding the workings of nature—and our place in it—expresses for me what is most noble and good in us. As for the applications of science, I am certainly not opposed to technology as a whole; I benefit greatly from it. But we cannot have advances in technology without an accompanying consideration of human values and quality of life.

How should this examination and questioning proceed? I don't know. It is not likely that government regulations would be effective. Our government, as well as other large institutions, understandably has an investment in allowing technology to develop unabated. The problem cannot be solved from the top down. It is a cultural problem. Perhaps we must regulate ourselves. Perhaps we each must think about what is truly important in our lives and decide which technologies to accept and which to resist. That is a personal responsibility. In the long run, we need to change our thinking, to realize that we are not only a society of production and technology but also a society of human beings.

Alan Lightman was born in Memphis, Tennessee, in 1948. He has worked in astrophysics at Cornell, as assistant professor of astronomy at Harvard, and as a research scientist at the Harvard-Smithsonian Center for Astrophysics. Lightman has published poems, essays, reviews, and short fiction, and his books have been translated into 30 languages.

1. ***Response***
   a. Write a paragraph explaining what the word *progress* means to you. Did Alan Lightman's essay affect your view of progress? Explain.
   b. Read the author biography for Lightman (above) and, if possible, do some additional research to learn more about him. In your view, do his qualifications make him a credible spokesperson on the topic of technological progress? Draw on your experience as a reader to draft five guidelines that you can use to establish a writer's credibility.
   c. Prepare a brief rebuttal to one of the arguments Lightman offers in support of his thesis. Use a concrete fact or personal experience to make your rebuttal more convincing.

2. ***Oral Language*** *Speech* Lightman encourages each person to "decide which technologies to accept and which to resist." Prepare a short speech that argues in favour of either accepting or resisting one specific technology.

3. ***Literature Studies*** *Rhetorical Questions* In the third paragraph of his essay, Lightman asks a series of eight rhetorical questions. Given that he doesn't answer the questions directly, why do you think he includes them? How do they affect the reader? Would you call the question in the final paragraph a rhetorical question? Explain.

4. ***Making Connections*** Create a chart that contrasts Lightman's position in "Progress" with Heather Proud's position in "Dis?Ability on the Internet." Are Lightman and Proud equally credible in your view? Would you say that the two essays are in direct opposition? Explain.

The *Time* Factor

By Gloria Steinem

Are you the type of person who already has your whole life mapped out? In this essay, Gloria Steinem argues that forward planning is a function of class and gender.

PLANNING AHEAD IS A MEASURE OF CLASS. The rich and even the middle class plan for future generations, but the poor can plan ahead only a few weeks or days.

I remember finding this calm insight in some sociological text and feeling instant recognition. Yes, of course, our sense of time was partly a function of power, or the lack of it. It rang true even in the entirely economic sense the writer had in mind. "The guys who own the factories hand them down to their sons and great-grandsons," I remember a boy in my high school saying bitterly. "On this side of town, we just plan for Saturday night."

But it also seemed equally true of most of the women I knew—including myself—regardless of the class we supposedly belonged to. Though I had left my factory-working neighbourhood, gone to college, become a journalist, and thus was middle class, I still felt that I couldn't plan ahead. I had to be flexible—first, so that I could be ready to get on a plane for any writing assignment (even though the male writers I knew launched into books and other long-term projects on their own), and then so that I could adapt to the career and priorities of an eventual husband and children (even though I was leading a rewarding life without either). Among the results of this uncertainty were a stunning lack of career planning and such smaller penalties as no savings, no insurance, and an apartment that lacked basic pieces of furniture.

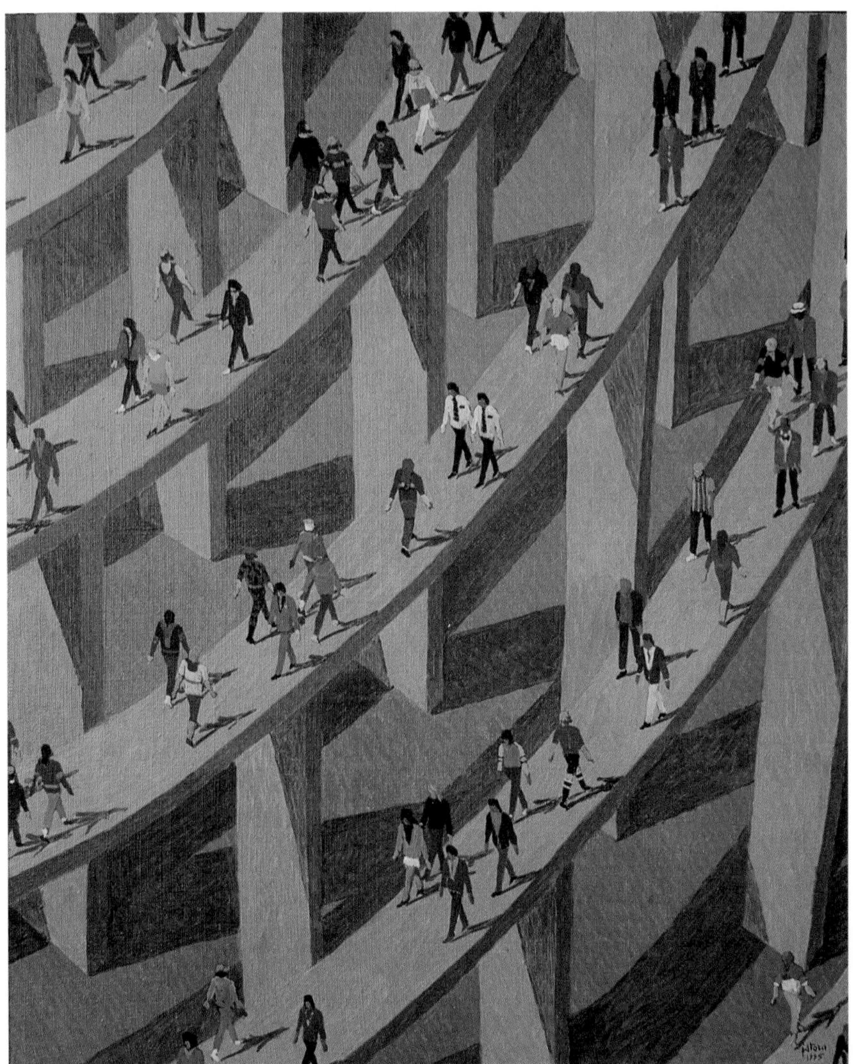

Allées Piétonnières by Jean-Pierre Stora

Examine and discuss this image. What kinds of lives do you think the people in this imaginary landscape must lead? Identify the specific visual elements that create this impression. What message does this image send?

On the other hand, I had friends who were married to men whose long-term career plans were compatible with their own, yet they still lived their lives in day-to-day response to any possible needs of their husbands and children. Moreover, the one male colleague who shared or even understood this sense of powerlessness was a successful black journalist and literary critic who admitted that even after twenty years he planned only one assignment at a time. He couldn't forget his dependence on the approval of white editors.

Clearly there is more to this fear of the future than a conventional definition of class could explain. There is also caste: the unchangeable marks of sex and race that bring a whole constellation of cultural injunctions against power, even the limited power of controlling one's own life.

We haven't yet examined time-sense and future planning as functions of discrimination, but we have begun to struggle with them, consciously or not. As a movement, women have become painfully conscious of too much reaction and living from one emergency to the next, with too little initiative and planned action of our own; hence many of our losses to a much smaller but more entrenched and consistent right wing.

Though the cultural habit of living in the present and glazing over the future goes deep, we've begun to challenge the cultural punishment awaiting the "pushy" and "selfish" women (and the "uppity" minority men) who try to break through it and control their own lives.

Even so, feminist writers and theorists tend to avoid the future by lavishing all our analytical abilities on what's wrong with the present, or on revisions of history and critiques of the influential male thinkers of the past. The big, original, and certainly courageous books of this wave of feminism have been more diagnostic than prescriptive.

> Thinking gets you nowhere. It may be a fine and noble aid in academic studies, but you can't think your way out of emotional difficulties. That takes something altogether different. You have to make yourself passive then, and just listen. Re-establish contact with a slice of eternity.
>
> Etty Hillesum

We need pragmatic planners and visionary futurists, but can we think of even one feminist five-year-plan? Perhaps the closest we have come is visionary architecture or feminist science fiction, but they generally avoid the practical steps of how to get from here to there.

Obviously, many of us need to extend our time-sense—to have the courage to plan for the future, even while most of us are struggling to keep our heads above water in the present. But this does not mean a flat-out imitation of the culturally masculine habit of planning ahead, living in the future, and thus living a deferred life. It doesn't mean the traditional sacrifice of spontaneous action, or a sensitive awareness of the present, that comes from long years of career education with little intrusion of reality, from corporate pressure to work now for the sake of a reward after retirement, or, least logical of all, from patriarchal religions that expect obedience now in return for a reward after death.

In fact, the ability to live in the present, to tolerate uncertainty, and to remain open, spontaneous, and flexible are all culturally female qualities that many men need and have been denied. As usual, both halves of the polarized masculine-feminine division need to learn from each other's experiences. If men spent more time raising small children, for instance, they would be forced to develop more patience and flexibility. If women had more power in the planning of natural resources and other long-term processes—or even in the planning of our own careers and reproductive lives—we would have to develop more sense of the future and of cause and effect.

An obsession with reacting to the present, feminine-style, or on controlling and living in the future, masculine-style, are both wasteful of time.

And time is all there is.

Gloria Steinem is best known for her work as a feminist–activist. In 1968, she co-founded *New York* magazine, and in 1971, co-founded *Ms. Magazine*. She wrote the bestsellers *Outrageous Acts and Everyday Rebellions* and *Revolution From Within: A Book of Self-Esteem.*

1. ***Response***

   a. Identify five key terms in "The Time Factor" (for example, *class, caste*) and write brief definitions of them in your own words.

   b. Gloria Steinem argues that females and males have different ways of viewing both time and life. Create a t-chart that shows those different ways. Do you agree with Steinem's analysis? Why or why not?

   c. "The Time Factor" was taken from a *Ms. Magazine* from 1980. In your opinion, is the essay still relevant today? Explain.

2. ***Language Conventions*** *Transition Words* Steinem uses a variety of **transition words** to help the reader follow her argument. Identify words that you would classify as transition words. Where do they usually occur, and why might this be so? Select a piece of your own writing and either highlight the transition words you used, or insert transition words appropriately.

Transition words indicate relationships between ideas. Writers use them to suggest links between sentences or paragraphs.

3. ***Literature Studies*** *Fact Versus Opinion* It's important for a reader to distinguish between fact and opinion when reading persuasive writing. A *fact* is a statement that can be proved correct. An *opinion* is a statement that expresses a belief that is open to question. Though all opinions can be debated, some opinions are easier to defend than others. Analyse the evidence Steinem presents, classifying individual statements either as fact or opinion. Present your findings. Based on your analysis, would you say Steinem's essay is convincing? Explain.

4. ***Critical Thinking*** Make a personal five-year plan. It should present goals related to education, employment, living arrangements, relationships, personal growth, and so on. Outline some plans for achieving these goals, as well. Compare your plan with someone else's and discuss the similarities and differences. Explain whether you feel that creating the plan was useful to you.

What makes a poem tick? Molly Peacock explains the poem "Filling Station" in her essay "Joy."

Joy

By Molly Peacock

Filling Station

By Elizabeth Bishop

Oh, but it is dirty!
—this little filling station,
oil-soaked, oil-permeated
to a disturbing, over-all
black translucency.
Be careful with that match!

Father wears a dirty,
oil-soaked monkey suit
that cuts him under the arms,
and several quick and saucy
and greasy sons assist him
(it's a family filling station),
all quite thoroughly dirty.

Do they live in the station?
It has a cement porch
behind the pumps, and on it
a set of crushed and grease-
impregnated wickerwork;
on the wicker sofa
a dirty dog, quite comfy.

Some comic books provide
the only note of color—
of certain color. They lie
upon a big dim doily
draping a taboret
(part of the set), beside
a big hirsute begonia.

Why the extraneous plant?
Why the taboret?
Why, oh why, the doily?
(Embroidered in daisy stitch
with marguerites, I think,
and heavy with gray crochet.)

Somebody embroidered the doily.
Somebody waters the plant,
or oils it, maybe. Somebody
arranges the rows of cans
so that they softly say:
ESSO—SO—SO—SO
to high-strung automobiles.
Somebody loves us all.

When you can't make sense of the world in any other way, merely to describe what you see before you leads to understanding. That is the lesson of the watching way of life, whether you are a detective tailing a suspect, or a bird-watcher, or a child. The clue to the life understood is observation. When Elizabeth Bishop was eight months old, her father died. Her mother's mental breakdowns and eventual institutionalization meant that by the age of five the young Elizabeth was shuttling back and forth between one set of grandparents in New England and the other in Nova Scotia, the beginning of a life in perpetual transit. For this poet, life was a tangle of travel due to mysterious circumstances; she developed a poetic art out of getting her bearings. After all, when you are at a complete loss as to how you came to be where you are, to describe what is before you is the beginning of restoration. This the lesson of fictional sleuths like Miss Jane Marple and Nero Wolfe, of naturalists like John James Audubon and Roger Tory Peterson: to describe, describe, describe the world, recording scrupulously, and thus also to watch a theory emerge. Description becomes knowledge. Details inform you of the shape of the world. Shape means perspective. If you are in a state of disorientation, you will gain a point of view. A point of view makes a sense of humor possible. And humor not only saves us from confusion, it paradoxically gives us the camera eye we need for sharp description. Not only is Elizabeth Bishop a noticing type of poet, she is funny. Capable of being amused, she amuses us, and it is a joy to read her. Joy is the inadvertent apotheosis of observation. The unexpected result of training your eye on detail is that the world becomes beautiful simply *because* it is noticed, and therefore appreciated. To have a sense of humor in an approving world—there is no fuller definition of enjoying where you are. And here we are with Bishop at a "Filling Station."

Oh, but it is dirty!
—this little filling station,
oil-soaked, oil-permeated
to a disturbing, over-all
black translucency.
Be careful with that match!

Oh, but it is dirty! she exclaims in the present tense. It seems we will be perennially in the filling station, getting gas, liquid nourishment to drive us forward—as vehicles for existence. The present tense, not the future tense, is the tense of forever because it pulses a current of "now" into all activity. *Be careful with that match!* she warns us. Bishop assumes her readers are her traveling companions, and by the end of the first stanza we share the intimacy of fellow travelers, passing through the world as witnesses. (Everything is interesting to observers; they are never bored.) Here we find ourselves at a place that is *oil-soaked, oil-permeated/to a disturbing, over-all/black translucency.*

Bishop revises what she says as she deepens what she sees. At first the station is *oil-soaked*, but then, as she notices more, it's *oil-permeated.* The oil is so embedded it changes the surfaces of things *to a disturbing, over-all/black translucency.* Each stage is ever more carefully scrutinized —and not neutrally. We are Bishop's chosen companions, after all; she claims us as her familiars—the sort of people who would find the oiliness *disturbing*—then pokes us in the ribs with her joke about the match. This is a place to escape from immediately!

Yet observers never escape; they see things through, instead. (That's the watching way.)

> *Father wears a dirty,*
> *oil-soaked monkey suit*
> *that cuts him under the arms,*
> *and several quick and saucy*
> *and greasy sons assist him*
> *(it's a family filling station),*
> *all quite thoroughly dirty.*

Within two stanzas, she's told us that the place and its inhabitants are *dirty* three times. Why, when the world is so exquisitely detailed, does she insist on that same word over and over again? Reusing the *dirty* word makes us feel that nothing seems to be happening. And so we learn the necessary patience of the watcher. When you are tailing a subject, the subject's world takes a lot of establishing. We have to trust, as Bishop does, that the closer the look, the greater the distance you possess—and the greater possibility for humor. When she says *Father* in her generic way, referring to the owner, we are in her confidence, sharing her point of view, and yet it is a point of view we would never have except for her. She's the one who catches the way his overall *cuts him under the arms*, and how the black gold keeps embedding itself, now in the *oil-soaked monkey suit.* There's that exact phrase, *oil-soaked,* again. With all her discriminating powers, why use it again? Because the return to the phrase, as to the word *dirty*, is a return to the key note. Bishop's recapitulation refocuses attention. The describer's eye returns to *clues,* Jane Marple's technique of understanding what happened.

The standard wisdom of the literary detective says that varied vocabulary is the key to sharp notation; a true scrutinizer rarely repeats. Yet Bishop's repetition is keen because it is reorienting—the way bird-watchers sweep the binoculars to the same tree in order to make sure of their bearings. Once gotten, descriptive precision is necessary again, and that's where Bishop's satisfyingly individual adjectives appear. The man's sons are *several quick and saucy/and greasy.* Those adjectives could be the names for the sons: Several, Quick, Saucy, and Greasy. Jaunty and cartoonish, they stand as if she had outlined them in Magic Marker. After she pokes our ribs *(it's a family filling station)*, she purses her lips as her grandmother might have done and spurns the joint: *all quite thoroughly dirty*. Not only does the refocusing on *dirty* reemphasize how grimy the place is, it deepens the judgment of those adverbs *quite thoroughly*. My own grandmother would have pursed her lips in the same way—and at a similar sight. The inescapability of the dirt teases out a question: *Do they live in the station?*

Yes, of course they do, I thought immediately when I first read this poem. My grandfather Gilbert Wright built one of the first gas stations in his part of upstate New York, a jerry-built structure, somewhere between house, store, and garage—and it was all three, presided over by our blind guard dog, Pal. The garage was a mishmash marvel of boxes of Model A parts stacked beneath a farmer's daughter calendar. The store wafted a heaven of smells: the dry sneeze-inducing flour, sugar, and laundry soap, the syrupy smell of root beer, Coca-Cola, and toffee, the rubbery whiff of windshield-wiper blades, and the smooth, crude smell of engine oil over all. The house behind, my grandmother's realm, smelled of molasses cookies and the starch of the embroidered doilies on the upright piano and the davenport. My grandmother Ruth battled the grease and dirt of La Grange Garage till her dying day; she would have hated Bishop's filling station.

It has a cement porch
behind the pumps, and on it
a set of crushed and grease-
impregnated wickerwork;
on the wicker sofa
a dirty dog, quite comfy.

Even though I suffered at first from Bishop's put-down of the station and the men in it, I soared at the idea that she wrote the poem at all. That a comfy dog, just like Pal, could be the subject of a poem made me recognize the value of this hearty dirtiness. La Grange Garage was an Esso station.

The ambivalence I feel reading this poem comes from the special conjunction of the facts that my grandparents shared the same values as Bishop but were in the very circumstances she describes. At first I felt ashamed to have La Grange Garage belittled, and elated that she also knew about those spots where filthy happiness prevails. Bishop herself must have experienced terrible shame at her own background. Having to tell people that your mother was in a mental hospital couldn't have been easy in 1916—it's difficult to pop into conversation today. Bishop's biographer, Brett Millier, tells us in *Elizabeth Bishop: Life and the Memory of It* that the poet saw her mother only a few times after the mother's breakdown and institutionalization. The story of her mother may have felt to Bishop like a secret too dirty to wash away. Yet as the oil-hyphenated words become doused with grease in the second stanza, and the wicker in the third becomes *grease-impregnated*, we begin to know that this place is so dirty it will never be clean; and this becomes the peculiar source of its happiness.

Often when an ebullient and self-possessed entity saunters into Bishop's poems, it seems to be in the shape of an animal. Toward the end of her life Bishop would write a poem called "Pink Dog," and in that poem would describe a mongrel mother dog at carnival time, out among the revelers. (Bishop lived for many years in Brazil.) When the speaker asks the dog where her babies are, the shadow of Bishop's mother seems to fly through the poem. The hairless pink dog, like a batty bag lady, conveys maternal presence, out among the crazies at carnival. The filling station seems also like a kind of benign nuthouse, where the *dirty dog is quite comfy*, right at home. The filling station itself is like a greasy Mardi Gras where everything is upside-down and saucy people can do exactly what they want, the whole scene held perennially in a comic moment.

Some comic books provide
the only note of color—
of certain color. They lie
upon a big dim doily
draping a taboret
(part of the set), beside
a big hirsute begonia.

Part of the watching way of life is watching *again*. Bishop notes, then *renotes* what she studies. *Some comic books provide/the only note of color*, she begins, then qualifies—*of certain color*. The poet models changing her mind, deepening her description, like a bird-watcher, wincing through her binoculars, narrating what she sees at first, second, third, and fourth glances. These lookings entail revisions, modifications, and corrections as the focus sharpens. She sweeps us into the process of observation; we are with her as she checks, then checks again. To us, her readers and intimates, Bishop displays a kind of imperfection because, quite transparently, she lets us see her re-visioning, re-noticing, getting it right.

Bishop doesn't produce a perfect surface of exact word in precise place; she works at correcting, if not mistakes, then the wrongness of immediate impressions. It's not that the comic books are the *only* color, it's that the place is so greasy you can't exactly tell what colors things *really* are. The comic books are placed, as the dog is in its chair, on *a big dim doily*, entirely out of place in this masculine world. It *drap[es] a taboret.* There, on an end table (an end table!) on the porch (a porch?) of a gas station is a doily (!) on which squats a huge, hairy houseplant—*a big hirsute begonia.* That hairy begonia is as fuzzy as Father and his sons. *Hirsute* is my favorite moment in the poem, because the use of this word next to *big, dirty*, and *pumps* is just like the appearance of the doily in the gas station to begin with. It is entirely unlikely, as bizarre as the noun *taboret* in this *oil-soaked* place. Now the subject of the poem reveals itself: unlikeliness. Isn't the world made up of peculiarly unlikely things—and isn't this what we have to explain to ourselves? Think of the orphaned Elizabeth explaining to herself why she lives with her grandparents, why others have parents who make a home, but she doesn't.

Unlikelihood always leads to the child's question, Why? And a series of why's composes the next three lines:

Why the extraneous plant?
Why the taboret?
Why, oh why, the doily?
(Embroidered in daisy stitch
with marguerites, I think,
and heavy with gray crochet.)

Each *Why* makes the incongruities all the more obvious, the vocabulary increasingly heightened and intellectualized. The plant is extraneous—a word people use for correcting compositions, not for describing filling stations. And this stanza rhymes *taboret* with *crochet* at the end. The utterly female order (I think of my own grandmother's variegated embroidery floss) against the male dishevelment (and my grandfather's grease-stained coverall and cap) is even a further disjuncture. Why are the yin of the world and its yang the way they are? The demands for understanding pile up and up, even as the descriptive words flood the stanza. Parentheses reappear. And inside them Bishop meditates on the type of embroidery—*daisy stitch/with marguerites, I think*—and the type of edging, *gray crochet*. The dirty and the clean mix up to form the unlikely world.

In forty-one lines, Bishop manages to use every type of punctuation we traditionally have. Punctuation lies entirely in the realm of the system of the sentence. It is what modulates the storyteller's voice; it is what unravels the sentence to our ears and reveals its rhythms. In the first line, she uses the most and the least frequently occurring types of punctuation, a comma and an exclamation point. With breezy confidence, she dares to open the poem with an exclamation, as if she were jotting down a postcard to us. Writing is a lonely art, and no one is lonelier than a writing orphan—or more befriended by an audience. Perhaps we, her future readers, are her imaginary friends.

Immediately after that daring exclamation, Bishop throws on another mark of punctuation before she utters another word—the dash. Letters and postcards, those vehicles of intimacy, are littered with them. Dashes mark a special kind of aside (different from the parentheses she will use three times later in the poem), and she poises a dash like a magnifying glass in the fourth stanza. In both cases, the dash ensures a closer look at the world. Though dashes in a sentence modify perception, they don't alter tone of voice. What lies on the other side of a dash is equally important—even though it is separate from the rest of the syntax. The dash is like the line between yin and yang in the familiar symbol: ☯ . The sentence, like a river, flows around the island contained within dashes.

On the other hand, parentheses are much more like a stage whisper, where an actor turns to address us, her audience, in confidence. Inside parentheses Bishop makes her jokes—*(part of the set)*, she says, raising an eyebrow. Parentheses are like two raised eyebrows set side by side to contain in print the very comment that the eyebrows would accompany in speech.

Many poets argue that the line stopping gives enough of a pause without adding a comma, but Bishop punctuates her poems exactly like prose. The tale she tells—like a dinner table anecdote—requires attention fine-tuned to the sentence. And so she brings the commas to show how likenesses and disparities hinge and attach, or separate and reattach. Semicolons are her great equalizers. Detaching the link of "and," they maintain the equal importance of the information on both their sides. The semicolon is like the balancer in the middle of a seesaw. Commas distribute weight, making the seesaw go up and down, allowing the balance to swing back and forth, readjusting always. But semicolons come to a balance point.

In the final stanza, Bishop uses a colon. A mystery is often solved by the words placed after a colon. The colon implies an opening out, a realization. It is used where information leads to understanding, where the clues all add up. And that is exactly what happens in Bishop's last stanza:

Somebody embroidered the doily.
Somebody waters the plant,
or oils it, maybe. Somebody
arranges the rows of cans
so that they softly say:
ESSO—SO—SO—SO
to high-strung automobiles.
Somebody loves us all.

When *the rows of cans/ … softly say:/ESSO—SO—SO—SO/to high-strung automobiles*, a newly resolved voice enters the poem. The whispery ss's of the cans, as carefully arranged as lines on a page, are artfully revealed as the answer to the way one goes about living a life—in search of what we will find on the other side of a conjunction, *so*, which means therefore and also is the first syllable of *Somebody* with a capital S. Here is the joining, after which materializes … the name of God, the comforter. After Bishop's three *so's* the Somebody who acts like God enters the poem. God is an arranger, like an artist, and positions the world. Somebody is the prime mover of a domestic life, the godly person who *waters the plant* and *arranges the rows of cans* and, finally, is the one who *loves us all.*

A comforting hand seems to be on Bishop's forehead, perhaps uttering the words *don't be afraid.* Bishop's hands, in turn, are on either side of her reader's head, turning it, directing our gaze. The reward of description—the tactic of noticing details when nothing in the world makes sense—is lucidity. As intelligibility comes from specifics, so does humor. Humor never exists *in general.* It is present only *in details.* And Bishop's saving humor is also godly. It emanates from an oil can that mutters *so* what? There's a *Somebody*, like a huge grandmother in the sky, who's looking out for us. And make no mistake, it's our own inner motors that make us high-strung automobiles.

So, whatever is bothering you doesn't matter. Whatever it is, is OK.

Kick down your motor. Somebody loves us all. Bishop's gesture is so complete it traces a kind of circle, like the letter of the alphabet in the middle of jOy.

Molly Peacock is the author of four books of poems—including *Original Love* and *Take Heart*—as well as a memoir—*Paradise, Piece by Piece*. Peacock is a contributing writer and poet to journals such as *The New Yorker* and *The Paris Review*. She works closely with new poets.

1. ***Response***
   a. Why is "Joy" an appropriate title for Molly Peacock's essay? What different things should a good title do? Give an example of titles (of essays, stories, poems, movies, CDs, et cetera) that you think are especially effective, explaining why.
   b. Does "Joy" have a formal or informal style? Use quotations from the essay to support your opinion.
   c. When you study a poem, what steps do you take to understand it? Reflect on the different methods you use and describe each one.
   d. Did Peacock's essay help you to understand "Filling Station"? Why or why not?

2. ***Literature Studies*** *Literary Essay* A **literary essay** usually considers both *content* (what the work says: its message and meaning) and *form* (how that meaning is expressed). Reread "Joy" and summarize the main points Peacock makes about the poem's content and the main points she makes about its form.

A **literary essay** presents an interpretation or explores some aspect of one or more works of literature.

3. ***Language Conventions*** *Punctuation* Review Peacock's discussion of Bishop's use of punctuation. ("In forty-one lines, Bishop manages to use every type of punctuation we traditionally have ...") Did this discussion help you to appreciate punctuation in a new way? Do you think that this is an effective section of the essay? Explain.

In this essay, Kristal Fung, a student, explains why a favourite piece of literature should be included in a high school anthology.

In Support of Nick Bantock's "Life Class"

By Kristal Fung

"Life Class," an excerpt from *The Artful Dodger: Images and Reflections*, by Nick Bantock, is laced with humorous first-person anecdotes. Bantock, who moved to Vancouver with his wife and young son in 1988, began to work on his own books ten years ago. As his skills as a writer developed, he unexpectedly found himself being swept along by the *Griffin & Sabine* phenomenon. Since then he has continued to expand and develop a genre of narrative books that integrate both text and images.

I found this excerpt, entitled "Life Class," to be both refreshing and amusing. In fact, this excerpt reminded me a little of the short story "A & P" in that it explores the workings of a young teenaged boy's mind when it comes to the opposite sex or, in this case, "a beautiful woman in her early twenties." Although this excerpt holds "less" literary merit when compared to works by Shakespeare or Margaret Atwood (such a highly acclaimed and honoured Canadian author), I found Bantock's take on his own life to be surprisingly witty and humorous.

"Life Class" addresses timeless idiosyncrasies of adolescent life and that is why it should be included in a new Grade 11 Anthology for academic students. Bantock's work would readily serve as great comic relief and, to be honest, every reader needs to have a good laugh in between readings of *The Rime of the Ancient Mariner* and *Paradise Lost*, as grand as these works may be. In addition, the author is immediately able to enrapture his audience through the use of sharp wit and uncanny humour. Furthermore, I am sure that teenagers around my own age would empathize with the characters as I did, upon reading this excerpt.

Nick Bantock's open approach to writing is invigorating and I was completely taken away by this humorous short story.

I was not at all offended by the fact that the narrator is openly excited by the prospects of seeing a naked woman for the first time in his life, for Bantock does not objectify the young woman. Robbie, however, who "frankly didn't know what all the kerfuffle was about" is able to successfully embarrass himself in front of the entire class and, of course, in front of the "truly celestial body." At this point, the reader is left hungry for more; yet Bantock forces the reader to draw his or her own conclusions.

Life Class
Excerpt from *The Artful Dodger: Images and Reflections*
by Nick Bantock

The really big event in my early days at art college was our first life-drawing class. I was barely sixteen and I'd never seen a naked woman before. I was both excited at the prospect and scared stiff that I'd find some way of embarrassing myself. I'd discussed the matter with my friend Steve, who was also suffering from heavy attacks of conflicting expectations. He and I used to travel on the train together, and on the morning of the great event, we noticed a beautiful woman in her early twenties sitting at the other end of the carriage. We laughed and joked about "Wouldn't it be fantastic if she was the model instead of some Bessy Bradock." (Bessy Bradock was an amiable but pudding-faced, rotund, middle-aged politician, who, for a pair of teenaged boys, has grown to symbolize the sexually unappealing.)

At college, we got into a conversation about the impending life class with Robbie, a big Scottish lad who was a couple of years our senior. According to Robbie, he'd been there, done that, and frankly didn't know what all the kerfuffle was about.

When the moment was finally upon us, we filed into the life room with our heads bent low and our smirks tucked carefully into the shadows of our collars. Needing a security blanket, I immediately went over and stood by my favorite easel. Steve took up a similar position on the other side of the room. Robbie, meanwhile, perched himself right next to me astride a donkey, a kind of long, low stool with a drawing board cradled at one end.

After a couple of minutes, our drawing teacher came in with, of all people, the beauty from the train. She had bare feet and was wearing a Chinese silk robe. It took me a few seconds to come to grips with the implications of this momentous occurrence. I shot

Steve a glance and could see that he was wearing a look of panicked ecstacy similar to my own. I snatched up a pencil and started sharpening it for all it was worth. (Funny: Back then, I never noticed how blatantly phallic that gesture was.) I was trying to compose myself, knowing that she still had to go behind the screen and undress. I told myself that I had plenty of time to prepare for the oncoming shock to my senses. But, as it turned out, things didn't quite go the way I'd imagined. Our model's conversation with the teacher ended abruptly. Instead of stepping over to the screen, she simply pirouetted, and, with a flick of her delicate thumbs, unhinged the robe. Even without comparison, I knew I was gawking like a guppy at a truly celestial body. For long seconds the room filled with an unearthly silence. Then, from my right, there came a faint creaking noise that was followed by the awesome vision of Robbie's spasticated arms and legs beating in futility at the air as he and his donkey keeled over and crashed to the floor, spraying the room with a shower of pencil shavings, drawing board chips, and charcoal dust.

Kristal Fung was born in Vancouver, British Columbia. She was first drawn into the world of art and literature at the age of five. Her passions include writing poetry, drawing, snowboarding, and eating sushi. Fung plans to continue her studies at the University of British Columbia.

1. ***Response*** Do you agree with Kristal Fung that this excerpt from Nick Bantock's book makes a good addition to a Grade 11 anthology? Why or why not? Discuss her assessment of it.

2. ***Research and Inquiry*** Kristal Fung found Bantock's anecdote and wrote this essay as part of an assignment. Your assignment is similar: Find a piece of literature you like—a short story, poem, or autobiography, for example—and that you think would appeal to a Grade 11 audience. Write a one-page rationale explaining the reasons for your choice.

3. ***Making Connections*** Kristal Fung and Lynn Coady ("The Importance of Being Earnest") both present arguments in favour of humour. What similarities and differences do you see in their positions?

In this essay, poet Sylvia Plath compares being a poet to being a novelist.

A Comparison

By Sylvia Plath

How I envy the novelist!

I imagine him—better say her, for it is the women I look to for a parallel—I imagine her, then, pruning a rosebush with a large pair of shears, adjusting her spectacles, shuffling about among the teacups, humming, arranging ashtrays or babies, absorbing a slant of light, a fresh edge to the weather and piercing, with a kind of modest, beautiful X-ray vision, the psychic interiors of her neighbors—her neighbors on trains, in the dentist's waiting room, in the corner teashop. To her, this fortunate one, what is there that *isn't* relevant! Old shoes can be used, doorknobs, air letters, flannel nightgowns, cathedrals, nail varnish, jet planes, rose arbors and budgerigars; little mannerisms—the sucking at a tooth, the tugging at a hemline—any weird or warty or fine or despicable thing. Not to mention emotions, motivations—those rumbling, thunderous shapes. Her business is Time, the way it shoots forward, shunts back, blooms, decays and double exposes itself. Her business is people in Time. And she, it seems to me, has all the time in the world. She can take a century if she likes, a generation, a whole summer.

I can take about a minute.

I'm not talking about epic poems. We all know how long *they* can take. I'm talking about the smallish, unofficial garden-variety poem. How shall I describe it?—a door opens, a door shuts. In between you have had a glimpse: a garden, a person, a rainstorm, a dragonfly, a heart, a city. I think of those round glass Victorian paperweights which I remember, yet can never find—a far cry from the plastic mass-productions which stud the toy counters in Woolworths. This sort of paperweight is a clear globe, self-complete, very pure, with a forest or village or family group within it. You turn it upside down, then back. It snows. Everything is changed in a minute. It will never be the same in there—not the fir trees, nor the gables, nor the faces.

So a poem takes place.

And there is really so little room! So little time! The poet becomes an expert packer of suitcases:

The apparition of these faces in the crowd;
Petals on a wet black bough.

There it is: the beginning and the end in one breath. How would the novelist manage that? In a paragraph? In a page? Mixing it, perhaps, like paint, with a little water, thinning it, spreading it out.

Now I am being smug, I am finding advantages.

If a poem is concentrated, a closed fist, then a novel is relaxed and expansive, an open hand: it has roads, detours, destinations; a heart line, a head line; morals and money come into it. Where the fist excludes and stuns, the open hand can touch and encompass a great deal in its travels.

I have never put a toothbrush in a poem.

I do not like to think of all the things, familiar, useful and worthy things, I have never put into a poem. I did, once, put a yew tree in. And that yew tree began, with astounding egotism, to manage and order the whole affair. It was not a yew tree by a church on a road past a house in a town where a certain woman lived … and so on, as it might have been, in a novel. Oh no. It stood squarely in the middle of my poem, manipulating its dark shades, the voices in the churchyard, the clouds, the birds, the tender melancholy with which I contemplated it—everything! I couldn't subdue it. And, in the end, my poem was a poem about a yew tree. That yew tree was just too proud to be a passing black mark in a novel.

Perhaps I shall anger some poets by implying that the *poem* is proud. The poem, too, can include everything, they will tell me. And with far more precision and power than those baggy, disheveled and undiscriminate creatures we call novels. Well, I concede these poets their steamshovels and old trousers. I really *don't* think poems should be all that chaste. I would, I think, even concede a toothbrush, if the poem was a real one. But these apparitions, these poetical toothbrushes, are rare. And when they do arrive, they are inclined, like my obstreperous yew tree, to think themselves singled out and rather special.

Not so in novels.

There the toothbrush returns to its rack with beautiful promptitude and is forgot. Time flows, eddies, meanders, and people have leisure to grow and alter before our eyes. The rich junk of life bobs all about us: bureaus, thimbles, cats, the whole much-loved, well-thumbed catalogue of the miscellaneous which the novelist wishes us to share. I do not mean that there is no pattern, no discernment, no rigorous ordering here.

I am only suggesting that perhaps the pattern does not insist so much.

The door of the novel, like the door of the poem, also shuts.

But not so fast, nor with such manic, unanswerable finality.

Sylvia Plath (1932–1963) was an American poet described as sensitive, intelligent, and compelled toward perfection. *Ariel, Crossing the Water, Winter Trees,* and *The Collected Poems of Sylvia Plath* were all published after her death.

1. ***Response***
   a. Look at the first two sentences of the essay. Do you think they make an effective beginning? Explain.
   b. In your own words, state the thesis Sylvia Plath expresses in "A Comparison." At what point in the essay does the thesis become clear to the reader? How does this compare with the placement of the thesis in other essays you have read?
   c. Reread the essay and find an example of figurative language that you think is especially effective. Why do you like it?

2. ***Literature Studies*** *Comparison* If you were asked to write a comparison of two methods of transportation, what kind of structure might you use for your essay? Create a diagram or outline that shows how that essay might be put together. Now reread "A Comparison." Is Plath's approach similar to, or different from, yours? In your opinion, did Plath use a sensible structure for her essay? Explain.

3. ***Language Conventions*** *Pronouns and Gender* Plath uses feminine pronouns (*she, her*) to refer to her imaginary novelist. What other options did she have? Do you think it would be fair to say her choice of pronouns is *sexist?* Why or why not?

4. ***Writing*** *Poetry* Take a story you have read or written this year and condense its essential meaning into a poem. When your poem is finished, briefly describe how you approached this task. What challenges did you face?

The Short Story Defined

By Peter Hung

Check several dictionaries for definitions of the term *short story*. How precise are these definitions? Which definition do you find the most useful?

In the following essay, student writer Peter Hung explores why it is not that easy to create a definition that truly captures the essence of the short story form.

zymurgy (zī′ mər jē) n. [ZYM (O) - + URGY] the branch of chemistry dealing with fermentation, as in making wine, ale, etc. **While in college, Mr. Budweiser got an "A" in Zymurgy 101**.

There. It was done. The last entry of my new, updated *Dictionary of the English Language, Thirty-Fifth College Edition* was finished. Even I was impressed. It contained over a billion lexicographical entries, spanned a thousand volumes, and would take up more than four hundred feet of shelf space. Best of all, it would be the first dictionary of mine to be bound in genuine Naugahyde, which looks like leather, but at a fraction of the cost. Yes, I was impressed. I, the lexicographer's lexicographer. I, Webster.[1]

I settled back in my chair, feeling quite content. But wait—something wasn't quite right, something I couldn't identify. It was not unlike the insistent buzzing of an invisible fly that is trapped in a room and cannot find its way out. Pensively, I reached for a chocolate-chip cookie from the plate of goodies I always keep on my desk. Eating helps me to think clearly, and in my line of work you do a lot of thinking.

"Ah, yes," I mumbled through cookie crumbs. I opened the rough copy of Volume 768 and flipped some pages. Scanning page 393, I found what I wanted:

[1] **Noah Webster:** (1758–1843). American educator, author, and lexicographer. It took him 27 years to prepare the original edition of *An American Dictionary of the English Language.*

shortstop (shôrt ′ stäp ′) n. Baseball **1** the infielder stationed between second and third base **2** the area covered by a shortstop. **I hate baseball, and I absolutely detest playing shortstop.**

short straw (shôrt ′ strô ′) n. The bad end of a deal, usually obtained through the process of drawing straws (see **draw straw**) or through some other lottery system. **Tom got the short straw; he, out of all the new prisoners at San Quentin, would be executed first.**

I had almost forgotten that I hadn't yet defined "short story." I had left a blank space between "shortstop" and "short straw," intending to fill it in later on. I have a habit of postponing the hardest terms, and "short story" is as hard as they come.

I went to the kitchen, got another plate of cookies, and returned to my desk. Picking up a pencil, I began writing.

short story (shôrt ′ stôr ′ ē) n. A kind of story that is short.

Well, it was a start. But I had to be more specific. After all, the dictionary might be consulted by, say, a high school student who must write an essay defining the short story. People around the world depend on me to shed light on all manner of topics, and I mustn't let them down. I bit into a cookie and continued.

short story (shôrt ′ stôr ′ ē) n. A kind of story that is short (i.e., no longer than thirty pages) with a simple plot and no more than ten characters.

Now that was more like it. I rewarded myself with another cookie. Munching steadily, I came up with another idea. I grabbed Volume 359, turned to page 410, and located the desired entry.

Hemingway (hem′ in wā ′), **Ernest** 1899–1961. U.S. novelist and short-story writer whose writing is characterized by the use of short, simple, declarative sentences (e.g., "Ad stood up," as in "The Battler"). Two of his favorite themes are man's internal struggle (as in "The Snows of Kilimanjaro") and trout fishing. Two interesting facts about Hemingway's short stories are that "The Short Happy Life of Francis Macomber" is thirty-five pages long, and "The Light of the World" has more than ten characters in it.

Hmp. This discovery was somewhat of a mixed blessing. Here I was reminded that the style of the short story is simple, and that its themes are man's internal struggle and trout fishing. Unfortunately, I was also reminded that short stories can have more than ten characters and thirty pages.

I erased my definition and started again.

short story (shôrt ′ stôr ′ ē) n. A kind of story that is short and deals with man's internal struggle or trout fishing; stylistically, it consists primarily of short, simple, declarative sentences, such as "Ad stood up."

This definition was, I felt, lacking something, so I chose a large molasses cookie from the diminishing pile and shoved it into my mouth. It had just the right consistency and texture, but not quite enough molasses. Just the same, it cleared my head, and I was able to delve into my memory for another appropriate reference. I pulled out Volume 299 and opened it to the right page.

Ellison (el ′ i sen), **Ralph** 1914– . U.S. writer who won acclaim with his novel *Invisible Man.* Also wrote short stories of note, such as "Battle Royal," in which a single event serves to illustrate the struggle of black Americans against racial discrimination and mistreatment. Ellison tends to use more complex sentences than Hemingway, as well as more adjectives, adverbs, and similes to produce vivid images; e.g., "The boys groped about like blind, cautious crabs crouching to protect their mid-sections, their heads pulled in short against their shoulders, their arms stretched nervously before them, with their fists testing the smoke-filled air like the knobbed feelers of hypersensitive snails."

This couldn't be happening. Ellison and Hemingway were as different as authors can be, and yet they both had produced these "things" that are categorized as short stories. Despite an increasing sense of vertigo, I swallowed my last cookie and turned to another entry, this time from Volume 745.

Salinger (sal ′ iŋ jer). **J(erome) D(avid)** 1919– . U.S. novelist and short-story writer. Salinger blends overtones of love and squalor in his brilliant short story "To Esmé—with Love and Squalor." He separates the squalid part from the rest by dividing the story into two distinct sections, with completely different settings and characters. The structure is very different from that of stories by Hemingway or Ellison, which develop in a continuous, unbroken manner.

I stared blankly down at my plate, now devoid of goodies except for a few crumbs. I licked up the crumbs in desperation. My head was fairly spinning, and I was, for the first time in my illustrious career, at a loss for words. "Get a grip on yourself, Web," I told myself. Putting down my pencil, I got up from my chair, walked slowly over to the couch, and sat down heavily, feeling lost and bloated.

I don't know when I fell asleep, but I did, which was a good thing, because I tend to think better when I am asleep than when I am awake, except when I'm eating cookies. So my mind subconsciously mulled over the various ways of defining "short story." Hemingway, Ellison, Salinger, Hemingway, style, simple, plot, Salinger, short, Ellison, complex, Battle of Snows and Squalor, J(erome) D(avid) Waldo, character, theme, Ernest, earnest, any earnest, some Salinger, every Esmé, Royal Macomber, Short Happy Story of Life, Love, and Light of, dark.

Somewhere along the line, I came to the conclusion that the short story could not be defined, for it was all these things and more. It was strange, but I saw the Short Story there. No, not the spirit of the short story, or the embodiment of the short story. But just the Short Story there. It was like a candle in the darkness, or the flash of a firefly at night, shining brightly and then gone. Yes, it was gone. But that moment of light revealed a part of life that had gone unnoticed before. Or perhaps had been noticed, but ignored.

At any rate, it wasn't anything you could put into a dictionary, even Webster's *Dictionary of the English Language, Thirty-Fifth College Edition*. I woke up, no longer at a loss, but still feeling bloated by an overdose of thought-provoking cookies. I returned to my desk, erased my definition of the short story, and began to write again.

short story (shôrt ′ stôr ′ ē) n. A section of a building that extends from the floor to the ceiling and is lower than usual in height. **My, that building has a short story!**

Peter Hung was a senior at San Diego High School in San Diego, California, when he wrote this story. After reading a lot of short stories, Peter concluded that this particular genre is not easy to pin down. To make his point in an imaginative and amusing way he shows us Webster—"the lexicographer's lexicographer"—struggling to define "short story" in an updated edition of his dictionary.

1. ***Response***

a. Peter Hung, the student who wrote "The Short Story Defined," chose a humorous tone for his essay. What details and techniques create the humour?
b. Did you like the humour? Do you think the humour strengthened or weakened the essay? Give reasons for your point of view.
c. Despite the light tone of this selection, what are the serious points it makes about the short story?

2. ***Literature Studies*** *Exploring Genre* Is "The Short Story Defined" more of an essay or a short story? In a group, develop a series of convincing arguments supporting the view that it is an essay. Then develop other arguments suggesting that it should actually be classified as a story. Present your arguments to the class.

3. ***Language Focus*** *Definitions* A good definition is short, precise, and easy to understand. With a partner, brainstorm three words that you will attempt to define. Try to choose words that are not yet in the dictionary—good candidates are specialty words related to a sport or hobby. Write the definitions. How can you test the quality of your definitions?

4. ***Research and Inquiry*** Three famous short story writers are mentioned in this selection—all of them male. Needless to say, female authors could also have been included in this attempt to define a short story. Research two classic female short story writers, such as Katherine Mansfield, Toni Cade Bambara, or Alice Munro, and write biographical entries similar to those the author created for Hemingway, Ellison, and Salinger.

"For now, I'm content to be alone, because loneliness is something that doesn't exist here."

The Shack

By Margaret Laurence

The most loved place, for me, in this country has in fact been many places. It has changed throughout the years, as I and my circumstances have changed. I haven't really lost any of the best places from the past, though. I may no longer inhabit them, but they inhabit me, portions of memory, presences in the mind. One such place was my family's summer cottage at Clear Lake in Riding Mountain National Park, Manitoba. It was known to us simply as The Lake. Before the government piers and the sturdy log staircases down to the shore were put in, we used to slither with an exhilarating sense of peril down the steep homemade branch and dirt shelf-steps, through the stands of thin tall spruce and birch trees slender and graceful as girls, passing moss-hairy fallen logs and the white promise of wild strawberry blossoms, until we reached the sand and the hard bright pebbles of the beach at the edge of the cold spring-fed lake where at nights the loons still cried eerily, before too much humanshriek made them move away north.

My best place at the moment is very different, although I guess it has some of the attributes of that long-ago place. It is a small cedar cabin on the Otonabee River in southern Ontario. I've lived three summers there, writing, bird-watching, river-watching. I sometimes feel sorry for the people in speedboats who spend their weekends zinging up and down the river at about a million miles an hour. For all they're able to see, the riverbanks might just as well be green concrete and the river itself flowing with molten plastic.

Before sunup, I'm awakened by birdvoices and, I may say, birdfeet clattering and thumping on the cabin roof. Cursing only slightly, I get up temporarily, for the pre-dawn ritual of lighting a small fire in the old black woodstove (mornings are chilly here, even in summer) and looking out at the early river. The waters have a lovely spooky quality at this hour, entirely mist-covered, a secret meeting of river and sky.

By the time I get up to stay, the mist has vanished and the river is a clear ale-brown, shining with sun. I drink my coffee and sit looking out to the opposite shore, where the giant maples are splendidly green now and will be trees of flame in the fall of the year. Oak and ash stand among the maples, and the grey skeletons of the dead elms, gauntly beautiful even in death. At the very edge of the river, the willows are everywhere, water-related trees, magic trees, pale green in early summer, silvergreen in late summer, greengold in autumn.

I begin work, and every time I lift my eyes from the page and glance outside, it is to see some marvel or other. The joyous dance-like flight of the swallows. The orange-black flash of the orioles who nest across the river. The amazing takeoff of a red-winged blackbird, revealing like a swiftly unfolded fan the hidden scarlet in those dark wings. The flittering of the goldfinches, who always travel in domestic pairs, he gorgeous in black-patterned yellow feathers, she (alas) drabber in greenish grey-yellow.

A pair of great blue herons have their huge unwieldy nest about half a mile upriver, and although they are very shy, occasionally through the open door I hear a sudden approaching rush of air (yes, you can hear it) and look up quickly to see the magnificent unhurried sweep of those powerful wings. The only other birds which can move me so much are the Canada geese in their autumn migration flight, their far-off wilderness voices the harbinger of winter.

Many boats ply these waterways, and all of them are given mental gradings of merit or lack of it, by me. Standing low in the estimation of all of us along this stretch of the river are some of the big yachts, whose ego-tripping skippers don't have the courtesy to slow down in cottage areas and whose violent wakes scour out our shorelines. Ranking highest in my good books are the silent unpolluting canoes and rowboats, and next to them, the small outboard motorboats putt-putting along and carrying patient fishermen, and the homemade houseboats,

> Literature is the last banquet between minds.
>
> Edna O'Brien

unspeedy and somehow cosy-looking, decorated lovingly with painted birds or flowers or gaudy abstract splodges.

In the quiet of afternoon, if no boats are around, I look out and see the half-moon leap of a fish, carp or muskie, so instantaneous that one has the impression of having seen not a fish but an arc of light.

The day moves on, and about four o'clock Linda and Susan from the nearby farm arrive. I call them the Girls of the Pony Express. Accompanied by dogs and laughter, they ride their horses into my yard, kindly bringing my mail from the rural route postbox up the road. For several summers it was Old Jack who used to drive his battered Volkswagen up to fetch the mail. He was one of the best neighbours and most remarkable men I've ever known. As a boy of eighteen, he had homesteaded north of Regina. Later, he'd been a skilled toolmaker with Ford. He'd travelled to South America and done many amazing things. He was a man whose life had taught him a lot of wisdom. After his much-loved wife died, he moved out here to the river, spending as short a winter as possible in Peterborough, and getting back into his cottage the first of anyone in the spring, when the river was still in flood and he could only get in and out, hazardously, by boat. I used to go out in his boat with him, later afternoons, and we would dawdle along the river, looking at the forest stretches and the open rolling farmlands and vast old barns, and at the smaller things close by, the heavy luxuriance of ferns at the water's rim, the dozens of snapping turtles with unblinking eyes, all sizes and generations of the turtle tribe, sunning themselves on the fallen logs in the river. One summer, Old Jack's eighty-fourth, he spent some time planting maple saplings on his property. A year later, when I saw him dying, it seemed to me he'd meant those trees as a kind of legacy, a declaration of faith. Those of us along the river, here, won't forget him, nor what he stood for.

After work, I go out walking and weed-inspecting. Weeds and wildflowers impress me as much as any cultivated plant. I've heard that in a year when the milkweed is plentiful, the Monarch butterflies will also be plentiful. This year the light pinkish milkweed flowers stand thick and tall, and sure enough, here are the dozens of Monarch butterflies, fluttering like dusky orange-gold angels all over the place. I can't identify as many plants as I'd like, but I'm learning. Chickweed, the ragged-leafed lamb's quarters, the purple-and-white wild phlox with its expensive-smelling free perfume, the pink and mauve wild asters, the two-toned yellow of the tiny butter-and-eggs flowers, the burnt orange of devil's paintbrush, the staunch nobility of the huge purple thistles, and, almost best of all, that long stalk covered with clusters of miniature creamy blossoms which I finally tracked down in my wildflower book—this incomparable plant bears the armorial name of the Great Mullein of the Figwort Family. It may not be the absolute prettiest of our wildflowers, but it certainly has the most stunning pedigree.

It is night now, and there are no lights except those of our few cottages. At sunset, an hour or so ago, I watched the sun's last flickers touching the rippling river, making it look as though some underwater world had lighted all its candles down there. Now it is dark. Dinner over, I turn out the electric lights in the cabin so I can see the stars. The black sky-dome (or perhaps skydom, like kingdom) is alive and alight.

Tomorrow the weekend will begin, and friends will arrive. We'll talk all day and probably half the night, and that will be good. But for now, I'm content to be alone, because loneliness is something that doesn't exist here.

Margaret Laurence was born in Neepawa, Manitoba, in 1926. After attending the University of Winnipeg she became a reporter for the *Winnipeg Citizen*. Along with her husband, she lived in England, Somalia, and Ghana, before returning to Canada. Her novel *The Stone Angel* became the first of five novels set in the fictional Manitoba town of Manawaka. Laurence was awarded the Governor General's Award twice for her writing.

1. *Response*

a. What does the term *personal essay* suggest to you? In what ways might a personal essay differ from a persuasive essay?
b. What do you think Margaret Laurence set out to accomplish in "The Shack"? Provide evidence from the essay to support your view.
c. What three words do you think would best describe the mood of "The Shack"?
d. Does Laurence's cedar shack sound like a place where you would like to spend some time? Explain what does or does not appeal to you about it.
e. Reread the last line of the essay. What does Laurence mean? Do you think the sentence makes a good conclusion to "The Shack"? Why or why not?

2. ***Literature Studies*** *Description* Reread the essay, paying special attention to the techniques Laurence uses to create a strong sense of place. Find examples of simile, metaphor, specific nouns and verbs, and vivid adjectives and adverbs. Choose one sentence or phrase that presents a particularly effective description, and explain why it appeals to you.

3. ***Writing*** *Descriptive Paragraph* Review what you learned in activity 2 above, and apply the same techniques in a paragraph of your own writing. Your paragraph should capture the essence of a favourite place or pastime. Was it challenging to use the techniques you observed in Laurence's writing? Suggest some strategies you could use to improve your ability to write descriptively.

4. ***Media*** *Storyboard* Assume that The National Film Board is planning to make a short film documenting Laurence's experiences at the shack. Create the storyboard that would be the first stage in producing the film. What aspects of the essay will you include and what will you omit? Develop at least ten frames for the storyboard, including the opening and closing shots of the film. Beneath each frame, include notes about the shot, narration, lighting, sound effects, music, and so on. Share your storyboard with peers, explaining what you have done and the choices you have made.

Photographer William DeKay's travels in rural Canada have produced thousands of pictures and the discovery that, geography or subject matter aside, many photos seem to pair off naturally. They form a study of life and times beyond the cities and a tribute (by a southern Ontario farmboy) to the people of country Canada.

Doubletake

Photos and captions by William DeKay

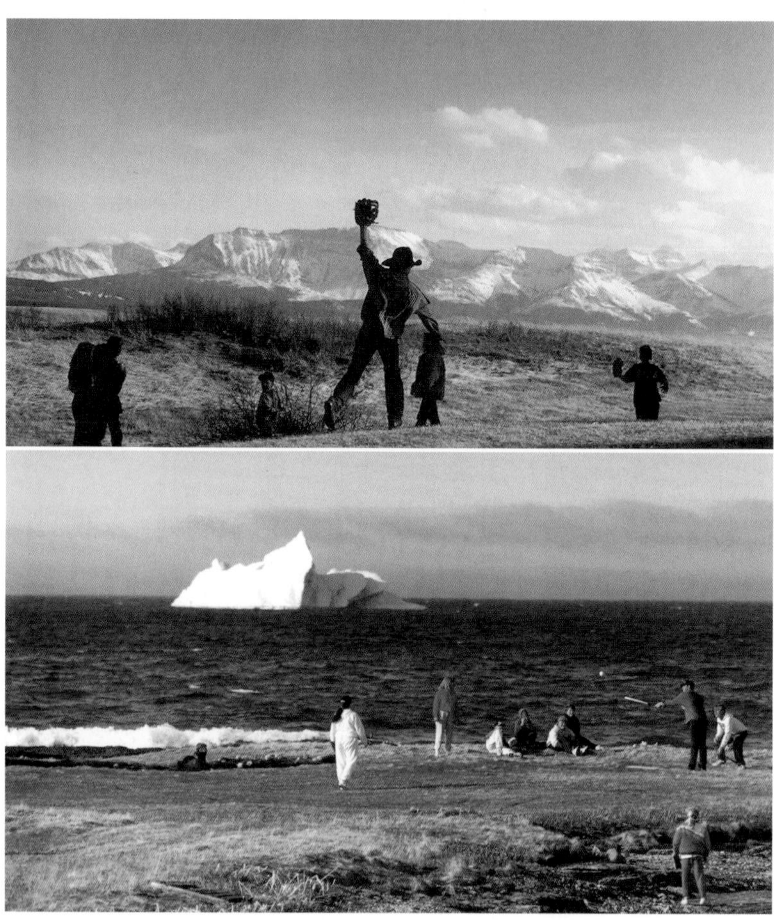

Top TWIN BUTTE, ALBERTA While their parents attend the Shoderee Ranch's Red Angus bull sale, kids play baseball on the sort of field dreams are made of.

Above EDDIES COVE, NEWFOUNDLAND I wonder if a baseball game has ever been called on account of icebergs.

Top TWIN BUTTE, ALBERTA Blaine Marr rolls a metal feeder across snow-covered pastureland. Slipped over a hay bale, it will provide a moveable feast for his hungry yearlings.

Above WHITEHORSE, YUKON Two boaters head upstream past Moccasin Flats, a more or less permanent community that survives despite the efforts of city council, which has for years been threatening to annex the land. I visited John Hutch, one of the squatters, in his home. A notice on the wall proclaimed: "I Do Precision Guesswork Based on Vague Assumptions and Unreliable Data of Dubious Accuracy Provided by Persons of Questionable Intellectual Capacity."

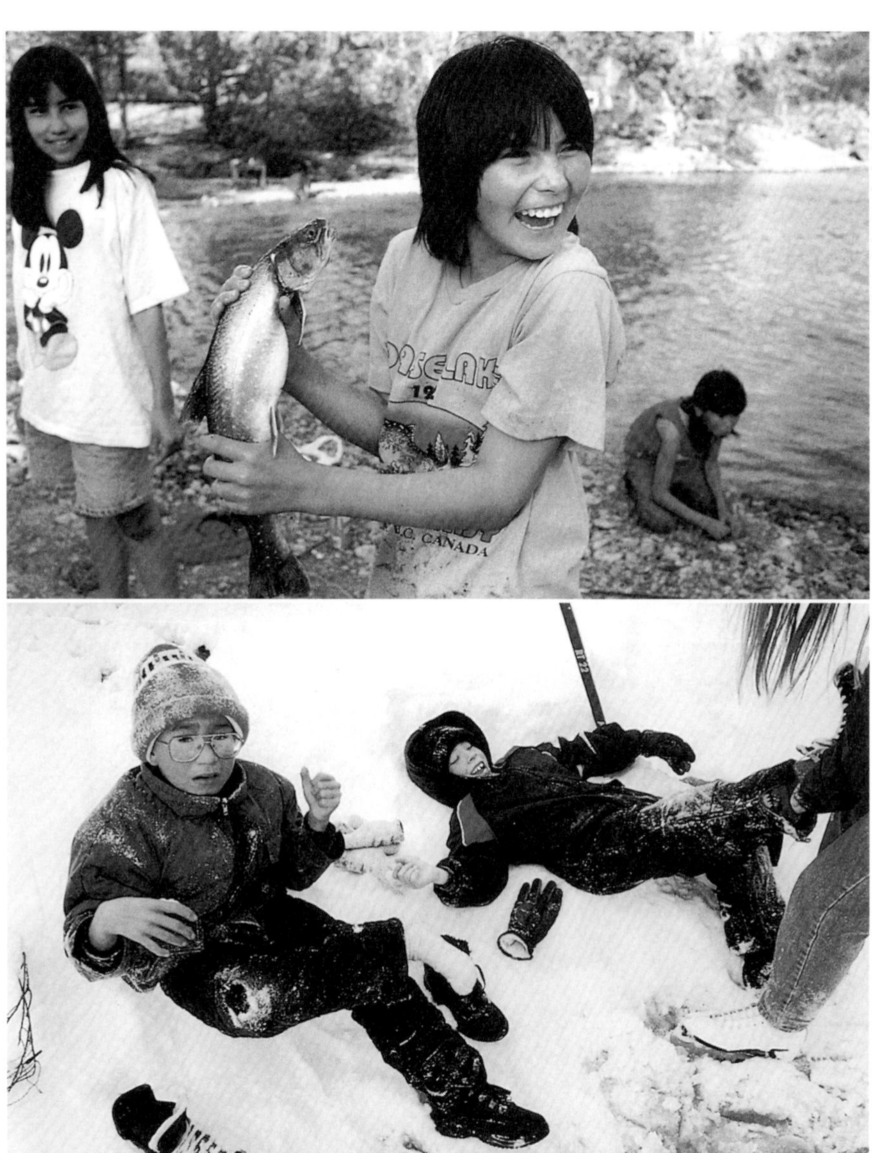

Top TELEGRAPH CREEK, BRITISH COLUMBIA Young girls play with a sockeye salmon, netted at Six-Mile Camp along the Stikine River.

Above POINTE AU BARIL, ONTARIO Andrew Dampeir looks like I felt. His hardier friend, Mark Madigan, gets an assist from his sister Heidi.

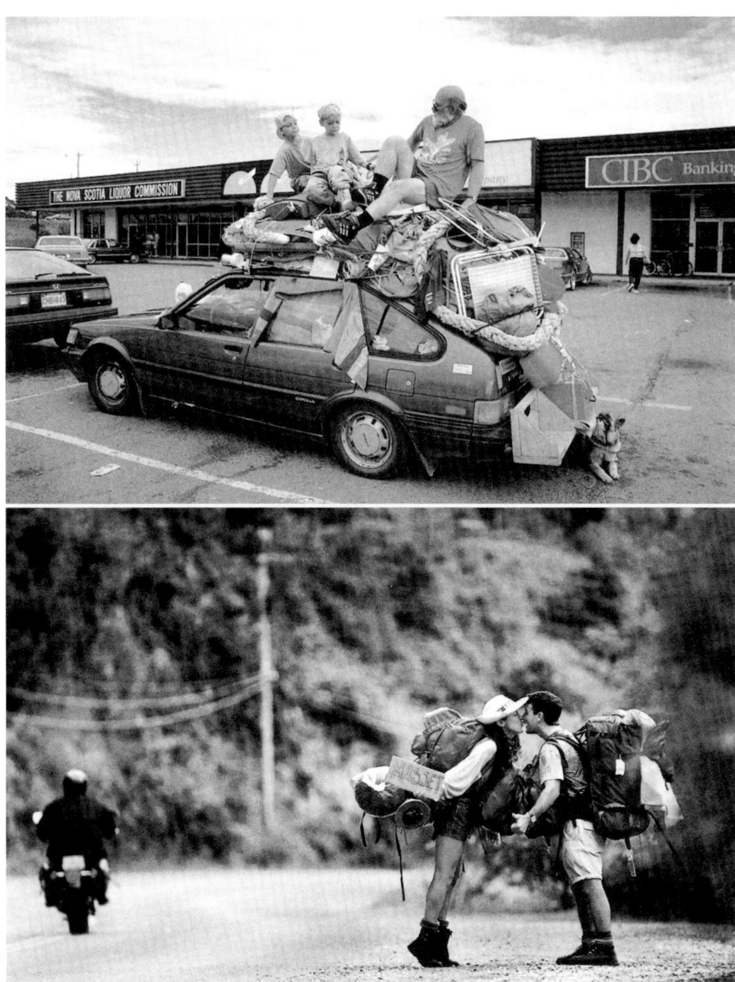

Top Sydney River, Cape Breton, Nova Scotia Darren and Keith Chomyn join their father Don atop their vacation home. They'd headed east from Alberta and had been on the road for three months. I asked if the amazing pile of goods strapped to the car had attracted the attention of the police. Don said that as long as the "stuff" was secured, it posed no problem. He'd had lots of double-takes, but no tickets. He went on to explain that his wife had died of cancer a short while back. "The boys really miss their mother," he said. "We're still hurting badly."

Above Queen Charlotte City, British Columbia Annick Blais and Francis Madore, two young Quebeckers, were taking a week's vacation from their summer job, planting trees for a forestry firm. I was glad to have company, and agreed to drive them to Masset, where they planned to camp on the beach.

William DeKay is a freelance photographer from London, Ontario. A graduate of Ryerson University, he has worked at the *London Free Press, National Geographic,* and the *Detroit Free Press.* He has won many state and national awards for his photojournalism.

1. ***Response***
   a. Photographer William DeKay says that "many photos seem to pair off naturally." Identify the similarities in each pairing of photos. Consider both content (subject matter) and form (colour, line, shadow, shape, and composition).
   b. Which single photo do you like best, and why?
   c. If you were going to photograph one thing, place, or person that would capture your perception of the essence of your community, what would it be? Explain the reasons for your choice.
   d. A photo essay develops a thesis or point of view through a combination of photos and text. Identify the thesis of DeKay's essay.

2. ***Visual Communication*** *Photo Essay* Create your own photo essay, preferably using photos you take yourself. (If you don't have access to a camera, you can create your photo essay with print or digital photos you obtain through research.) Explore subject matter that interests you, and do not be afraid to be experimental with your photography. Remember that the artistry of the photo essay lies not only in taking the photographs and writing the captions, but also in arranging the photos in sequence, and in positioning photos and text on the page.

3. ***Critical Thinking*** Consider the relationship between text and photos in "Doubletake." Obviously the photos are central, but would they be as interesting or effective if presented on their own? What functions are served by the text?

The poet George Faludy recalls his experiences in Hungary's concentration camps, and how he survived.

Arming the Spirit

By George Faludy

Some years ago in Hungary I found myself, for the second time in my life, in a concentration camp. There were some thirteen hundred inmates: democrats, Catholics, liberals, socialists and people without any political preferences, most sentenced to hard labor on trumped-up charges, though a few were there without having been sentenced or even charged. We could neither write nor receive letters or parcels; we had no books, newspapers, radios, or visitors. We cut stones from dawn to dusk 365 days a year, except for May Day. We did this on a diet of 1200 calories a day. Our situation was thus better than in a Nazi concentration camp, but much worse than in the present-day [1978] Soviet camps recently described by Bukovsky and others.

At first we returned to the barracks at night deadly tired, with no strength even to pull off our army boots and fall asleep on the rotten straw sacks. Our lives seemed not to differ from those of the slaves that built the pyramids, and our futures seemed equally bleak. But already on the day of my arrest, in the Black Maria that took me away, I had met young friends who had been denied a university education because of the war. Their faces had lit up: "You can lecture us in the camp," they said, "and we'll get our university education that way." After about a week in the camp two of them approached me and insisted that I start my lectures immediately after lights-out.

We were by then even more exhausted than on the day of our arrival. At first four men sat beside my pallet, and we were jeered at by the others. Eventually twelve prisoners gathered beside my straw sack every night for an hour or two. We recited poems, Hungarian poems, and foreign poems in translation. Among the English ones the "Ode to the West Wind" became the favorite. Then I would speak on literature, history or philosophy and my lecture would be discussed by all.

I was by no means the only prisoner to deliver such lectures. A former member of the short-lived democratic government knew *Hamlet* and *A Midsummer Night's Dream* by heart, and recited both to an enthusiastic audience. There were lectures on Roman Law, on the history of the Crusades, narrations of large parts of *War and Peace*, courses in mathematics and astronomy avidly listened to, sometimes by men who had never entered a secondary school. There was even a former staff colonel who whistled entire operas. Those of us who lectured ransacked our memories to keep alive a civilization from which we were hopelessly—and, it seemed, permanently—cut off.

There were prisoners who looked on all this with disgust, maintaining that we were insane to spend our sleeping time in lectures when we were all going to die anyway. These men, intent on survival, retreated into themselves, becoming lonely, merciless with others, shutting out thought and even speech.

By the second winter of our imprisonment it began to happen when we were at work that once, twice or even three times in the course of a day a prisoner would suddenly stop work and stagger off through the deep snow. After twenty or thirty yards of running he would collapse. In each case the man would die a day or two later, usually without regaining consciousness. Those who died in this way were always the men who had been most determined to survive, those who had concentrated on nothing but food, sleep and warmth. For my part, owing perhaps to large doses of pragmatism and positivism in my youth I was reluctant to admit the obvious: that delighting in a good poem or discussing Plato's Socratic dialogue could somehow arm the spirit to the point that it could prevent the body's collapse.

But then I was presented with proof. While I was washing myself in the snow before the barracks one evening, one of my pupils, a former government official, a strong young man, came up to tell me that he would not attend the lecture that night, nor indeed any other night. He wanted to survive and was going to sleep rather than talk; he was going, he said, to live the life of a tree or a vegetable. He waited before me as if expecting my objection. I was indescribably tired, and closing my eyes I saw scenes from my childhood, the sort of hallucinations one has in a state of semi-starvation. Suddenly it occurred to me that I must dissuade the man. But he was already gone. He slept perhaps twenty yards from me, but I never summoned the strength to argue with him. Five days later we saw him stop work, begin to run towards the trees, and then collapse in the snow. His death has been on my conscience ever since. But without exception all those who lectured, and all those who listened, survived.

It does not seem to me far-fetched to apply this lesson in the infinitely more pleasant society of this country. It justifies, I think, the Platonic view that man as given by nature owes it to himself to obey the dictates of his higher nature to rise above evil and mindlessness. Those in the camp who attempted this, survived; although physical survival had not been their aim. And those who for the sake of physical survival vegetated, perished in large numbers. It seems to me that the mentality of these latter is, *mutatis mutandis*,[1] analogous to the mentality of the consumer societies of the world, of those who seem obsessed with producing and consuming an ever-growing mountain of things to ensure comfort and survival; who have addicted themselves to energy as if to morphine until they are ready to destroy all nature to increase the dosage; who have, indeed, increased our life span but have failed to mention that the brain requires jogging even more than the heart if that life span is to mean anything.

The other conclusion I have drawn from my camp experience, and have tried to embody in my own poetry, is that our whole fragile tradition of art and thought is neither an amusement nor a yoke. For those who steep themselves in it, it provides both a guide and a goal for surpassing all the half-baked ideologies that have blown up at our feet in this century like land mines. Sitting comfortably in the present and looking forward to longevity in an unknown future does nothing to ensure our survival nor even to make it desirable. In any case we do not live in the future; we live in the present, and all we have to guide us in this present is the accumulated thought and experience of those who have lived before us.

For all the deficiency of my own learning, then, this is what I have attempted to voice in my work, and at this point in my life I feel safe in echoing the words of Petronius: *Pervixi: neque enim fortuna malignior umquam eripiet nobis quod prior hora dedit*—I have lived, and no evil fate can ever take away from us what the past has given. I believe we will do ourselves a favor if we extend the meaning of the author of the *Satyricon* to include the past of all humanity.

[1]***mutatis muntandis:*** Latin phrase meaning "with the necessary changes"

George Faludy is a Hungarian-born poet. His book *Selected Poems 1933–80*, edited and translated by Canadian Robin Skelton, was published in 1985.

1. ***Response***
   a. Why might "Arming the Spirit" be described as a personal essay?
   b. This speech was given as a convocation address to students at the University of Toronto in 1978. Why would the topic of the essay have been appropriate for that audience? Describe your own response to "Arming the Spirit."
   c. Do you think George Faludy is right to feel guilty about the young man who died? Explain.
   d. In the third-last paragraph of the essay, Faludy broadens the scope of his argument. Paraphrase the point he is making. Do you think the essay is strengthened by this paragraph? Why or why not?
   e. The editors of this anthology chose the title "Arming the Spirit" for this selection, which was untitled. Discuss this title. What else could it have been called?

2. ***Critical Thinking*** In a group, discuss Faludy's theory that "the brain requires jogging even more than the heart if that life is to mean anything." Do you agree with this theory? How could it be tested, and what evidence might provide convincing support? Present your ideas to the class.

3. ***Oral Language*** *Speech* Faludy uses his own experience to inspire others in this speech. Develop an inspirational speech based on your own experiences, or the experiences of someone you know. Rehearse your speech in front of a small group, getting feedback on presentation—body language, projection, pacing, and tone. Once you have delivered your speech, assess your oral communication skills and how they might be improved.

4. ***Research and Inquiry*** Using resources in your library, select one important work of art (literature, music, or visual art) created before 1900 and conduct research to learn why that work is culturally important. Present your findings to the class.

The Internet: "... a bright new window into a room that traditionally has been very dark."

Dis?Ability on the Internet

By Heather Proud

Over the past twelve years I have learned much by working, counselling, socializing, studying, advocating, observing, playing, and interacting with individuals with disabilities (IWD). It is still amazing to me that I have adjusted to being paralyzed for over half of my young life, and yet I feel so fortunate to have a good quality of life. I am excited and interested to learn about the Internet—the ways it has opened up vast new worlds to IWD by greatly increasing our interactivity and functionality in the world. We are using the Internet to be productive in countless creative and therapeutic ways.

People with disabilities face an ongoing and unique set of issues and challenges that many able-bodied individuals do not understand or are even aware of. As a person living with a disability for the last 18 years, I have gained tremendous experience and insight regarding the daily problems IWD face on so many levels. I've worked in the local disabled community for many years as an advocate, fundraiser, peer counsellor, educator, and case manager, and as director of a small spinal cord injury support group. From this experience I have learned about the physical, emotional, mental, spiritual, and economic challenges that IWD face.

The physical challenges vary widely for every individual,

according to their disability, from those who can live independently to those who are completely unable to take care of their physical needs. The physical limitations may not be obvious when you see someone in a wheelchair, yet even someone who is independent will generally find something in the "able-bodied" world which is a barrier to their accessibility. Even two or three stairs into a building or home means an individual in a wheelchair is excluded. In addition to the obvious barriers there are also hidden physical problems, such as chronic pain, which can make participating in ordinary life very difficult.

We all face mental, emotional, and spiritual issues as we live out our lives. We struggle with our inner conflicts and the need for love and acceptance from our world. For the individual with a disability, many issues such as self-esteem, optimism, and faith in ourselves, God, and our fellow humans are much more challenging. One reason for this is the physical separateness which leads to loneliness and a feeling of personal isolation. Relationships, both personal and romantic, become harder when the individual with a disability has so many needs. It can be overwhelming to a partner, making it more difficult to create and maintain healthy romantic relationships. Marriages often fail after disability occurs.

Adding to the personal physical limitations, IWD face societal limitations in order to be successful and reach their goals financially, educationally, professionally, and creatively. Not only are there fewer jobs and professions in which IWD can participate, there is often an inability to accommodate their needs. On the brighter side, advocacy groups, individuals, and family members have brought about the Americans with Disabilities Act and have been dramatically increasing the overall awareness of the need for accessibility, accommodation, and integration of IWD into mainstream life.

The Internet has also changed and expanded the capacity of IWD to function in the world. A wide variety of assistive technology devices have been developed, creating easy access to both computers and the Internet. Unfortunately these devices are still very expensive and continue to disenfranchise a large percentage of the disabled community who cannot afford them. I have been lucky. After researching what is available and what would make it possible for me to continue my education and become more employable, I received a state-of-the-art computer system from the State of Hawaii that allows me, as a quadriplegic, to go to school. I have never had a computer before or spent more than a couple of hours on the Internet at a friend's house. My experience with this class over the past two months has shown me the incredible vastness of information and ability to interact that one can experience while on the Net. I've come to realize that for IWD, this environment offers amazing freedom. The Internet is exceptionally supportive to those IWD who have always experienced so many limitations in the able-bodied world. It's like a bright new window into a room that traditionally has been very dark.

In a disabled person's world, the concept of space and time is very different. Most are often unable to devote the large chunks of continuous time that our society demands of its participants in employment/school/social settings. I personally cannot sit comfortably in a wheelchair for more than a few hours at a time. Until recently, I have not been able to "work" because of this. The fact that the Internet opens up new possibilities to work and go to school from one's home is an outstanding development for the disabled community who has been waiting a very long time for just such an opportunity to participate in mainstream/cutting edge life.

The Internet not only creates quality business and educational connections, but also healthy personal support systems. Networking through the Internet allows thousands of connections to be made which enhance our awareness that others are coping with the same situation. Knowing that someone is out there to talk with about a variety of disability issues helps ease the sense of isolation. A feeling of belonging combats loneliness. The disabled community has a strong presence on the Internet with numerous chat rooms and news groups available to discuss issues. I've been exploring now for two months and still feel that I have barely scratched the surface of what's out there. I want to know more!!

Individuals with disabilities are using the Internet to produce better lives for themselves both personally and economically. Many of these individuals have Web sites. They are sharing their personal stories of how they became disabled and how they have adjusted and accepted living with their disability. Their stories are inspiring and poignant. These people are addressing their issues and challenges in positive ways that encourage excellence within the global disabled village. By doing this they are an inspiration to others and are able to express their own personal creativity. This information is particularly helpful to people who have recently become disabled.

As I have been writing this essay, my awareness of IWD on the Internet has been radically broadened; a learn-as-you-go project. It has been enlightening and inspiring beyond my imagination. The Internet in no way takes away from my personal real-life interactions, but has enhanced and expanded my perspective of the unlimited possibilities and opportunities in the virtual world.

1. ***Response***

a. What is Heather Proud's thesis and how does she support it? Summarize her main argument.

b. The body of Proud's essay can be divided into two sections. Where would you put the dividing line? Why?

c. How does Proud's perspective on disability compare with your own? What knowledge and insight did you gain from her essay?

d. Proud says that "a large percentage of the disabled community" is *disenfranchised.* What specific problem is she emphasizing at that stage of her essay? In a group, brainstorm some possible solutions to that problem.

e. Explain the possible meanings of the title, and its use of typography.

2. ***Writing*** *Personal Essay* Proud uses this essay to explore the potential of the Internet for individuals with disabilities. Develop a short personal essay that describes your own experience with the Internet (or another technology). Remember that your introduction should engage the reader's interest, introduce your thesis, and preview the essay's organization. The body of your essay should develop your arguments logically, and include relevant supporting evidence. Your conclusion should summarize your key points and present a closing insight that is related to your thesis.

3. ***Language Focus*** *Preferred Terminology* Examine the language Proud uses to refer to those with disabilities. Why might the term *individuals with disabilities* be preferred to the expression *disabled individuals?* Provide some other examples of terminology that is preferred by a certain group or community. Do you think it is right for a community to encourage the general public to accept its preferred terminology? Explain your position.

4. ***Media*** *Web Sites* Investigate the Internet to find out what sites are designed for or targeted at individuals with disabilities. Describe any special features you find on these sites. What suggestions would you make to someone who wanted to design a Web page that is accessible to individuals with disabilities?

Chicken-Hips

By Catherine Pigott

When you look in the mirror, what do you see? In this essay, Catherine Pigott explains how a visit to Africa raised questions about her image of herself.

The women of the household clucked disapprovingly when they saw me. It was the first time I had worn African clothes since my arrival in tiny, dusty Gambia, and evidently they were not impressed. They adjusted my head-tie and pulled my *lappa,* the ankle-length fabric I had wrapped around myself, even tighter. "You're too thin," one of them pronounced. "It's no good." They nicknamed me "Chicken-hips."

I marvelled at this accolade, for I had never been called thin in my life. It was something I longed for. I would have been flattered if those ample-bosomed women hadn't looked so distressed. It was obvious I fell far short of their ideal of beauty.

I had dressed up for a very special occasion—the baptism of a son. The women heaped rice into tin basins the size of laundry tubs, shaping it into mounds with their hands. Five of us sat around one basin, thrusting our fingers into the scalding food. These women ate with such relish, such joy. They pressed the rice into balls in their fists, squeezing until the bright-red palm oil ran down their forearms and dripped off their elbows.

I tried desperately, but I could not eat enough to please them. It was hard for me to explain that I come from a culture in which it is almost unseemly for a woman to eat too heartily. It's considered unattractive. It was even harder to explain that to me thin is beautiful, and in my country we deny ourselves food in our pursuit of perfect slenderness.

That night, everyone danced to welcome the baby. Women swivelled their broad hips and used their hands to emphasize the roundness of their bodies. One needed to be round and wide to make the dance beautiful. There was no place for thinness here. It made people sad. It reminded them of things they wanted to forget, such as poverty, drought and starvation. You never knew when the rice was going to run out.

I began to believe that Africa's image of the perfect female body was far more realistic than the long-legged leanness I had been conditioned to admire. There, it is beautiful—not shameful—to carry weight on the hips and thighs, to have a round stomach and heavy, swinging breasts. Women do not battle the bulge, they celebrate it. A body is not something to be tamed and moulded.

The friends who had christened me Chicken-hips made it their mission to fatten me up. It wasn't long before a diet of rice and rich, oily stew twice a day began to change me. Every month, the women would take a stick and measure my backside, noting with pleasure its gradual expansion. "Oh Catherine, your buttocks are getting nice now!" they would say.

What was extraordinary was that I, too, believed I was becoming more beautiful. There was no sense of panic, no shame, no guilt-ridden resolves to go on the miracle grape-and-water diet. One day, I tied my *lappa* tight across my hips and went to the market to buy beer for a wedding. I carried the crate of bottles home on my head, swinging my hips slowly as I walked. I felt transformed.

In Gambia, people don't use words such as "cheating," "naughty," or "guilty" when they talk about eating. The language of sin is not applied to food. Fat is desirable. It holds beneficial meanings of abundance, fertility and health.

My perception of beauty altered as my body did. The European tourists on the beach began to look strange and skeletal rather than "slim." They had no hips. They seemed devoid of shape and substance. Women I once would have envied appeared fragile and even ugly. The ideal they represented no longer made sense.

After a year, I came home. I preached my new way of seeing to anyone who would listen. I wanted to cling to the liberating belief that losing weight had nothing to do with self-love.

> An essay is a work of literary art which has a minimum of one anecdote and one universal idea.
>
> Carol Bly

Family members kindly suggested that I might look and feel better if I slimmed down a little. They encouraged me to join an exercise club. I wandered around the malls in a dislocated daze. I felt uncomfortable trying on clothes that hung so elegantly on the mannequins. I began hearing old voices inside my head: "Plaid makes you look fat.... You're too short for that style.... Vertical stripes are more slimming.... Wear black."

I joined the club. Just a few weeks after I had worn a *lappa* and scooped up rice with my hands, I was climbing into pink leotards and aerobics shoes. The instructor told me that I had to set fitness goals and "weigh in" after my workouts. There were mirrors on the walls and I could see women watching themselves. I sensed that even the loveliest among them felt they were somehow flawed. As the aerobics instructor barked out commands for arm lifts and leg lifts, I pictured Gambian women pounding millet and dancing in a circle with their arms raised high. I do not mean to romanticize their rock-hard lives, but we were hardly to be envied as we ran like fools between two walls to the tiresome beat of synthesized music.

We were a roomful of women striving to reshape ourselves into some kind of pubertal ideal. I reverted to my natural state: one of yearning to be slimmer and more fit than I was. My freedom had been temporary. I was home, where fat is feared and despised. It was time to exert control over my body and my life. I dreaded the thought of people saying, "She's let herself go."

If I return to Africa, I am sure the women will shake their heads in bewildered dismay. Even now, I sometimes catch my reflection in a window and their voices come back to me. "Yo! Chicken-hips!"

Catherine Pigott has worked as a print journalist at the Kingston *Whig Standard*, a teacher in a Gambian college, and an editor for *CBC Radio News*. She has also worked as a producer of CBC's radio broadcasts *Morningside*, and *Sunday Morning*.

1. ***Response***

   a. In your own words, state the implicit thesis of this essay. Compare your wording with that of some classmates and discuss the differences.
   b. Refer to the description of organizational patterns in "Whose Lathe?" What pattern has Catherine Pigott used in "Chicken-Hips"? How is this pattern appropriate to her topic?
   c. Pigott describes some differences between life in Africa and life in Canada. Summarize those differences. In your opinion, how accurate is her portrayal of each place? Explain.
   d. Do you think that teenagers' perceptions about their bodies are strongly influenced by media images and peer attitudes? Explain your answer. Would you say that you are more or less susceptible to these pressures than other teens? Why?
   e. Do you think Canadians have changed their views about ideal body shape over the past 50 years? What kind of evidence could help you to answer this question, and where could you find it?

2. ***Vocabulary*** Pigott says, "In Gambia, people do not use words such as 'cheating,' 'naughty,' or 'guilty' when they talk about eating." In a group, discuss the good or bad connotations that many food words (for example, *chocolate, dessert, butter, carrots, tofu,* and so on) have. Design and administer a survey that will help you to investigate the connotations of some specific food-related words. Present your findings to the class.

3. ***Oral Communication*** *Debate* Soon after she returned to Canada, Pigott joined a health club. Brainstorm the most compelling arguments for and against that decision. Prepare for an informal debate in which you will either defend or attack Pigott's decision. During your preparation you should seek evidence to support your arguments, and you should practise delivering your position in a forceful way. After the debate, assess whether brainstorming arguments on both sides was a valuable first step.

4. ***Media*** *Image Analysis* With a small group, choose one medium—TV, movies, or magazines, for example—and analyse the messages about body type and body image. What seem to be the most common explicit messages, and how do they compare with the implicit messages? What conclusions can you draw? Provide concrete examples to support your view.

"I write for my dying cactus."

What Colour Is a Rose?

By Drew Hayden Taylor

As a Native writer there are always three questions I get asked, *ad nauseam,* whenever I give a lecture or a reading for a non-Native audience. Question one: "What do you feel about cultural appropriation?" My answer: "About the same as I feel about land appropriation." Question two: "When you write your plays or stories, do you write for a specifically Native audience or a White audience?" My answer: "I'm usually alone in my room when I write, except for my dying cactus. So I guess that means I write for my dying cactus." The final, and in my opinion, most annoying question I often get asked is: "Are you a writer that happens to be Native, or a Native that happens to be a writer?"

I was not aware there had to be a difference. I was always under the impression that the two could be and often were, synonymous. But evidently I am in error. Over the past few years of working as a professional writer, I have slowly begun to understand the rules of participation in the television and prose industry in terms of this difference. It seems there is a double standard. Surprise, surprise.

It is not uncommon, though deemed politically incorrect, for White writers to write satires about Native people quite freely, particularly on television. Notice many of the "people of pallor" script credits on such shows as *North of 60* (which, granted, does have one talented Native writer), *Northern Exposure* (I guess I'll have to move to the North since it seems that's where all the Native people live), and movies like *Where the Spirit Lives* or *Dance Me Outside.* All these shows have strong, identifiable Native characters created by non-Natives.

However, should a Native writer want to explore the untrodden world outside the Aboriginal literary ghetto, immediately the fences appear, and opportunities dry up. Evidently, the Powers That Be out there in the big cruel world have very specific ideas of what a Native writer can and can't do. Only recently, a friend of mine submitted a story to a new CBC anthology series in development, about Native people, called *The Four Directions*.

His story outline was soon returned with an explanation that the producers thought the story wasn't "Native enough" for their purposes. I myself submitted a story to the producers, and during our first story meeting, I received a stirring and heartfelt lecture about how they, the producers, were determined to present the Native voice as authentically and accurately as possible, and how committed they were to allowing us Native-types the chance to tell our stories our way. I was then asked if I could cut the first eight pages of my twenty-seven-page script. Oddly enough, they seemed puzzled by my sudden burst of laughter.

I once wrote an episode of *Street Legal* and accidentally caught a glimpse of a memo from the producer to a story editor asking him to rewrite the dialogue of my Native Elder to "make him more Indian." I guess as a Native person, I don't know how real "Indians" talk. Bummer. These are just a few examples of the battle Native writers often face.

I hereby pose a question to these people who judge our stories. I personally would like to know by what set of qualifications these people examine Native stories. Is there an Aboriginal suitability quotient posted somewhere? If there is, I would love the opportunity to learn more about how I should write as a Native person.

For a story to be "Native enough," must there be a birch bark or buckskin quota? Perhaps there are supposed to be vast roaming herds of moose running past the screen. Oh geez, I guess I'm not Native enough. I momentarily forgot, moose don't herd, they just hang out with flying squirrels that have their own cartoon show.

Or maybe I's got be good writer like dem Indians whats W.P. Kinsella writes about. It no sound like any Indian I ever hears, but what the hell, I maybe win bunch of awards. On second thought, you never mind. I get headache trying write like this.

So what's a writer to do? Damned if he does, damned if he doesn't. And what if I want to write stories about non-Native people? It's possible, but will I be given a chance? I'm sure I could do it. I've learned enough about how White people really live from watching all those episodes of *Married With Children* and *Baywatch*.

This all brings us back to the original question. Am I a writer who happens to be Native, or a Native that happens to be a writer? Do I have a choice? I think that the next time I get asked that, I'll ask the equally deep and important question: "Is a zebra black with white stripes, or white with black stripes?"

Just watch. They'll make that into a racial question.

Scriptwriter **Drew Hayden Taylor** has written *The Bootlegger Blues*, which won the Canadian Authors Association Award for Drama, and *Only Drunks and Children Tell the Truth*, which won the Dora Award for most outstanding new play. Taylor also writes essays and commentaries for *The Globe and Mail, The Toronto Star* and *This Magazine*.

1. ***Response***
   a. In your own words, state the "double standard" that Drew Hayden Taylor is commenting on in his essay.
   b. Taylor uses the term *cultural appropriation*. What does it mean? Give an example of a situation that could be described as cultural appropriation.
   c. What is the tone of the essay? Select three quotations that provide good examples. As a reader, how did you respond to this tone? Did it appeal to you? Do you think Taylor's approach is effective? Explain.
   d. Did you find Taylor's anecdotal evidence convincing? Why or why not?

2. ***Language Conventions*** *Language Level* "What Colour Is a Rose?" is written in an informal, conversational style. Identify the specific techniques Taylor uses to create this style, providing one or two examples of each. Pay attention to aspects such as sentence structure, punctuation, and diction. Using a conversational style yourself, write a paragraph that tells about the advantages and/or disadvantages of using informal language in an essay.

3. ***Making Connections*** The title of Taylor's essay may be a literary allusion to two famous quotations that also contain the word *rose*. How could you find out what they are? Try to identify what those quotations might be. How does the title of Taylor's essay relate to the main point of his essay? Are the quotations also appropriate to this message? Explain.

Have you ever considered the beauty of a toad? In this essay, George Orwell explores what makes toads such a wonderful sight.

Some Thoughts on the Common Toad

By George Orwell

Before the swallow, before the daffodil, and not much later than the snowdrop, the common toad salutes the coming of spring after his own fashion, which is to emerge from a hole in the ground, where he has lain buried since the previous autumn, and crawl as rapidly as possible towards the nearest suitable patch of water. Something—some kind of shudder in the earth, or perhaps merely a rise of a few degrees in the temperature—has told him that it is time to wake up: though a few toads appear to sleep the clock round and miss out a year from time to time—at any rate, I have more than once dug them up, alive and apparently well, in the middle of the summer.

At this period, after his long fast, the toad has a very spiritual look, like a strict Anglo-Catholic towards the end of Lent. His movements are languid but purposeful, his body is shrunken, and by contrast his eyes look abnormally large. This allows one to notice, what one might not at another time, that a toad has about the most beautiful eye of any living creature. It is like gold, or more exactly it is like the golden-coloured semi-precious stone which one sometimes sees in signet-rings, and which I think is called a chrysoberyl.

For a few days after getting into the water the toad concentrates on building up his strength by eating small insects.

Presently he has swollen to his normal size again, and then he goes through a phase of intense sexiness. All he knows, at least if he is a male toad, is that he wants to get his arms round something, and if you offer him a stick, or even your finger, he will cling to it with surprising strength and take a long time to discover that it is not a female toad. Frequently one comes upon shapeless masses of ten or twenty toads rolling over and over in the water, one clinging to another without distinction of sex. By degrees, however, they sort themselves out into couples, with the male duly sitting on the female's back. You can now distinguish males from females, because the male is smaller, darker and sits on top, with his arms tightly clasped round the female's neck. After a day or two the spawn is laid in long strings which wind themselves in and out of the reeds and soon become invisible. A few more weeks, and the water is alive with masses of tiny tadpoles which rapidly grow larger, sprout hind-legs, then forelegs, then shed their tails: and finally, about the middle of the summer, the new generation of toads, smaller than one's thumb-nail but perfect in every particular, crawl out of the water to begin the game anew.

I mention the spawning of the toads because it is one of the phenomena of spring which most deeply appeal to me, and because the toad, unlike the skylark and the primrose, has never had much of a boost from the poets. But I am aware that many people do not like reptiles or amphibians, and I am not suggesting that in order to enjoy the spring, you have to take an interest in toads. There are also the crocus, the missel-thrush, the cuckoo, the blackthorn, etc. The point is that the pleasures of spring are available to everybody, and cost nothing. Even in the most sordid street the coming of spring will register itself by some sign or other, if it is only a brighter blue between the chimney pots or the vivid green of an elder sprouting on a blitzed site. Indeed it is remarkable how Nature goes on existing unofficially, as it were, in the very heart of London. I have seen a kestrel flying over the Deptford gasworks, and I have heard a first-rate performance by a blackbird in the Euston Road. There must be some hundreds of thousands, if not millions, of birds living inside the four-mile radius, and it is rather a pleasing thought that none of them pays a halfpenny of rent.

As for spring, not even the narrow and gloomy streets round the Bank of England are quite able to exclude it. It comes seeping in everywhere, like one of those new poison gases which pass through all filters. The spring is commonly referred to as "a miracle", and during the past five or six years this worn-out figure of speech has taken on a new lease of life. After the sort of winters we have had to endure recently, the spring does seem miraculous, because it has become gradually harder and harder to believe that it is actually going to happen. Every February since 1940 I have found myself thinking that this time winter is going to be permanent. But Persephone, like the toads, always rises from the dead at about the same moment. Suddenly, towards the end of March, the miracle happens and the decaying slum in which I live is transfigured. Down in the square the sooty privets have turned bright green, the leaves are thickening on the chestnut trees, the daffodils are out, the wallflowers are budding, the policeman's tunic looks positively a pleasant shade of blue, the fishmonger greets his customers with a smile, and even the sparrows are quite a different colour, having felt the balminess of the air and nerved themselves to take a bath, their first since last September.

Is it wicked to take a pleasure in spring and other seasonal changes? To put it more precisely, is it politically reprehensible, while we are all groaning, or at any rate ought to be groaning, under the shackles of the capitalist system, to point out that life is frequently more worth living because of a blackbird's song, a yellow elm tree in October, or some other natural phenomenon which does not cost money and does not have what the editors of left-wing newspapers call a class angle? There is no doubt that many people think so. I know by experience that a favourable reference to "Nature" in one of my articles is liable to bring me abusive letters, and though the key-word in these letters is usually "sentimental", two ideas seem to be mixed up in them. One is that any pleasure in the actual process of life encourages a sort of political quietism. People, so the thought runs, ought to be discontented, and it is our job to multiply our wants and not simply to increase our enjoyment of the things we have already. The other idea is that this is the age of machines and that to dislike the machine, or even to want to limit its domination, is backward-looking, reactionary and slightly ridiculous. This is often backed up by the statement that a love of Nature is a foible of urbanised people who have no notion what Nature is really like. Those who really have to deal with the soil, so it is argued, do not love the soil, and do not take the faintest interest in birds or flowers,

> Over increasingly large areas of the United States, spring now comes unheralded by the return of the birds, and the early mornings are strangely silent where once they were filled with the beauty of bird song.
>
> Rachel Carson

except from a strictly utilitarian point of view. To love the country one must live in the town, merely taking an occasional week-end ramble at the warmer times of year.

This last idea is demonstrably false. Medieval literature, for instance, including the popular ballads, is full of an almost Georgian enthusiasm for Nature, and the art of agricultural peoples such as the Chinese and Japanese centres always round trees, birds, flowers, rivers, mountains. The other idea seems to me to be wrong in a subtler way. Certainly we ought to be discontented, we ought not simply to find out ways of making the best of a bad job, and yet if we kill all pleasure in the actual process of life, what sort of future are we preparing for ourselves? If a man cannot enjoy the return of spring, why should he be happy in a labour-saving Utopia? What will he do with the leisure that the machine will give him? I have always suspected that if our economic and political problems are ever really solved, life will become simpler instead of more complex, and that the sort of pleasure one gets from finding the first primrose will loom larger than the sort of pleasure one gets from eating an ice to the tune of a Wurlitzer. I think that by retaining one's childhood love of such things as trees, fishes, butterflies and—to return to my first instance—toads, one makes a peaceful and decent future a little more probable, and that by preaching the doctrine that nothing is to be admired except steel and concrete, one merely makes it a little surer that human beings will have no outlet for their surplus energy except in hatred and leader worship.

At any rate, spring is here, even in London N.1, and they can't stop you enjoying it. This is a satisfying reflection. How many a time have I stood watching the toads mating, or a pair of hares having a boxing match in the young corn, and thought of all the important persons who would stop me enjoying this if they could. But luckily they can't. So long as you are not actually ill, hungry, frightened or immured in a prison or a holiday camp, spring is still spring. The atom bombs are piling up in the factories, the police are prowling through the cities, the lies are streaming from the loudspeakers, but the earth is still going round the sun, and neither the dictators nor the bureaucrats, deeply as they disapprove of the process, are able to prevent it.

George Orwell was the pen name of British author, Eric Blair, who was born in India in 1903. During World War II, Orwell was a war correspondent for the BBC and the *Observer*. Best-known for his satire, Orwell wrote non-fiction, essays, criticism, documentaries, and novels, including *Animal Farm* and *Nineteen Eighty-Four*.

1. ***Response***

a. Who was George Orwell and what were his politics? When and where is the essay set? Explain how this contextual information can help a reader better appreciate "Some Thoughts on the Common Toad."

b. Orwell makes a reference to Persephone, a figure from Greek mythology. Who was she and why is she often associated with spring?

c. How does this work differ from a typical essay about politics? In your view, are these differences strengths or weaknesses? Why?

d. Who do you think was the audience Orwell was writing for? Is the essay relevant to a wider audience? Explain.

2. ***Language Focus*** *Simile* Identify the unusual simile that Orwell introduces in the fifth paragraph. In what way is this simile surprising? Why is it appropriate to the context and topic of the essay? Create three similes of your own that could have the effect of surprising the reader.

3. ***Literature Studies*** *Satire* "Some Thoughts on the Common Toad" could be classified as a gentle satire. What features of the work support that classification? Express Orwell's satirical message in your own words. If you were going to write a satire, what would be your target?

4. ***Writing*** *Monologue* Take the toad's point of view and write a monologue about Orwell, as he is taking notes in early spring. Your monologue could be satiric. Read your monologue aloud for an audience. Use your voice expressively in order to convey the tone of your writing.

In this expository essay Marjorie Doyle describes her experience in Barcelona; her description brings the city and its people to life.

Homage to Barcelona

By Marjorie Doyle

Barcelona. No wonder it's madness, with four million people trying to squeeze into a comparatively tiny space. Here is a city emerging from a long dictatorship; that may explain the resentment towards any law that hints at impinging on individual rights. Or it may be a deep-rooted love of anarchy that goes back to long before Franco. In any event, there is a pervasive scorn for anything that inconveniences the individual for the collective good. A request to a neighbour to lower his stereo at 4:00 a.m. is greeted with outrage. Not only is this a denial of basic rights, but where's the problem? You're free to play your stereo louder and later tomorrow night. And so it goes.

Take parking, for example.

The accepted system—which works, sort of—is to park where you want, when you want. If you find yourself hemmed in on all sides, you simply sit in your car and blow your horn until the guilty parties come forth. Except they're not guilty parties here. No apology; not even a glance or nod is exchanged. It's a problem, then, only for a foreigner who's reluctant to add more decibels to what must surely be the noisiest city on earth. An *extranjera* doesn't feel comfortable sitting with her hand glued to the horn for, say, twenty minutes. But this is a city in which volume is a virtue. How noisy is it? Imagine that city council is working on your street with a jackhammer, there's a house under construction next door, every youngster on the street has just been given a ghetto blaster and a motorcycle, and the muffler's gone on your car, your neighbour's car and your neighbour's neighbour's car. That would be a quiet moment in Barcelona.

Louder is better, the motto seems to be, and everyone does his best to live up to it. On the street there's the continual blare of horns as cars park and unpark, and there are thousands of muffler-less scooters. In the *bodegas* (cafes or bars), there are TV sets, gambling machines and coffee grinders that seem especially designed to rub your nerves raw. I retreat to my flat in grateful anticipation of a few moments' solitude with my electric piano. But even with top volume I still hear only the neighbour's radio, the schoolchildren playing next to my terrace, and the Andalusian singing floating down seven flights from the maid upstairs. I begin to accompany her—it's good practice for my ear—but eventually I give up. I don't know then that the real noise doesn't begin until the hot summer nights when everyone eats (late, as the Spanish do) on their terraces. There'll then be countless sleepless nights with a clashing of cutlery that sounds like one big swordfight. In retrospect, this will seem a quiet time.

So you can't be in and you can't be out. Maybe the parks are quiet, and there'll be grass, a precious commodity in a dry climate. I think there are two patches: one is in a little English garden tucked inside the walled protectorate of the British Consulate; the other is here, in the park. Your poor hardened toes are just beginning to sink into the soft stuff when the shrill whistle of the Guardia Civil suggests that grass is only to be seen. One look at his hat, more persuasive than his weapons, and concrete doesn't seem so bad. When you've reached the noise saturation level, you head back to your apartment building and descend three floors below sea level. But you can only hide out so long in a parking garage.

So you climb around the jungle city, crossing six lanes of traffic to get your morning croissant at the neighbourhood bakery. Not a bad life, really. It's just that when you find yourself in a crowd of fifty waiting to brave the crossing, you suddenly notice there's an equal number ready to attack from the other side. Experience in the Metro has taught you a law of physics you didn't know before—two people can occupy the same place at the same time. Or, at least, there's a strong conviction here to that effect. With the vague hope that tackle football can be learned on the job, you hunch your shoulders, duck and charge. The lucky ones make it to the other side. If you had a *peseta* for every person you touched and tackled along the way, you could even buy a second croissant—chocolate, maybe. So you return from the battlefield for a little reprieve, sit and contemplate. The thought of the fruit and vegetables finally wins out, and off you go again.

And here, in the *fruteria*, you come face to face with one of the peculiar ironies of Barcelona. In the midst of a city of madness and anarchy, there is an orderliness that would challenge a Swiss. You enter the store and call out, who's last? I, someone answers, and you fix your eyes on her, anxious not to miss your turn. It would be easy to in the scramble—there are two or three shopkeepers continually calling, who's next? who's next? and you've also got your responsibility to shout "I" to the person who enters the store after you. If by chance you do miss your turn, there's nothing for it but to leave and enter again. As with most things, this system is learned the hard way. It's easy for a foreigner to violate the order. War erupts, in two languages. In Catalan (the language of this region) and Castellano (Spanish) there are cries of: this lady was before that old man, that old man was before this young girl, that handsome young one was before that woman there, I was before her, she was before him, he was before me ... The shopkeepers remain silent. Whose fault is this anyway? the customers are shouting. Somewhere in the corner is a quiet Newfoundlander admiring the size of the avocados and noting that lettuce *is* green. *La inglesa*, they finally notice, *es la inglesa*. Ah well, so the Brits take the rap.

The sense of propriety continues when you are served. A kilo of oranges, half a kilo of bananas and four apples, you rush to tell her. You quickly learn all requests are ignored except the first. After your oranges are brought from the bin, weighed, priced and placed ceremoniously in your shopping basket, you're asked, what more? And on it goes, item by item. If you want one apple and one orange and they are next to each other in the bins, you learn to tell only about the apple at first. The apple is carried to the scale, priced and deposited. Then, and only then, is the subject of the orange addressed.

This sense of concentrated devotion to the activity is even more pronounced at the butcher shop, where you go to buy, say, a rabbit. You wait at least twenty minutes to be served, but then you are given the butcher's fullest attention; she will carefully and wholeheartedly do anything you want with the poor little thing in front of you. The butchers are usually raised on a rostrum behind the counter; this, and the fact that all eyes are on her, turn the activity into a show. The requests are thorough and varied: a chicken or rabbit will be skinned, boned, quartered, shredded, turned into patties, prepared for stew, the liver for this, the kidney for that; every conceivable direction is given. By the time you get your little rabbit home, you're intimate with it. Underneath this procedure in all the shops there is the continuous rhythm of: *Ultimo? Yo. Quien es? Que más? Algo más?* Who's next? What more? Something more? You eventually get the hang of the system.

You don't waste much time worrying about your performance in the *fruteria* as another reality of Barcelona hits you on the way home. This is the sight of the countless poor rummaging through the huge dumpsters that stand on every corner. You try to convince yourself at first that they're scrounging for odds and ends, but before long you have to face it: they are hunting for food. This, and all the begging in Barcelona, is something you never get used to. Poverty and unemployment manifest themselves here in various ways. There are the hundreds of homeless who huddle in shop doorways at night, carefully guarding their few possessions—usually more scraps of thin clothing. Then there are the men, in their twenties and thirties, who frequent the public plazas. Some sit on the sidewalks with a sign placed in front of them: I am hungry, I have no work, I have six children. Others kneel and hang the same sign around their necks, a posture that is disturbing as much for its self-abasement as for the confused sense of guilt it seems to suggest. And it's not uncommon for a pair of small boys to enter the Metro. One stands still and cries out a prepared speech: my mother is sick, my father has no work, I have seven brothers and sisters, we are hungry. The other walks through the car with his hand cupped. At the next station, they hurry onto the next car, and so they pass the day. Sometimes one boy will have an accordion; he can't play it (he's barely big enough to carry it), but he opens and closes it and some sort of wail comes out. One night, walking up the famed Ramblas, I literally tripped over a baby bottle, nipple up. I looked down to find a young woman sitting on the pavement with an infant in her arms and a baby (maybe ten months older?) lying across her lap. She and others are there every night, right in the path of Barcelona's wealthiest, the opera patrons pouring out of the opulent Liceo, dressed in furs it's never cold enough to wear. There is money in this city, a lot of it. Money is made, and money is saved. (A local joke says that copper wire was invented by two Catalans fighting over a *peseta*.) The Catalans pride themselves on their industry and are always careful to make the distinction between themselves and the Spanish.

Yes, indeed, the Catalans are separatist. When my choir was in France performing with a local choir, the conductor asked at the first rehearsal, where is the French choir? and they identified themselves. A moment later, where is the Spanish choir? I hauled my hand back just in time. Silence. After the conductor repeated his question, a strong, clear voice announced: *Nous sommes Catalans*.

In Barcelona, a Spaniard means someone from Spain; this is Catalunya. It's easy to understand the Catalan position. During the *dictadua* (the Franco regime of about 35 years), their language and culture were suppressed. Most Catalans over a certain age can't read or write their language. In an office, for example, in which nearly everyone is Catalan, the memos and correspondence will inevitably be in Spanish. On the other hand, there are some Catalans (usually women who've never worked outside the home) who haven't spoken Spanish since their school days. A few women whom I saw regularly told me they never speak Spanish. They did it with me as a concession, although I was asked more than once why I was learning Spanish when I wasn't living in Spain.

The Catalans are proud of their language and insist that foreigners learn it. But they are a warm and indulgent people and they'll never refuse to speak Spanish. In fact, they'll tolerate any mistake and struggle to understand the wildest attempt at pronunciation. (It's only when you cross the border to France that you remember what linguistic snobbery is—if you're one shade off one vowel sound in an otherwise respectable sentence, they look at you uncomprehendingly, making you wonder if you've slipped into some rare Beothuk dialect.) Nevertheless, trying to learn Spanish in a Catalan city is not easy. When I first arrived in Barcelona I heard enough vaguely familiar sounds to think I could fall back on my old church Latin, but relationships are somewhat limited when all you can do is confess and praise.

Barcelona, you thought: skiing trips to Andorra, weekends in the Pyrenees and wonderful *menus del dia* (those three-course meals, with wine, offered for $5 at midday in all restaurants), sitting on the Ramblas sipping cool *sangria* and nibbling on *tapas* it takes you months to work off. Yes, that too is life in Barcelona, and the joys of the city are not to be underestimated, as the initiated well know. But the pleasure pales when your status turns from tourist to *livyere*.

After a few months home to breathe clean air and bask in quiet (cold quiet, I might add), I returned to the insanity known as Barcelona. Before there was time to be defeated by the city's noisy madness, I realized what it was that had made my time there enriching. It isn't easy to move from an island like Newfoundland to a city as dense as Barcelona (second to Calcutta, they say), but when you break down the dreaded crowds and seek out the individuals, you find a generous, tolerant, humane people. And to add to their charm, some of them now speak broken English with traces of a St. John's accent.

"So, you come back," a former student smiles at me over lunch.

"Yes," I say, delighted that we can now converse at a comfortable level of English. This is the student who always told me on rainy days to put my umbrella in the chicken. (It was one of those attractive mistakes I never had the heart to correct, knowing that my Spanish was just as colourful.)

"I say me today, how is doing Marjorie?" she tells me warmly.

"I've been thinking about you, too," I respond.

She raises her cup of champagne in a welcome back toast and I follow suit.

"Cheese," she smiles at me, proudly.

"Cheese," I echo, my teaching days over.

Marjorie Doyle was born in Newfoundland and Labrador shortly after it joined Canada, which fostered her later interest in the study of that province. She holds an M.A. from Memorial University. Her first book, *A View of Her Own*, was published in 1996, followed by *Newfoundlander in Exile*, in 1997. Doyle has worked on various CBC Radio programs, including *Arts National, The Doyle Bulletin,* and *That Time of the Night.* Her columns have appeared in *The Globe and Mail, The Ottawa Citizen,* the *Evening Telegram,* and *This Magazine.*

1. *Response*

a. How does Marjorie Doyle create the feeling of what it is like to live in Barcelona? In your answer, refer to both the content and the form of her writing.

b. Doyle frequently uses the second-person point of view ("But you can only hide out so long in a parking garage.") What might be some reasons for doing this? In what other kinds of writing might you find the second-person point of view?

c. Did Doyle's essay spark your interest about Barcelona? Would you visit Barcelona if you had the chance? Explain.

d. Comment on whether travel is a means of understanding one's self and the world at large. Reflect on how your attitudes about travel have been shaped—through personal experience or in some other way?

2. ***Language Conventions*** *Parentheses* Parentheses ( ) can serve a variety of purposes. Explain some of those purposes, using quotations from "Homage to Barcelona" as examples. How does Doyle's use of parentheses contribute to the style of the essay? Rewrite some of the quotations so they contain no parentheses. Describe the difficulties you faced and your solutions.

3. ***Drama*** *Improvisation* In a group, improvise one of the scenes that Doyle describes. Try to represent all the details she records in that scene. Before you present your scene, have a group discussion to assign roles and decide generally what will happen during your improvisation.

4. ***Media*** *Brochure* Use the Internet or library resources to learn more about Barcelona. Use your findings to design and write a travel brochure that promotes Barcelona as a desirable travel destination. Before you create your brochure, decide on a specific audience (families or business travellers, for example); then use visuals and language that are appropriate to that audience. How does the Barcelona depicted in your brochure compare with Doyle's Barcelona? Which one do you think is closer to the "real" Barcelona? Explain.

"It is a terrible irony that as formal development reaches more deeply into rain forests, deserts and other isolated environments, it tends to destroy the only cultures that have proved able to thrive in these environments."

Lessons From a Walk in a Rain Forest

By David Suzuki

FROM CHOCO FOREST, COLOMBIA—To most Canadians the name Colombia conjures up images of coffee or drugs. But to biologists, Colombia is home to one of the richest ecosystems on the planet, the Choco tropical rain forest pinched between the Pacific Ocean and the Andes mountain range. It extends from Panama through Colombia to Peru.

Chugging from Bahia Solano to Utria National Park on the *Jestiven*, a wooden boat, I am accompanied by Francis Hallé, a French expert on tropical forests. Hallé is famous for having created a huge, pneumatic platform that can be erected on the canopy where researchers can explore 600 to 800 square metres of the treetops.

Hallé points out the thick cloak of trees extending to the water line. "The first thing people do when they invade such a virgin forest," he says, "is to clear the trees along the shore." Despite the difference in vegetation, the tree-covered mountains and pristine bays remind me of British Columbia.

Utria National Park was formed in 1987 and covers 54,300 hectares of spectacular forest. In a heavy rain, I set off alone to walk across a peninsular saddle along a thin path that is a slimy ribbon of red mud. Serpentine tree roots coil along the forest floor to suck nutrients from the thin topsoil and anchor the immense trunks in place. Though impediments on level ground, the roots provide welcome hand and footholds on the steep hills.

In the forest, temperature and light intensity immediately drop. Thirty metres overhead, the canopy blocks out the sky, preventing growth of the heavy underbrush we think of as jungle. The steady rainfall is intercepted by foliage so the water doesn't pound onto the soil. Even though it has rained constantly, the water in the creeks is crystal clear.

The ground is littered with leaves. In Canada, we classify

trees as deciduous or evergreens, but here the trees shed leaves year round. However, instead of building up to form thick humus, they quickly become food for insects and fungi and thus are recycled back up into the forest biomass.

It's easy to walk along creek beds or through the trees with little vegetation to hamper movement. The noise is constant, a cacophony of buzzing, clicking, and humming of insects and frogs. Walking quietly and slowly, eyes adapting to the shadows and shapes, one begins to notice movement that betrays a frog, a butterfly, a bird. A cosmos of complexity opens up.

Back on the boat, Hallé informs me that "jungle" is a word from India referring to the tangle of secondary growth that results after the initial forest is cleared. It is an insult to call a primary forest a jungle, he says. He draws my attention to trees with special properties—the hard white "tagwa" seeds, six to a cluster within an armoured shell, that can be carved like ivory; fruit trees; parasitic air-breathing plants, lianes, orchids. But when I bring a seed or leaf, he often admits he has no idea what it is. When I ask how much taxonomists know of the species residing in tropical rain forests, Hallé makes a gesture of futility and replies: "It's an impossible mess." He tells me individuals of one species are usually spaced far apart and each may house different spectra of associated species. A lifetime could be spent studying the organisms in a few square metres while an adjacent section could take another lifetime. That's the reason our ignorance is so vast.

Hallé believes the fabled diversity within a tropical rain forest gives it its stability. When one or a few trees are removed, the opening in the canopy allows light to reach the forest floor and stimulates a succession of plants. Over time, like a small nick in the skin, the opening is healed and filled in. But remove a large section of trees and like a mortal wound, the forest cannot repair itself.

Here a destructive parasite is controlled because its target species is not concentrated in an area the way species are in temperate forests. "There's no need for pesticides," Hallé tells me, "because the forest is too diverse to allow an outbreak." Similarly, an introduced exotic species can't explode like rabbits in Australia or purple loosestrife in Canada because there are too many predators able to attack them. So biodiversity is not just a descriptive property of tropical rain forests, it is the very mechanism of its stability for survival.

World demand for lumber and pulp continues to rise while forest plantations cannot deliver wood of quality or quantity. That's why deforestation continues to claim the great forests of the planet and threatens the Choco.

The Choco is the traditional home of perhaps 30,000 aboriginal people belonging to three main groups—Embera, Waunana, and Cuna—who continue to live as they have for thousands of years, depending on the forest for their food, medicines, and materials.

From the airport at Bahia Solano, we take a bus up the coast to the village of El Valle, which is populated by descendants of African slaves who were brought to mine gold more than 400 years ago. We rent a dugout with a motor and guide to take us up the Boro Boro River. After about three hours, we finally leave the plantations, cleared fields, sugar cane, and breadfruit trees to enter primary rain forest. As the river narrows, we drag the dugouts across shallow riffles and around fallen trees and logjams. At one point, we unload the boat and sink it to push it under a huge log blocking the river.

Night falls early and quickly in the tropics and as the light fades, we know we are still hours away from our destination, the Embera village of Boro Boro at the junction with the Mutata River. Five hours after nightfall, we finally reach the settlement, exhausted, wet, but exhilarated by the adventure. Hammocks and mosquito nets are slung in the tiny school, and we soon join the frog calls with snores.

Boro Boro is home for eighty-four people living under thatched huts built on supports two metres above the ground. The tiny cluster of buildings is surrounded by small fields of domesticated plants. Life here revolves around the river for bathing, laundry, food, and transportation. A three-hour hike up the Mutata ends at spectacular falls that drop 400 metres into a huge pool that is considered the source of life and power in the river. The people of Boro Boro fear the power of the place and stay away. Only the shaman goes to the pool to perform rituals to ensure the fecundity of the river and forest.

The villagers tell us they want to keep their culture and way of life. They have heard of proposals to develop the area, which one prime minister referred to as Colombia's "piggy bank." The Pan American Highway, nearly finished, was stopped only when the minister of the newly formed

> The challenge of nonfiction is to marry art and truth.
>
> Phyllis Rose

environment ministry threatened to resign if it wasn't. There are other proposals to build superports on the coast, a network of highways to link the ports to cities, and huge dams to deliver electricity to isolated villages. The familiar notion of "development" by extracting the resources of the forest is irresistible in Colombia too.

Colombia's forests, of which Choco is an important part, have the most known bird species (19.4 percent of all the world's known species compared to 17.6 percent in Brazil and 15 percent in Africa) and orchids, the second most amphibians, the third most reptiles, and one of every five bats. This rich tapestry of living things is beyond any scientific comprehension and, if destroyed, will never be duplicated or recreated.

There are people who have had the knowledge and expertise to make a living from these forests for millennia, but their futures are as uncertain as the fragile ecosystems that are their homes. The 1987 United Nations report *Our Common Future* stated: "It is a terrible irony that as formal development reaches more deeply into rain forests, deserts and other isolated environments, it tends to destroy the only cultures that have proved able to thrive in these environments."

Indigenous people throughout Colombia are organizing to resist incursions into their land. In the Choco, OREWA was formed to represent the Embera, Waunana, and Cuna. But in the government discussions about the future of the Choco, the indigenous people who have always occupied the forests are seldom involved.

The predicament is complicated by an Afro-Colombian population that outnumbers the aboriginal people by ten to one. After escaping slavery, they were able to survive in coastal villages for 200 to 300 years. Lacking the indigenous culture and knowledge base built around the forest, the blacks have eked out a living and are desperate for the material benefits of modern life.

In negotiations with the government, OREWA has included Afro-Colombians as stakeholders in the forest lands. But impoverished people are easy prey to the blandishments of developers. Promises of jobs, electricity, and television tempt them to welcome roads and ports. To them, the forest is a resource that can be converted to money. If we in Canada haven't been able to resist the siren's call of development, why should people who start out with far less?

Environmentalists in industrial nations of the North are concerned about the fate of tropical rain forests that have been labelled the "lungs of the planet" and the "wellsprings of biodiversity." Here in Colombia, Latin

Americans demand to know why they are expected to save the forests when countries in the North haven't protected theirs. In the debate over vanishing forests, the people who live in them are often forgotten.

Travelling through the Choco rain forest along mud tracks, one can't help but wonder why magnificent forests like this are being traded for squalid towns and villages of impoverished people and of scrawny cattle grazing on barren hills. Is there no other way to create income for the human residents while preserving the forest ecosystem?

According to Francis Hallé there is. He has spent his life studying plant growth in the canopy of tropical rain forests. When I ask him whether we know enough to cut down the likes of the Choco and regrow it, he replies, "Absolutely not!" He points out that a tree plantation is not a forest and that rapidly growing species like eucalyptus or pine imported from other parts of the world seldom perform as expected. Hallé says ideas developed from northern temperate forests are inappropriate for the tropics, where vegetation and soil are completely different.

The secret to the resilience and productivity of a tropical rain forest is its tremendous variety of living forms. As long as the forest is intact, people can cut into it as the indigenous inhabitants have for thousands of years, and the cut will heal. But if the clearing is large, then like a spider web that loses too many threads, the system collapses.

Throughout tropical countries of Africa, South America, and southeast Asia, Hallé finds a sophisticated human practice called agroforestry (AF) that has sustained communities for hundreds, if not thousands, of years. Hallé has observed carvings on Indonesian temples depicting AF practices about A.D. 1000.

AF requires a profound knowledge of plants that can be used for a variety of needs. Useful plants are collected from intact primary forests and deliberately planted in a surrounding AF Buffer Zone. Here one finds small shrubs, medicinal plants, parasitic lianes for rope and furniture, and large trees that yield wood, edible leaves, and fruits.

Fifty percent of the biodiversity present in the primary forest can be found in an AF Buffer Zone. In fact, says Hallé, it has only been in the past century that foresters recognized that the AF Buffer Zone is human-created and not a natural forest. Domesticated animals are grazed in the Buffer Zone, where the huts and villages are also located. The primary forest remains intact to provide new material during collecting expeditions.

Hallé says, "Agroforesters are true capitalists; their capital is biological and it is constantly growing." Usually, they live off the interest but when they are confronted with an emergency, they may harvest more than they usually take, sure in the knowledge that over time, the forest will grow back.

Hallé's description of agroforestry makes one wonder why it isn't being pushed everywhere as a sustainable alternative to massive clearing of tropical forests. Hallé's explanation is: "AF is always local and small-scale. People are constantly coming out of the villages with baskets of fruits, vegetables, meat, and plant products for trade or sale, but that doesn't yield the large and quick profits that governments and multinational companies want."

Since all useful organisms are harvested from the Buffer Zone, the primary forest is protected as a priceless source of genetic material. Communities practising AF don't need outside help or expertise because they depend on their own time-tested indigenous knowledge.

Hallé observes that practitioners of AF are always women. Men may be recruited to cut trees down or lift heavy things, but women are in charge. He believes it reflects women's concerns with food and children's health. "Large-scale monoculturing seems to be more of a male impulse, while diverse, small-scale ventures seem more feminine," Hallé says.

AF exposes the insanity of destroying tropical forests for a one-time-only recovery of cash. AF rests on the fundamental capital of nature, which, if protected, can sustain communities and ecosystems indefinitely. But that flies in the face of the current suicidal path of global economics that glorifies human creativity and productivity above all.

Dr. David Suzuki was born in Vancouver, B.C., in 1936. He is an award-winning scientist, broadcaster, and environmentalist, and Chair of the David Suzuki Foundation—a charity concerned with environmental issues. Suzuki is well known as the host of CBC's science TV series, *The Nature of Things,* and is the author of over 30 books. He has received numerous awards for his work, including the Order of Canada, and is internationally recognized for his work in the field of ecology.

1. ***Response***

a. Create a map that would be a useful accompaniment to David Suzuki's essay.

b. What did you know about David Suzuki before you read "Lessons From a Walk in a Rain Forest"? Summarize your prior knowledge. Do you regard Suzuki as a credible commentator on ecological issues? Explain.

c. In point form, note the factual information about rain forests contained in the essay. What steps could you take to establish the reliability of this information?

d. Make a list of environmental issues (local, national, or global) that interest you. Choose one of the issues and write a brief explanation of why that issue is important generally, and to you in particular.

2. ***Literature Studies*** *Expository Writing* The *purpose* of expository writing is to convey information to the reader, but the *challenge* is to keep the reader interested. Reread "Lessons From a Walk in a Rain Forest" and note the techniques Suzuki uses to hold the reader's attention. Provide specific examples of each technique. Did Suzuki meet the challenge of engaging your interest? Why or why not?

3. ***Writing*** *Fact Sheet* In activity 1. d above, you selected one environmental issue of interest to you. Your task is to draft a **fact sheet** covering that issue. Do some research to gather background information. Your fact sheet might provide some or all of the following: statistics, definitions, answers to frequently-asked questions, predictions, graphs, maps, resource lists, and so on. When you present your fact sheet, explain what was most difficult about preparing it

A **fact sheet** presents key information about a particular topic, issue, or organization. It provides concise answers to basic questions. Some fact sheets are written in point form, others in full sentences.

4. ***Critical Thinking*** A critical thinker seeks out information from a variety of sources before coming to a conclusion. In a group, make a plan for obtaining additional perspectives about rain forest management and preservation; then carry out that plan. What difficulties did you face in locating and analysing the information? Based on your experience, develop five guidelines or principles for obtaining and evaluating multiple points of view on an issue.

"W.O. Mitchell was larger than life, even in life."

In Memory of W.O. Mitchell

By Fred Stenson

In 1974, when I published my first book, a book which aspired to be funny, a reviewer wrote, "Stenson is trying to be Western Canada's next W.O. Mitchell." It was a strange statement, not least of all because the job was taken and remained so for twenty-four years. But that was what the reviewer wrote and, having established what my goal was, he went on to demonstrate, illustrate and prove that I wasn't apt to attain it. It was a negative review, no doubt about it, but I was thrilled. One way or another I had been mentioned in the same sentence as W.O. Mitchell, and I was honoured.

Asked to speak at this tribute, to speak about W.O. Mitchell's humour, I am honoured again. Part of how I will pay tribute to W.O. will be to illustrate, once again, that, when it comes to being funny, I can't hold a candle to him. Few people could.

Twenty-two years ago, in a large gathering of Canadian writers, W.O. Mitchell came up to me and gave me a powerful hug. Lifted me right off the floor. He had mistaken me for Andreas Schroeder. He expressed his delight at seeing me.

I expressed my delight at seeing him. After a time, we moved on. I remember that, by then, he was looking somewhat perplexed. I tell that story now because of how much I wished at the time that the exuberance of that greeting had been meant for me. I was about 23 years old and I admired W.O. Mitchell greatly. He was a writer and he was funny—and those were the two things in life that I most hoped to be.

I actually did meet W.O. Mitchell not long after, when he was teaching at the Banff Centre and I was working there too. I was working in the farthest corner of the Cameron Hall basement in a room with blacked out windows. I called out numbers—sort of like a bingo announcer—16, 29—to two fellows who spun wheels and pushed buttons on a giant animation camera called "The Oxberry."

The people in the writing program at Banff were kind enough to invite me to some of their parties and, if I could escape the Oxberry, I went. A mushroom-coloured, half-starved gnome who scoffed as much Camembert and red wine as possible. And the great attraction of those evenings was the opportunity to watch and listen to W.O. Mitchell in action.

I hope my writer friends will forgive me for saying so, but writers are usually a little smaller in life than in print. And why not? In print you get as many runs at a thing as you care to take. In life, you get one chance and often you blow it. But, in the case of W.O. Mitchell, this was not true. W.O. Mitchell was larger than life, even in life.

Whatever his mood, sunny or furious, he dependably poured forth a stream of verbiage that was original, irreverent, unexpected—and funny. I was just one of the admiring many and I didn't get to know him well. I expect he wondered why the hell, in the full-blown glory of both youth and summer, I didn't go out and get myself some sun. As for me, I listened and laughed until my face was sore.

Though I was never an official student of W.O. Mitchell's, I learned a lot from him, by watching and listening. I learned about pacing, at which he was a master, and pausing, and turning abruptly against the flow of your own story, and writing dialogue between people who aren't listening to a damn thing the other is saying. I learned about mixing high and low diction, and repeating a joke so that people will laugh more each time they hear it—and when to stop at the peak of that arc, before it starts going the other way.

> Biography lends to death a new terror.
>
> Oscar Wilde

I learned what happens to a bull's ass in fly time, and about the nervousness of cats in rooms full of rocking chairs, and about the speed achieved by manure in its passage through a goose. I learned that the correct words for expressing the song of the meadowlark are: "*Tar Tar Diddly Boo.*"

I learned that humour is a serious craft and that one of its fundaments is the breaking of taboo. I remember W.O. explaining one time, very seriously, that if you want a child to laugh, what you must say is PEE PEE. POO POO. If you want to make an adult laugh, what you should say is PEE PEE. POO POO. And if they're still not laughing, say "FART." He had discovered that people don't change much from when they're children, and that often the job of the humorist is to say the taboo things on behalf of others, especially those who can't themselves.

I remember another time when W.O. Mitchell was giving a reading in a small town in eastern Alberta, one renowned as the heart of the bible belt, or at very least a valve in that heart. It was a full house as usual and W.O. Mitchell out and performed one of his more scatological stories. (There's a five dollar word for you. Scatological.) And that audience, which looked very like a rural church audience, all dressed up and permed, laughed until they cried. No one looked offended, or even vaguely uncomfortable. W.O. Mitchell was calling a bull's ass a bull's ass, on all our behalfs, and we were grateful.

On that same occasion, W.O. invited me to have dinner with him and Andy Russell—and I couldn't go, or I thought I couldn't. I have kicked myself ever since. I decided solemnly that when your life is so complicated that you can't sit down to dinner with two of the people you most admire, it's time to get a new life.

Anyway, the invitation came as W.O. was sitting in the lobby taking snuff and a small boy had come up to ask what he was doing. A lot of adults would not have bothered to explain but W.O. did. He explained in great detail, in great seriousness. He demonstrated frequently. He explained snuff-taking to that small boy as if it were something we must all do eventually and that it was his duty to make sure that the boy grew up knowing how to do it right. The teaching was done the way Jake would have taught the Kid, or like Daddy Sherry would have taught young Keith. Small boys, whose fathers are dead or otherwise not of much use, was always a big theme in the writing and humour of W.O. Mitchell. The job of the men who taught the boys was mostly to counteract the forces of society that aspire to regulate and restrict fun. W.O. Mitchell's message, expressed in this way, was that it was okay to have fun, that most of what you are told is bad might be good at least once in a while, and that it's best to find out for yourself in any case.

One of the great things about being young is that you simply *are*. Only as a grown-up do you find out *what* you are. In my case, I found out that I was a rural Western Canadian, which made me different than what most other folks were. I discovered the uniqueness of the culture I had grown up in.

In my opinion, rural Western Canadians are some of the funniest people on this earth. When I go home to Twin Butte, Alberta, I don't tell many stories or jokes. Mainly, I listen. And I laugh. And I marvel at how these people seem to effortlessly contain within them the art of humour. I think W.O. Mitchell must have discovered that too—in places like Weyburn and Castor and High River—how, in the cigar smoke around the potbelly stove at the curling rink on a night in the dead of winter, some of the funniest stories anywhere were told by people who would never stand on a stage or write much more than their names on a cheque, or an IOU. I believe W.O. Mitchell heard those stories, and ingested the secrets of their manufacture, and made a brilliant career out of never forgetting where he came from.

Sometimes I worry that my parents' generation—almost to the birth year, the W.O. Mitchell generation—will be forgotten; swept aside by the current, and I think deeply foolish and empty, fad of globalization. Nobody lives globally. W.O. Mitchell knew that. I expect he also knew that the thing closest to global is a good, "regional" story, well told. In that sense, in the sense that his books will always exist like a rosetta stone for the rediscovery of Western Canadian rural life, W.O. Mitchell has done more for the West than any of the powers of righteousness and wrath he used to counsel small boys to guard against.

It makes me very proud to have been asked to come here and speak about the humour of W.O. Mitchell. He was a profoundly, and seriously, funny man.

Fred Stenson has written the novels *Last One Home,* and *Lonesome Hero,* and the short story collections *Working Without a Laugh Track* and *Teeth.* He has also written for series on *History TV* and *Discovery.*

W.O. Mitchell. Photo by Charles Clarke

Do you think this photo portrait of W.O. Mitchell is a good representation of the qualities Stenson describes in his essay? Explain.

1. ***Response***

a. What purposes do you think Fred Stenson had in mind when he wrote this tribute? How well does he achieve those purposes? Explain.

b. Do some research to obtain background information about W.O. Mitchell, then create a time line that traces his achievements as a writer.

c. Paraphrase what Stenson means by the last line of his tribute. What examples does Stenson provide to help him make this point?

d. In the second-last paragraph, Stenson calls Mitchell's writing a *rosetta stone*. Define this term, and explain what Stenson is suggesting with this comparison. Do you think any writer's work can be a rosetta stone for a whole community or nation? Provide reasons, and evidence if possible, for your view.

e. If someone were writing a tribute in your honour, what personal achievements and qualities would you want them to mention?

2. ***Language Focus*** *Colloquial Language* In his tribute, Stenson chooses to quote several examples of W.O. Mitchell's use of *colloquial language* (everyday, informal language). What explanation does Stenson offer in defence of colloquialism? How does he demonstrate that he has considered the appropriateness of using this language? Do you agree with its use? Why or why not?

3. ***Oral Language*** *Reading Aloud* "A Tribute to W.O. Mitchell" was meant to be delivered as a speech. Select a passage (about four or five paragraphs) and practise reading it aloud. Before you present your reading, experiment with pacing, volume, and tone of voice. Do you enjoy public speaking? Give your view on the rewards and/or challenges of addressing an audience.

4. ***Writing*** *Tribute* Discuss the features of a tribute, referring to this selection as a model. Write your own tribute to someone you know and admire.

5. ***Making Connections*** Read an example of W.O. Mitchell's work, and write a brief review of it. Describe your critical assessment of the work, as well as your personal response to it. Include quotations that support your conclusions.

Steve Mann: Genius or Lunatic?

Mann and Machine

from *Contemporary Canadian Biographies*

FEW PEOPLE KNOW EXACTLY WHAT to make of Steve Mann, a pioneer in the field of wearable computers. "A physicist once said he felt that I had the intelligence of a dozen experts in his discipline," Mann told Steve Ditlea of MIT's *Technology Review*. "A few minutes later, someone else said they thought I was mentally handicapped." Despite the mixed reactions, Mann's faith in wearable computers has never faltered. "Some things look crazy now," he told *Business Day*, "but will make sense in about 20 years."

Mann's interest in wearable electronic devices seems to run in the family. His father was a hobbyist who built what may have been the first wearable radio in the 1950s. As a high-school student in Hamilton, Ontario, Mann was known as Computer Steve. He would do strange things, like show up at school dances wearing a sound-controlled device with a light-emitting diode that changed colour in time with the music. He also built a Walkman and a boombox before the commercial versions were on the market. In the 1970s, he came up with portable battery-powered light sources he called photographer's assistants; he used them to create altered perceptions of visual reality that he dubbed light paintings.

In 1981, Mann built his first true wearable computer, using an Apple II placed in a knapsack. It transmitted and received information through antennae mounted in a helmet. These early prototypes, made from scavenged computer parts, electronic camera flashes and toy walkie-talkies, weighed as much as 45 kilograms and made him look like an alien creature. "People would cross the street to avoid me," he told Ditlea.

Mann's wearable computers have been in a continuous process of evolution ever since. In 1982, he began to experiment with building components directly into his clothing. In his first year at McMaster University, he built a rig that allowed him to connect—through a serial data cable—with a friend. He added sensors that monitored his heart rate and other physiological signals and later created something he called a vibravest, which remains part of his technological repertoire today. The vest used radar to trigger vibrations that showed the size of objects in his path, as well as how far away they were.

By the mid-1990s, Mann's rig consisted of a computer clipped to his belt, a one-handed keyboard called a Twiddler, a helmet-mounted video camera with antennae, and a visor with a built-in monitor that enabled him to watch computerized video images as they were being

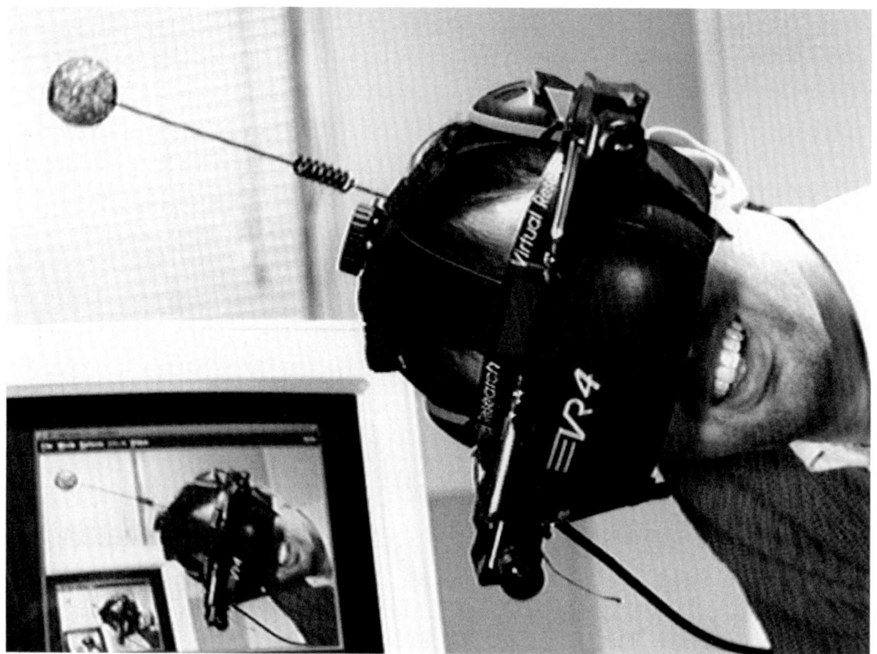

Steve Mann

What elements of this photo suggest that it was carefully thought out and composed? In a sentence or two, state what this image tells the viewer about Steve Mann.

recorded. WearComp7, the name of the current version of his creation, includes a hard drive, miniature keyboard and radio equipment that are strapped across his back and chest. His sweater conceals sensors that monitor body temperature, breathing and heart rate. Sensors in his shoes monitor each step and chunky black sunglasses called WearCam conceal a tiny camera and laser beam that write patterns directly onto his eye, so that images and text seem to hover on objects that exist in the real world. Mann calls the resulting combination of human and computer a cyborg—short for "cybernetic organism," a term coined by author Manfred Clynes in 1960 to describe a technologically augmented human being.

The effect of this equipment can be disconcerting, to say the least. In conversation, wrote Jan Cienski of Associated Press: "(Mann's) eyes often shift between the person he is talking with and his computer screen, depending on which is more interesting." Mann defends the effect of the technology on others. "There are times when you want to be isolated. You still want to be aware of your surroundings but scale them out. I often turn the outside world gray while I do my work. All those things can be better done with a curtain between me and the outside world."

In 1991, Mann enrolled at the Massachusetts Institute of Technology in Cambridge, Massachusetts. His aim was to earn his Ph.D. at the school's Media Lab, which had been founded in 1985 by Nicholas Negroponte. At first, Negroponte told Judith Gaines of the Fort Worth *Star-Telegram*, Mann's ideas were "very much on the lunatic fringe." In fact, for several years, he was the only person working on the concept. Eventually, however, the faculty and students became intrigued, and Mann established what would become the Media Lab's Wearable Computer Project. It wasn't until 1995, Mann told Ditlea, that his work began to attract serious attention from his peers. By 1997, the "lunatic fringe" was becoming almost mainstream; that year, a conference Mann had proposed to the Institute of Electrical and Electronic Engineers' Computer Society attracted more than 700 researchers, and the accompanying fashion show drew an audience of more than 3,000. After graduating from MIT in 1997, Mann joined the department of electrical and computer engineering at the University of Toronto.

In fact, Mann's ideas had been attracting the attention of a curious public and the media long before they became professionally acceptable. In the 1980s, he found himself becoming a kind of cyborg performance artist as he began receiving invitations to demonstrate his wearable computer at galleries and other events. In 1994, his Wearable Wireless Webcam, a helmet-mounted camera that transmitted images of whatever he was looking at through antennae to his Web page, drew a great deal of media comment. As a result, Mann began receiving as many as 30,000 e-mail messages every day from visitors to his Web site. When he invited the public to experience a virtual reality version of Boston's First Night New Year's Eve festivities in 1995, so many people tried to connect that his system crashed under the load. Mann even made the pages of the *National Enquirer* when he replaced the broken thermostat in his apartment with a radio receiver that used signals from sensors in his underwear to control the heat by measuring his body temperature. The headline read, "Web Man Walking."

Though he welcomes the attention, Mann and others are convinced that his technology is much more than a freaky media fad. They believe that his work will enable people to create new forms of communication; for example, Mann's wife is able to help him pick out the ripest fruits and vegetables at the grocery store even when she isn't physically present. "If everyone has this sort of connection, then we all become more productive," Mann told Dylan Jones of *People Weekly*.

A variety of uses have been suggested for the rig. It could function as a personal safety device, both as a sort of personal black box that records information and as part of a virtual community of individuals watching out for one another. The device could assist victims of Alzheimer's by helping them remember where they put things. For the visually impaired, it could connect a camera to a computer that would recognize faces or compress visual images into a smaller area for people with limited peripheral vision. At the 1997 Beauty and the Bits wearable computer show in Cambridge, Massachusetts, a design called Accessor-eyes featured a navigational system that would guide the blind by using audible directional clicks. "This way, you don't have to reconfigure the world, you just have to reconfigure the individuals," Mann told Robert Everett-Green of *The Globe and Mail*.

Mann has also suggested that the machine could have a more political purpose. He objects to the video cameras that have become almost omnipresent in urban environments and used his wearable computer to produce a short film titled *Shooting Back*. It explored the issue of what he calls "unreciprocated video surveillance." He also uses his wearable computer as part of a personal crusade against advertising. "I see it as personal empowerment," he told J. L. O'Brien of *Computer Dealer News*. "If the eye is the window to the soul, shouldn't it have some locks on it? Right now, we walk around with things unlocked and our minds are open for anybody to shove anything they want in there, and that is theft of my solitude. Billboards are theft. Nobody asked my permission to put that image of Calvin Klein underwear into my head."

Mann uses his computer to replace advertisements with something he would rather look at—images of his own choosing, for example, or e-mail messages. He calls this mixture of real and electronic worlds "mediated reality." It's something very different from virtual reality, he insists. "Virtual reality is flawed because you are shutting out the real world. It's like putting on a blindfold," he told Mark Nusca of *The National Post.* "Mediated reality connects you to the real world." In effect, his wearable computer enables Mann to place a thin electronic membrane between himself and the world.

There is a sense that Mann's real interest in wearable computers stems from his earliest experiments with photography. He sometimes calls the system his visual memory prosthetic. His most recent versions constantly record visual information in a memory buffer. If something unusual happens, sensors pick up the sudden change in Mann's heart rate, and the video record of the event can be pulled from the buffer into permanent storage. For Mann, this represents a step forward in the relationship between human and machine. "Your brain is using the machine as a second brain, and it's using your brain as a second CPU," he told Everett-Green. "It's a two-way street. My machine modifies me and I modify it." This is a prime example of what Mann calls "humanistic intelligence," a collaboration between human and computer, which he views as different from artificial intelligence. "My point is that computers are really good at some things and humans are really good at others," he told Nusca. He believes that the wearable computer will bring out the best in both human and machine.

Others, too, have ideas about the potential of wearable computers. At a 1996 conference on wearable computers, many possible applications were discussed and, since then, some of these have become reality. For example, Xybernaut Corp., based in Fairfax, Virginia, recently released the fourth generation of its Mobile Assistant, a wearable computer used in manufacturing situations where workers not only need to use computers but must also be able to move around the factory or have both hands free for their work. The United States Army is testing prototypes that map a soldier's location, show where the enemy is hiding, and enable him or her to aim and fire a weapon without being exposed to the enemy. The Army is also testing a T-shirt made of cotton woven with fibre optics that can relay medical information from wounded soldiers.

All this means that the wearable computer could be big business. Research in the field is sponsored not just by Microsoft and IBM, but by Nike, Levi-Strauss and Swatch. Sony owns the rights to the name WebMan, and is planning a consumer version of the wearable computer. Companies like Nokia, Motorola, Hewlett-Packard and Samsung are also interested in the concept.

In September 1998, Mann introduced University of Toronto students to what he calls the world's first course on how to be a cyborg. Flyers advertising the course were posted around the campus. They read: "You will be assimilated. Become the world's first 'cyborgs.' " The course attracted 20 electrical engineering students who explored the theory, philosophy and practice of wearable computers and used the machines to produce collaborative digital visual art. Though Xybernaut donated 20 Mobile Assistants to the class, students quickly became aware of the shortcomings of the technology. There were complaints about its weight and short battery life, as well as its reliance on voice-recognition software. "I despise the whole idea (of operating the equipment by voice recognition)," Mann told Everett-Green. "If I'm on the subway talking to myself, people will think I'm crazy." Despite these technical limitations, however, the course was a success, and most of the students are planning to pursue further studies in the field.

For Mann, the next step is to make the equipment less obtrusive. In the beginning, he told Everett-Green, "There was a freakish, outlandish essence to it that I'm trying to shake now. The early stuff used to look a little dorky. I got a lot of gee-whiz reactions." He is certain that as the machines continue to develop, they will become smaller, lighter and less noticeable.

Mann and machine have become inseparable. He removes the devices only to sleep, shower, or swim. "I wouldn't live any other way," he wrote in MIT's *Technology Review*. "I have melded technology with my person and achieved a higher state of awareness than would otherwise be possible ... Every morning I decide how I will see the world that day. Sometimes I give myself eyes in the back of my head. Other days I add a sixth sense, such as the ability to feel objects at a distance." He can use visual effects—a stroboscope, for example—to see things he would otherwise be unable to see.

Despite his enthusiasm for the devices, Mann acknowledges that there is a downside to wearable computers. On his Web site, he warns those who would build their own machines of the potential dangers of faulty wiring, long-term exposure to radio waves, eye damage, reduced attention span and flashbacks. There is another problem associated with the technology, too. Speaking at a 1996 conference, Mann wryly confessed: "I do find myself in a somewhat confused and bewildered state when my system goes down."

1. *Response*

a. Reread the profile and list the words and phrases used to describe Steve Mann, including descriptions appearing in statements by Mann himself and others. Sort the expressions into categories. How do you account for the wide variation? Write a description that expresses your own view of Mann.

b. In your own words, explain how *mediated reality* differs from *virtual reality*, and how *humanistic intelligence* differs from *artificial intelligence*.

c. Reread the description of WearComp7 that appears in the fifth paragraph. Look as well at the capabilities of the technology as described in the second-last paragraph. Would you want to try WearComp7 yourself, becoming what Mann calls a "cyborg"? Give reasons for your answer.

d. Mann says, "Nobody asked my permission to put that image of Calvin Klein underwear into my head." Do you think Mann's solution to omnipresent advertising makes sense? Explain your point of view and suggest alternative ways of coping.

2. *Media* *Ad* Mann seems to have high expectations for the technology he is developing, as do many prominent businesses. Develop an ad that conveys the value and potential of one of Mann's computer innovations. Create your ad for a medium of your choice.

3. *Writing* *Science Fiction* Is it true that "the wearable computer will bring out the best in both human and machine"? Write a short science fiction story that provides your perspective on that proposition.

4. *Language Conventions* *Comma Use* Commas have more functions than any other punctuation mark. Their uses include separating items in a series, separating the different parts of a place name, dividing a subordinate clause from a main clause, marking the beginning and end of an appositive or a non-restrictive clause, and inserting a pause before a quotation. Reread "Mann and Machine" to find examples of each of these uses of the comma. If necessary, use a reference book to clarify the rules for using commas.

In 1962, Nelson Mandela went to Algeria for military training and was arrested for leaving South Africa illegally and for incitement to strike. Mandela was jailed for five years and, while in prision, was charged with sabotage and sentenced to life imprisonment.

from Long Walk to Freedom

The Autobiography of Nelson Mandela

By Nelson Mandela

We were awakened at 5:30 each morning by the night warder, who clanged a brass bell at the head of our corridor and yelled, "*Word wakker! Staan op!*" (Wake up! Get up!) I have always been an early riser and this hour was not a burden to me. Although we were roused at 5:30, we were not let out of our cells until 6:45, by which time we were meant to have cleaned our cells and rolled up our mats and blankets. We had no running water in our cells and instead of toilets had iron sanitary buckets known as "ballies." The ballies had a diameter of ten inches and a concave porcelain lid on the top that could contain water. The water in this lid was meant to be used for shaving and to clean our hands and faces.

At 6:45, when we were let out of our cells, the first thing we did was to empty our ballies. The ballies had to be thoroughly cleansed in the sinks at the end of the hallway or they created a stench. The only pleasant thing about cleaning one's ballie was that this was the one moment in those early days when we could have a whispered word with our colleagues. The warders did not like to linger when we cleaned them, so it was a chance to talk softly.

During those first few months, breakfast was delivered to us in our cells by prisoners from the general section. Breakfast consisted of mealie pap porridge, cereal made from maize or corn, which the general prisoners would slop in a bowl and then spin through the bars of our cells. It was a clever trick and required a deft hand so as not to spill any of the porridge.

After a few months, breakfast was delivered to us in the courtyard in old metal oil drums. We would help ourselves to pap using simple metal bowls. We each received a mug of what was described as coffee, but which was in fact ground-up maize, baked until it was black, and then brewed with hot water. Later, when we were able to go into the courtyard to serve ourselves, I would go out into the courtyard and jog around the perimeter until breakfast arrived.

Like everything else in prison, diet is discriminatory.

In general, Coloureds and Indians received a slightly better diet than Africans, but it was not much of a distinction. The authorities liked to say that we received a balanced diet; it was indeed balanced—between the unpalatable and the inedible. Food was the source of many of our protests, but in those early days, the warders would say, "Ag, you kaffirs[1] are eating better in prison than you ever ate at home!"

In the midst of breakfast, the guards would yell, "*Val in! Val in!*" (Fall in! Fall in!), and we would stand outside our cells for inspection. Each prisoner was required to have the three buttons of his khaki jacket properly buttoned. We were required to doff our hats as the warder walked by. If our buttons were undone, our hats unremoved, or our cells untidy, we were charged with a violation of the prison code and punished with either solitary confinement or the loss of meals.

After inspection we would work in the courtyard hammering stones until noon. There were no breaks; if we slowed down, the warders would yell at us to speed up. At noon, the bell would clang for lunch and another metal drum of food would be wheeled into the courtyard. For Africans, lunch consisted of boiled mealies, that is, coarse kernels of corn. The Indian and Coloured prisoners received samp, or mealie rice, which consisted of ground mealies in a souplike mixture. The samp was sometimes served with vegetables whereas our mealies were served straight.

For lunch we often received *phuzamandla*, which means "drink of strength," a powder made from mealies and a bit of yeast. It is meant

[1]**kaffir:** a derogatory term for a black person, used mainly in South Africa, especially during the apartheid era

to be stirred into water or milk and when it is thick, it can be tasty, but the prison authorities gave us so little of the powder that it barely colored the water. I would usually try to save my powder for several days until I had enough to make a proper drink, but if the authorities discovered that you were hoarding food, the powder was confiscated and you were punished.

After lunch we worked until four, when the guards blew shrill whistles and we once again lined up to be counted and inspected. We were then permitted half an hour to clean up. The bathroom at the end of our corridor had two seawater showers, a saltwater tap, and three large galvanized metal buckets, which were used as bathtubs. There was no hot water. We would stand or squat in these buckets, soaping ourselves with the brackish water, rinsing off the dust from the day. To wash yourself with cold water when it is cold outside is not pleasant, but we made the best of it. We would sometimes sing while washing, which made the water seem less icy. In those early days, this was one of the only times that we could converse.

Precisely at 4:30, there would be a loud knock on the wooden door at the end of our corridor, which meant that supper had been delivered. Common-law prisoners were used to dish out the food to us and we would return to our cells to eat it. We again received mealie pap porridge, sometimes with the odd carrot or piece of cabbage or beetroot thrown in—but one usually had to search for it. If we did get a vegetable, we would usually have the same one for weeks on end, until the carrots or cabbage were old and moldy and we were thoroughly sick of them. Every other day, we received a small piece of meat with our porridge. The meat was usually mostly gristle.

For supper, Coloured and Indian prisoners received a quarter loaf of bread (known as a *katkop*, that is, a cat's head, after the shape of the bread) and a slab of margarine. Africans, it was presumed, did not care for bread as it was a "European" type of food.

Typically, we received even less than the meager amounts stipulated in the regulations. This was because the kitchen was rife with smuggling. The cooks—all of whom were common-law prisoners—kept the best food for themselves or their friends. Often they would lay aside the tastiest morsels for the warders in exchange for favors or preferential treatment.

At 8 P.M., the night warder would lock himself in the corridor with us, passing the key through a small hole in the door to another warder outside. The warder would then walk up and down the corridor, ordering us to go to sleep. No cry of "lights out" was ever given on Robben Island because the single mesh-covered bulb in our cell burned day and night. Later, those studying for higher degrees were permitted to read until ten or eleven.

The acoustics along the corridor were quite good, and we would try to chat a bit to each other before going to sleep. But if we could hear a whisper quite clearly, so could the warder, who would yell, *"Stilte in die gang!"* (Quiet in the passage!) The warder would walk up and down a few times to make sure we were not reading or writing. After a few months, we would sprinkle a handful of sand along the corridor so that we could hear the warder's footsteps and have time to stop talking or hide any contraband. Only when we were quiet did he take a seat in the small office at the end of the passage where he dozed until morning.

One morning ... we were taken to the head office. The head office was only about a quarter of a mile away and was a simple stone structure that resembled our own section. Once there, we were lined up to have our fingerprints taken, which was routine prison service business. But while waiting, I noticed a warder with a camera. After our fingerprints had been taken, the chief warder ordered us to line up for photographs. I motioned to my colleagues not to move, and I addressed the warder: "I would like you to produce the document from the commissioner of prisons authorizing our pictures to be taken." Photographs of prisoners required such authorization.

It was always valuable to be familiar with regulations, because the warders themselves were often ignorant of them and could be intimidated by one's superior knowledge. The warder was taken aback by my request and was unable to offer any explanation or produce anything in writing from the commissioner of prisons. He threatened to charge us if we did not consent to have our photographs taken, but I said that if there was no authorization, there would be no pictures, and that is where the matter remained.

As a rule, we objected to having our pictures taken in prison on the grounds that it is generally demeaning to be seen as a prisoner. But there was one photograph I did consent to, the only one I ever agreed to while on Robben Island.

> A word is not a crystal, transparent and unchanged; it is the skin of a living thought, and may vary greatly in color and content according to the circumstances and the time in which it is used.
>
> Oliver Wendell Holmes

One morning, a few weeks later, the chief warder, instead of handing us hammers for our work in the courtyard, gave us each needles and thread and a pile of worn prison jerseys. We were instructed to repair the garments, but we discovered that most of these jerseys were frayed beyond repair. This struck us as a curious task, and we wondered what had provoked the change. Later that morning, at about eleven o'clock, the front gate swung open, revealing the commanding officer with two men in suits. The commanding officer announced that the two visitors were a reporter and photographer from the *Daily Telegraph* in London. He related this as if visiting members of the international press were a regular diversion for us.

Although these men were our first official visitors, we regarded them skeptically. Firstly, they were brought in under the auspices of the government, and second, we were aware that the *Telegraph* was a conservative newspaper unlikely to be sympathetic to our cause. We well knew that there was great concern in the outside world about our situation and that it was in the government's interest to show that we were not being mistreated.

The two journalists walked slowly around the courtyard, surveying us. We kept our heads down concentrating on our work. After they had made one circuit, one of the guards plucked me by the shoulder and said, "Mandela, come, you will talk now." In those early days, I often spoke on behalf of my fellow prisoners. The prison service regulations were explicit that each prisoner was permitted to speak only for himself. This was done to negate the power of organization and to neutralize our collective strength. We objected to this rule, but made little headway. We were not even permitted to use the word *we* when we made complaints. But during the first few years, when the authorities needed one prisoner to speak on behalf of others, that individual would be me.

I talked to the reporter, whose name was Mr. Newman, for about twenty minutes, and was candid about both prison and the Rivonia Trial. He was an agreeable fellow, and at the end of our talk, he said he would like the photographer to take my picture. I was reluctant, but in this case relented because I knew the photograph would only be published overseas, and might serve to help our cause if the article was even the least bit friendly. I told him I would agree provided Mr. Sisulu could join me. The image shows the two of us talking in the courtyard about some matter that I can no longer remember. I never saw the article or heard anything about it. The reporters were barely out of sight when the warders removed the jerseys and gave us back our hammers....

In jail, all prisoners are classified by the authorities as one of four categories: A, B, C, or D. A is the highest classification and confers the most privileges; D is the lowest and confers the least. All political prisoners, or what the authorities called "security prisoners," were automatically classified as D on admission. The privileges affected by these classifications included visits and letters, studies, the opportunity to buy groceries and incidentals—all of which are the lifeblood of any prisoner. It normally took years for a political prisoner to raise his status from D to C.

We disdained the classification system. It was corrupt and demeaning, another way of repressing prisoners in general and political prisoners in particular. We demanded that all political prisoners be in one category. Although we criticized it, we could not ignore it: the classification system was an inflexible feature of prison life. If you protested that, as a D Group prisoner, you could receive only one letter every six months, the authorities would say, Improve your behavior, become a C Group prisoner, and you will be able to receive two letters every six months. If you complained that you did not receive enough food, the authorities would remind you that if you were in A Group, you would be able to receive money orders from the outside and purchase extra food at the prison canteen. Even a freedom fighter benefits from the ability to buy groceries and books.

The classifications generally ran parallel to the length of one's sentence. If you were sentenced to eight years, you would generally be classified as D for the first two years, C for the next two, B for the following two, and A for the last two. But the prison authorities wielded the classification system as a weapon against political prisoners, threatening to lower our hard-won classifications in order to control our behavior.

Though I had been in prison for nearly two years before I was taken to Robben Island, I was still in D Group when I arrived. While I desired the privileges that came with the higher classifications, I refused to compromise my conduct. The fastest way to raise one's classification was to be docile and not complain. "Ag, Mandela, you are a troublemaker," the warders would say. "You will be in D Group for the rest of your life."

Every six months, prisoners were called before the prison board to have their classifications evaluated. The board was meant to assess our behavior in terms of prison regulations, but we found that it preferred to act as a political tribunal rather than a mere evaluator of behavior. During my first meeting with the board, the officials asked me questions about the ANC and my beliefs. Although this had nothing to do with the classification system, I was vain enough to answer and think that I might convert them to my beliefs. It was one of the few times we were treated as human beings, and I for one responded. Later I realized that this was simply a technique on the part of the authorities to glean information from us, and I had fallen for it. Shortly afterward, we agreed among ourselves not to discuss politics with the prison board.

As a D Group prisoner, I was entitled to have only one visitor, and to write and receive only one letter every six months. I found this one of the most inhumane restrictions of the prison system. Communication with one's family is a human right; it should not be restricted by the artificial gradations of a prison system. But it was one of the facts of prison life.

Visits and letters were restricted to "first degree" relatives. This was a restriction we not only found irksome but racist. The African sense of immediate family is far different from that of the European or Westerner. Our family structures are larger and more inclusive; anyone who claims descent from a common ancestor is deemed part of the same family.

In prison, the only thing worse than bad news about one's family is no news at all. It is always harder to cope with the disasters and tragedies one imagines than with the reality, however grim or disagreeable. A letter with ill tidings was always preferable to no letter at all.

But even this miserable restriction was abused by the authorities. The anticipation of mail was overwhelming. Mail call took place once a month, and sometimes six months would go by without a letter. To be allowed one letter in six months and then not to receive it is a great blow. One wonders: What has happened to my wife and children, to my mother and my sisters? When I did not receive a letter I felt as dry and barren as the Great Karroo desert. Often the authorities would withhold mail out of spite. I can remember warders saying, "Mandela, we have received a letter for you, but we cannot give it to you." No explanation of why, or whom the letter was from. It required all my self-discipline not to explode at such times. Afterward, I would protest through the proper channels, and sometimes get it.

When letters did arrive, they were cherished. A letter was like the summer rain that could make even the desert bloom. When I was handed a letter by the authorities, I would not rush forward and grab it as I felt like doing, but take it in a leisurely manner. Though I yearned to tear it open and read it on the spot, I would not give the authorities the satisfaction of seeing my eagerness, and I would return slowly to my cell as though I had many things to occupy me before opening a letter from my family.

During the first few months, I received one letter from Winnie, but it was so heavily censored that not much more than the salutation was left. The island's censors would black out the offending passages in ink, but they later changed this when they realized we could wash away the ink and see what was underneath. They began to use razors to slice out whole paragraphs. Since most letters were written on both sides of a single piece of paper, the material on the other side would also be excised. They seemed to relish delivering letters in tatters. The censorship delayed the delivery of mail because warders, some of whom were not proficient in English, might take as long as a month to censor a letter. The letters we wrote were censored as well; they were often as cut up as the letters we received.

At the end of August, after I had been on the island less than three months, I was informed by the authorities that I would have a visitor the following day. They would not tell me who it was. Walter [Sisulu] was informed that he, too, would have a visitor, and I suspected, I hoped, I wished—I believed—that it would be a visit from Winnie and Albertina.

From the moment Winnie learned we had been brought to the island, she had been trying to arrange a visit. As a banned person, Winnie had to receive a special dispensation from the minister of justice, for she was technically not permitted to communicate with me.

Even with the help of the authorities, visiting Robben Island was not an easy proposition. Visits were a maximum of thirty minutes long, and political prisoners were not permitted contact visits, in which the visitor and prisoner were in the same room.

Visits did not seem to be planned in advance by the authorities. One day, they would contact your wife and say, "You have permission to visit your husband tomorrow." This was enormously inconvenient, and often had the effect of making visits impossible. If a family member was able to plan a visit in advance, the authorities would sometimes deliberately delay issuing a permit until after the plane had departed. Since most of the men's families lived far from the Cape and had very little money, visits by family members were often far beyond their means. Some men who came from poor families did not see their wives for many years at a time, if at all. I knew of men who spent a decade or more on Robben Island without a single visit.

The visiting room for noncontact visits was cramped and windowless. On the prisoner's side, there was a row of five cubicles with small square pieces of glass that looked out on identical cubicles on the other side. One sat in a chair and looked through the thick, smudged glass that had a few small holes drilled into it to permit conversation. One had to talk very loudly to be heard. Later the authorities installed microphones and speakers in front of the glass, a marginal improvement.

Walter and I were called to the visitors' office in the later morning and took seats at the far end of the room. I waited with some anxiety, and suddenly, filling out the glass on the other side of the window was Winnie's lovely face. Winnie always dressed up for prison visits, and tried to wear something new and elegant. It was tremendously frustrating not to be able to touch my wife, to speak tenderly to her, to have a private moment together. We had to conduct our relationship at a distance under the eyes of people we despised.

I could see immediately that Winnie was under tremendous strain. Seeing me in such circumstances must have been trying. Just getting to the island itself was difficult, and added to that were the harsh rituals of the prison, the undoubted indignities of the warders, and the impersonality of the contact.

Winnie, I later discovered, had recently received a second banning order and had been terminated from her job at the Child Welfare Office as a result. Her office was searched by the police shortly before she was fired. The authorities were convinced that Winnie was in secret communication with me. Winnie loved her job as a social worker. It was the hands-on end of the struggle: placing babies with adoptive parents, finding work for the unemployed and medical help for the uninsured. The banning and harassment of my wife greatly troubled me: I could not look after her and the children, and the state was making it difficult for her to look after herself. My powerlessness gnawed at me.

Our conversation was awkward at first, and was not made easier by the presence of two warders standing directly behind her and three behind me. Their role was not only to monitor but to intimidate. Regulations dictated that conversation had to be in either English or Afrikaans—African languages were forbidden—and could involve family matters only. Any line of talk that departed from the family and verged on the political might mean the abrupt termination of the visit. If one mentioned a name unfamiliar to the warders, they would interrupt the conversation, and ask who the person was and the nature of the relationship. This happened often, as the warders were generally unfamiliar with the variety and nature of African names. It was frustrating to spend precious minutes of one's visit explaining to the warder the different branches of one's family tree. But their ignorance also worked in our favor: it allowed us to invent code names for people we wanted to talk about and pretend that we were referring to family members.

That first visit was important, for I knew that Winnie was anxious about my health: she had heard stories that we were being physically abused. I quickly informed her that I was fine and she could see that I was fit, though a bit thinner than before. She, too, was thinner, something I always attributed to stress. After a visit in which Winnie's face looked drawn or tense, I would urge her to put on a bit of weight. She was always dieting, and I was always telling her not to. I inquired one by one about all the children, about my mother and sisters, and Winnie's own family.

Suddenly, I heard the warder behind me say, "Time up! Time up!" I turned and looked at him with incredulity. It was impossible that half an hour had passed. But, in fact, he was right; visits always seemed to go by in the blink of an eye. For all the years that I was in prison, I never failed to be surprised when the warder called, "Time up!" Winnie and I were both hustled from our chairs and we waved a quick farewell. I always felt like lingering after Winnie left, just to retain the sense of her presence, but I would not let the warders see such emotion. As I walked back to the cell, I reviewed in my head what we had talked about. Over the next days, weeks, and months, I would return to that one visit again and again. I knew I would not be able to see my wife again for at least six months. As it turned out, Winnie was not able to visit me for another two years.

Nelson Rolihlahla Mandela was born near Umtata in the Transkei, South Africa, on 18 July, 1918. At the University College of Fort Hare, he participated in a protest boycott and was expelled. In 1944, he helped found the African National Congress (ANC) Youth League and organized resistance to discriminatory legislation, countrywide. He was one of the accused in the Treason Trial and, when the ANC was banned after the Sharpeville massacre in 1960, he was detained until 1961, when he went underground to lead a campaign for a new national convention. The military wing of the ANC, Umkhonto we Sizwe (MK) was established in the same year.

Mandela was finally released from prison in 1990 and, shortly afterwards, he and his delegation agreed to the suspension of armed struggle. He was inaugurated as the first democratically elected State President of South Africa on 10 May 1994. He retired in 1999 and currently resides in his birthplace.

1. ***Response***

a. In a group, discuss what you know about South Africa, apartheid, and Nelson Mandela. Make point-form notes of the key information you cover in your discussion.
b. How does the information you learn in this excerpt fit in with what you already know about life in South Africa before the end of apartheid?
c. What was done to the prisoners to intimidate them and break their spirit? How did Mandela react?
d. Mandela writes, "My powerlessness gnawed at me." Was he entirely without power during these years in prison? Explain, using references to the selection.
e. What was your personal response to Mandela's account?
f. Make a list of five questions you would like to ask Mandela after reading this excerpt from his autobiography.

2. ***Language Focus*** *Diction* Find examples of words and phrases that help to create the formal tone that characterizes Mandela's writing. How do you think the warders and officials would have responded to Mandela's formality? What inferences might you draw about Nelson Mandela's character from the way he writes?

3. ***Literature Studies*** *Biography and Autobiography* Though biographies and autobiographies both focus on an individual's life story, they have different strengths and weaknesses. What do you think you could learn from Mandela's autobiography that no biography could offer? What might a biography of Mandela offer instead? Make some suggestions about what a reader should keep in mind when reading both formats.

4. ***Visual Communication*** *Create a Presentation* Research Mandela's life after he was released from prison. Prepare a visual presentation (a collage, time line, or PowerPoint slide show, for example) of the major events in Mandela's life. Include a commentary that tells the impact Mandela had on his country.

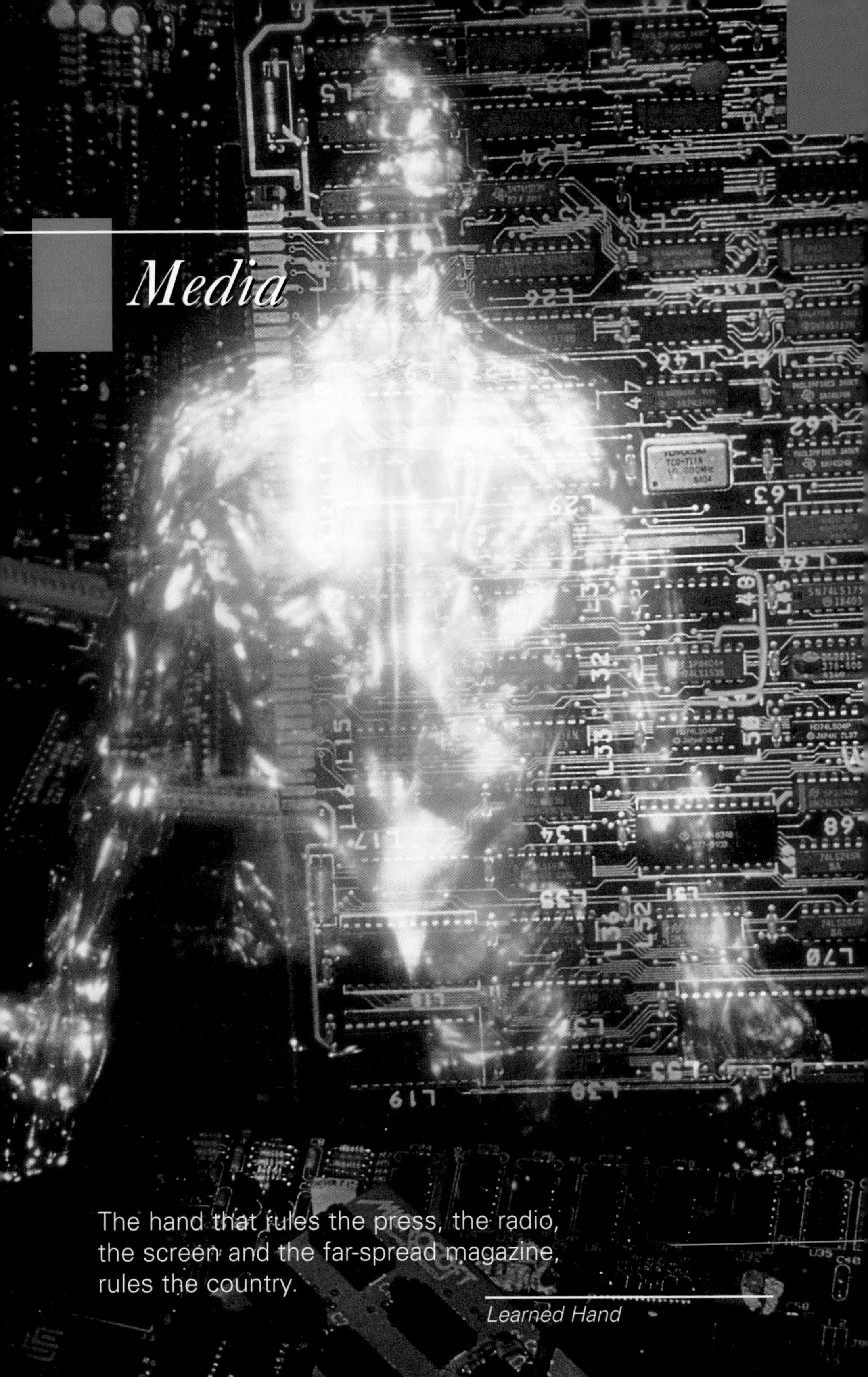

Media

The hand that rules the press, the radio, the screen and the far-spread magazine, rules the country.

Learned Hand

Looking at the Media

Essay by Cam MacPherson

A *medium* of communication is any method by which we spread information. The human voice was the first medium; our voices enabled us to develop spoken language and become a race of speechmakers and storytellers. Thousands of years later, various societies developed written language which allowed much more complex civilizations to emerge. With written language, we could record information accurately and send it long distances. No longer was the human memory our only storage device. Using tablets, scrolls, and finally printed books, we could store knowledge and accumulate it over generations. As increasing numbers of people learned to read and write, there was an increasing demand for printed material. Through the medium of the printed page, information became accessible to ordinary people, not just the wealthy and privileged.

Over the past few centuries, science and technology have provided us with different and more powerful ways of recording, storing, and transmitting words, sounds, and images. Today, in our information-rich society, we spend more time using the media than performing any other activity except, perhaps, sleep.

Consider the amount of time you spend watching movies and TV; reading books, magazines, and newspapers; surfing the Internet; listening to music on the radio, computer, or compact disc player; and looking at advertisements. In addition to the mass media that transmit the same information to everyone, there are also a growing number of personal media devices that keep individuals in touch with each other, such as pagers, the telephone, and e-mail.

mass media: any method by which a message is communicated to a large audience at the same time—movies, radio, TV, books, magazines, the Internet

media text: any media product—movie, radio show, CD, TV program, et cetera—that is selected for critical examination

deconstruction: With any media text that is created from many components, *deconstruction* is the process of taking it apart to analyse its component parts.

Why Understanding the Media Is Important

Here are five good reasons to increase your understanding of the media:

1. The media are our major source of entertainment. Think about the time and the money that you, and your family, spend every year to enjoy movies, watch TV, and listen to music. In addition to buying tickets at the local multiplex cinema, many families invest thousands of dollars in TV, stereo, and computer equipment, and probably pay hundreds of dollars a year to a TV cable, or Internet provider. To get the best return for the money you're spending, you need to understand the steadily evolving technology you use, as well as the program and product choices that are available.

2. The media are a major area of employment. One of the fastest growing sectors of our economy is involved with making the shows we watch, the music we listen to, and the computer software that manages our information at school and at work. There are hundreds of career choices available in the media for students who take the time to examine the possibilities and obtain the right training.

3. The media control much of our knowledge and understanding of the world. Most of what we know does not come from direct, personal experience, but through TV, radio, the Internet, and other media sources. How truthful and accurate is this information? Who controls what we see and hear? We need to ask questions about the information the media gives us, and not accept it uncritically.

4. Advertising and public relations messages pay for much of the media content we enjoy, but the purpose of these messages is to persuade us to buy products, accept ideas, and support governments and corporations. We need to examine the persuasive techniques that lie behind these messages so that we can make informed decisions and avoid being easily manipulated.

5. As they entertain us and inform us, the media shape our attitudes and values in a number of ways. The actors and models that are featured in programs and ads influence our ideas of how we should look, dress, and speak. These performers present us with images against which we measure ourselves and those around us. The lifestyles and occupations of people in the media influence our own ideas of how we should live our lives. Unlike our own multicultural society, the societies we see in many of our favourite media programs lack diversity.

Analysing Media Texts

When we analyse or "deconstruct" media texts we need to remember that every product of the media has three main components. We can understand each component better when we ask some basic questions:

About the text—the product itself—the movie, CD, et cetera
What category does this text fall into? (for example, romance, comedy)
Does the text tell a story or connect to a larger story?
Does the text follow a formula or familiar pattern?
What are the characters in the text like—are they like me?
What do I need to know to understand this text?

About production—the manufacture and distribution process
Where does this text come from? Who created it?
How is this text made? What techniques were used?
How is this text distributed or sold to the public?
What rules or laws affect this text?
Who owns it?
How could I produce a similar text?

About the audience—the reactions of consumers
How does this text appeal to me? What do I like/dislike?
Who is the intended target audience? How do I know?
How does this text appeal to its intended audience?
In what different ways do people use or consume this text?
How would I change this text to make it more enjoyable?

Key Concepts of Media Studies

Another way to organize our understanding and analysis of media texts is to apply what are called the "key concepts"—fundamental principles that apply to all media texts.

1. All media are constructions:
Media stories, characters, and settings may look natural and completely realistic, but they are artificial, and are only made to look real. Just as performers are carefully made up, dressed, and photographed to create a certain image for the part they are playing, so is the entire text a construction. Everything we see and hear is the product of the skills and decisions of the people who have created and produced the text.

2. The media construct reality:
Much of what we know and believe about the world we have learned through the media. Therefore, our understanding of reality is a

"construct" put together by others. Our impression of a city or country, for example, as shaped by the media, may be quite different from the impression we get when we actually visit the place.

3. Audiences negotiate meaning:
What we get out of a media text—how we respond to it—depends on who we are and what we bring to the text. Our age, gender, education, ethnic background, religion, and other factors influence our response. If one person enjoys a certain kind of music, another person may hate the same music. Whose response is the "right" one? They're both right.

4. Media have commercial implications:
While some individuals may produce a media text just to satisfy their artistic impulses, media products are almost always manufactured to make money. As a result, most media products are designed to have maximum audience appeal, and to increase this appeal the appearance and content of the text may be greatly affected.

5. Media contain ideological and value messages:
The media reflect the values of their creators and sponsors, and often stress the values of consumerism, and a middle-class, western way of looking at the world. Most TV shows, for example, deal with the lives of successful, attractive, middle-class people. Similarly, while some movies may glamorize criminals, they almost always get caught in the end.

6. Media have social implications:
Media products are powerful and persuasive. As a result, they can influence how we think, shop, dress, behave, judge other people, and feel about ourselves. Media celebrities are good symbols of this power. Their personal and professional lives are the subject of constant media chatter. As well, they can exert great influence on fashion trends and body image for their audiences, simply by changing their own appearance.

Today, we recognize the media as an essential component of our daily lives. Those who control our TV networks, radio stations, and other sources of information, shape what we know about the world and the people in it. At the same time, the media sells us products to buy, celebrities to admire, and lifestyles to envy. Much of our education, outside of school, is provided by the media, and we must not accept what we are taught uncritically. The better we understand how media products are created and sold to us, the better we are able to make informed choices. ◗

What did media guru, Marshall McLuhan, envision as a "classroom without walls"? This article was written in 1957. How has our view of media changed?

Classroom Without Walls

Essay by Marshall McLuhan

It's natural today to speak of "audio and visual aids" to teaching, for we still think of the book as norm, of other media as incidental. We also think of the new media—press, radio, movies, TV—as MASS MEDIA & think of the book as an individualistic form.

Individualistic because it isolated the reader in silence & helped create the Western "I." Yet it was the first product of mass production.

With it everybody could have the same books. It was impossible in medieval times for different students, different institutions, to have copies of the same book. Manuscripts, commentaries, were dictated. Students memorized.

Instruction was almost entirely oral, done in groups. Solitary study was reserved for the advanced scholar. The first printed books were "visual aids" to oral instruction.

Before the printing press, the young learned by listening, watching, doing. So, until recently, our own rural children learned the language & skills of their elders. Learning took place outside the classrooms. Only those aiming at professional careers went to school at all.

Today in our cities, most learning occurs outside the classroom. The sheer quantity of information conveyed by press-mags-film-TV-radio *far exceeds* the quantity of information conveyed by school instruction & texts. This challenge has destroyed the monopoly of the book as a teaching aid & cracked the very walls of the classroom, so suddenly, we're confused, baffled.

In this violently upsetting social situation, many teachers naturally view the offerings of the new media as entertainment, rather than education. *But this view carries no conviction to the student.*

Find a classic which wasn't first regarded as light entertainment. Nearly all vernacular works were so regarded until the 19th century.

Many movies are obviously handled with a degree of insight &

maturity at least equal to the level permitted in today's textbooks. Olivier's *Henry V* & *Richard III* assemble a wealth of scholarly & artistic skill which reveal Shakespeare at a very high level, yet in a way easy for the young to enjoy.

The movie is to dramatic representation what the book was to the manuscript. It makes available to many & at many times & places what otherwise would be restricted to a few at few times & places. The movie, like the book, is a ditto device. TV shows to 50,000,000 simultaneously. Some feel that the value of experiencing a book is diminished by being extended to many minds. This notion is always implicit in the phrases "mass media," "mass entertainment"—useless phrases obscuring the fact THAT *English itself is a mass medium.* Today we're beginning to realize that the new media aren't just mechanical gimmicks for creating worlds of illusion, *but new languages with new & unique powers of expression.* Historically, the resources of English have been shaped & expressed in constantly new & changing ways. The printing press changed, not only the quantity of writing, but the character of language & the relations between author & public. Radio, film, TV pushed written English towards the spontaneous shifts & freedom of the spoken idiom. They aided us in the recovery of intense awareness of facial language & bodily gesture. If these "mass media" should serve only to weaken or corrupt previously achieved levels of verbal & pictorial culture, it won't be because there's anything inherently wrong with them. *It will be because we've failed to master them as new languages in time to assimilate them to our total cultural heritage.*

These new developments, under quiet analytic survey, point to a basic strategy of culture for the classroom. When the printed book first appeared, it threatened the oral procedures of teaching, and created the classroom as we now know it. Instead of making his own text, his own dictionary, his own grammar, the student started out with these tools. He could study, not one, but several languages. Today these new media threaten, instead of merely reinforce, the procedures of this traditional classroom. It's customary to answer this threat with denunciations of the unfortunate character & effect of movies & TV, just as the comic book was feared & scorned & rejected from the classroom. Its good & bad features in form & content, when carefully set beside other kinds of art & narrative, could have become a major asset to the teacher.

Popular magazines multiply while the library shelves remain undisturbed.

Elisabeth Marbury

Where student interest is already intensely focused is the natural point at which to be in the elucidation of other problems & interests. *The educational task is not only to provide basic tools of perception, but to develop judgement & discrimination with ordinary social experience.*

Few students ever acquire skill in analysis of newspapers. Fewer have any ability to discuss a movie intelligently. *To be articulate & discriminating about ordinary affairs & information is the mark of an educated man.*

It's misleading to suppose there's any basic difference between education & entertainment. *This distinction merely relieves people* of the responsibility of looking into the matter. *It's like setting up a distinction between* didactic & lyric poetry on the ground that one teaches, the other pleases. *However, it's always been true* that whatever pleases teaches more effectively.

(Herbert) Marshall McLuhan was born in 1911 in Edmonton, Alberta. He taught in schools and at St. Michael's College of the University of Toronto, where he became director of the Centre for Culture and Technology. McLuhan is well known for his theories about the role of the electronic media in mass popular culture. He prophesied that printed books would become obsolete, killed off by TV and other electronic information technology.

1. *Response*

a. What is the thesis of this essay? What points in McLuhan's essay prove his thesis?

b. Is there any statement in this essay that you agree or disagree with strongly? What is it? What is your viewpoint?

c. This article was written in 1957, before the introduction of the Internet. How do you think McLuhan would have responded to the Internet? How would his essay change if it were written today?

d. Examine the use of italics, capital letters, and symbols within this essay. How does the typography the author has chosen to use affect the reader? The essay's meaning?

e. Who do you think McLuhan's target audience is? What is his purpose in addressing this audience? What makes you think so? How has he created a voice appropriate to his audience and purpose?

2. ***Research and Inquiry*** Consider how media have been used in the past to help educate the masses—whether students or the general public. For example, in the late nineteenth/early twentieth centuries in England, suffragettes handed out pamphlets and carried signs to help persuade the general populace that women deserved the right to vote. And in Germany in the 1930s, film documentaries and radio were used to spread propaganda and build support for the Nazi party.

Choose a time period and region and research how media were used to persuade the masses. Speculate on the effectiveness of the media for causing change or educating people.

Alternatively, you could research the impact of one medium—such as radio—on education, or on people in general.

3. ***Media*** *Choose a Format* Produce a media work that will convince your board of education to use media more widely in the classroom. You could choose to design a Web page, a print ad, a TV show, or a poster, for example. Your use of language, visuals, and design should reflect your audience and purpose.

4. ***Literature Studies*** *Diction* Examine the author's choice of words and explain which of the following most aptly describes McLuhan's diction: formal, colloquial, abstract, concrete, literal, figurative.

Identify the thesis statement in "The Psychological Power of Radio." As you read the rest of the essay, list the arguments the author uses to support his thesis.

The Psychological Power of Radio

Essay by Tim Crook

When you consider the history of the twentieth century, broadcasting skits or hoaxes are more associated with radio than with television. This is because radio was the first electronic medium of mass entertainment, and radio is a more psychological medium. Its relationship with its audience is based on an emotional and imaginative bond. Today radio has not lost its importance as a huge and significant source for news and entertainment and the opportunity to hoodwink the audience is as strong as it has ever been.

There are few people who are unaware of the panic created by the Mercury Theatre on Halloween night, 1938. The radio adaptation of H. G. Wells' novel *The War of the Worlds* had been transformed into a close representation of an American entertainment programme interrupted by urgent news bulletins. Orson Welles is credited with the idea, Howard Koch is credited with writing the script and the outstanding acting of the cast is credited with convincing hundreds of thousands of people that the Martians really were invading New Jersey.

Professor Hadley Cantril at Princeton University researched and published the only study into the relationship between the power and effectiveness of a broadcast of this kind and the reaction of the audience. "The Invasion From Mars: A Study in the Psychology of Panic" remains one of the most significant sociological and psychological studies of radio.

We can now say that the panic was the result of a mischievous determination to shock and confuse by Orson Welles, as well as the unusual circumstances of the period. The evidence available to us indicates quite strongly that Welles deliberately sought to create alarm, although he did not anticipate the scale of the panic.

CBS was aware of the risks of listeners being taken in by the realism of the writing and performance. Documentary evidence shows that producers insisted on changing real place names to fictitious ones, but the place names still had a ring of authenticity. Welles was conscious of the psychological impact of Herbert Morrison's emotional ad-libbed radio description of the destruction of the *Hindenburg*[1] just over a year before. In fact the actor playing the reporter in the production was directed to listen to and study the broadcast in a CBS booth during the rehearsals. An attempt was made to mimic the voice of President Roosevelt, and the production imitated the texture of contemporary networks which were continually interrupting music and soap opera broadcasts to bring the latest news developments from European crises.[2]

The rest, as they say, is interesting history. The power of radio was established, Orson Welles' name reverberated around the world, Campbell's Soups decided to sponsor the programme, and Welles later readily acknowledged that his plan to "make a radio splash" got him to Hollywood to make *Citizen Kane*. In fact his entrée to Hollywood was exceptional in the degree of artistic freedom given him.

The hysteria and controversy surrounding the *War of the Worlds* broadcast was also intensified by the hostility of the newspaper media which had seen the infant, and now adolescent, radio medium aggressively competing for advertising revenue. Here was an opportunity to exaggerate the degree of the panic. It does not appear that anyone died as a result, but listeners were treated for shock, hysteria and even heart attacks. Somewhat suspiciously there were more newspaper offices than police stations swamped with frantic queries: "What is happening? Where's the nearest bomb shelter? What must we do?"

The author of the original novel, H. G. Wells, was not particularly impressed. On the following day he is reported as saying "the dramatisation was made with a liberty that amounts to a complete rewriting and made the novel an entirely different story. It's a total unwarranted liberty." By 1940 his attitude had somewhat mellowed and he was happy to meet and be interviewed by Welles on live American radio. Why had

[1]***the* Hindenburg:** a Zeppelin, an early type of airship, which exploded and crashed May 6, 1934, killing 35 people

[2]***European crises:*** political unrest in Europe before the outbreak of World War II

his early objections evaporated? It might have something to do with the fact that the broadcast and publicity had boosted sales of one of his more obscure novels.

Attempts have been made to imitate the *War of the Worlds* scam within regulatory controls. Not surprisingly the US Federal Communications Commission launched an urgent enquiry and produced a raft of laws for US broadcasters to guard against deception of this kind again. Regulators in other countries followed suit.

The 1996, BBC Radio One FM's production of *Independence Day* on Nicky Campbell's show is an example of imitation. The invasion of British locations by aliens had powerful parallels. The Phoenix, Arizona radio station KTAR 620AM lovingly produced a 1995 version placing the *War of the Worlds* story in contemporary Arizona and engaging their entire on-air and production talent in the project. Producer Doren Fronterhouse went to St. Mary's Basilica in downtown Phoenix to record the bells as they chimed on Halloween night 1995. The station also warned its audience for many weeks that this programme was going to be aired as their special Halloween "trick or treat."

Television has never been able to match up to radio for the force and terror of "broadcast panics." A British ghost-hunting programme created a murmur of alarm one Halloween night in the 1990s and BBC Television's early *Panorama* April Fool's joke about the spaghetti harvests in Switzerland had a fair number of people fooled in 1957. Television was a relatively new medium of mass communication and the authoritative introduction and endorsement by Richard Dimbleby[3] helped emboss the item with credibility.

Orson Welles' 1938 portrayal of the expert astronomer, Professor Pierson, who is lost for words and has nothing to say in *War of the Worlds*, underlines how the audience's reliance on experts and information icons can be used to deceive and panic.

It is also worth bearing in mind that the year 1957 belonged to an era when recreational travelling abroad was still the preserve of only the few. So faked pictures of growing spaghetti combined effectively with the voice over:

> "Spaghetti cultivation in Switzerland is not on anything like the scale of the Italian spaghetti farms . . . Many of you will have seen the huge spaghetti plantations in the Po Valley."

---

[3] ***Richard Dimbleby:*** a British actor

Richard Dimbleby's sign off cue "And that is all from *Panorama* on this first day of April" was too subtle a remark for those who had been easily deceived. Viewers wrote in to ask where they could buy spaghetti plants and one viewer asserted that the programme had got it wrong; spaghetti grew horizontally, not vertically.

In recent decades, radio has been effective in developing a "skit genre" which engages the listeners in ironic entertainment rather than fooling them. This is the realm of the spoof broadcaster who uses mimicry to deceive ordinary people, politicians and public figures into making fools of themselves. *Candid Camera* is the television equivalent. It is copied across the world and provides huge entertainment. It also has the capacity to satirise and play a subversive role. In Britain, Chris Morris has developed the technique on Radio One FM and has transferred these skills to his Channel Four *Brass Eye* television series. He has achieved a sophisticated level of entertainment as well as exposing the cynicism of the media's relationship with politicians and pressure groups.

America's legendary shock jock Howard Stern has used "spoofing" as just one of the many subversive mechanisms to lampoon the world around him. But the radio spoofer of the century award should probably go to Montréal's Pierre Brassard whose *Blue Powder Drive Home Show* on station CKOI has successfully duped His Holiness the Pope and Her Majesty the Queen.

In October 1995, Brassard convinced the Queen that he was Canadian Prime Minister Jean Chrétien. He was able to persuade her in a 17-minute telephone conversation that it would be a good idea if she could broadcast an appeal to the French-speaking province of Québec not to break away from Canada in yet another nail-biting referendum. Part of the extraordinary conversation was in French with Brassard asking "Are you wearing a costume for Halloween?" She replied: "No, no. It's for the children." This scam was achieved through the skill of Brassard's cheek and mimicry and the Queen's misfortune that her officials could not confirm the authenticity of the call beforehand because Chrétien had been out campaigning.

The development of phone-in and talkback programming in the last 25 years has provided the opportunity for audience interactivity so that listeners can now turn the tables against the broadcasters themselves. The limited amount of time and resources available to check phone-in contributors provides an environment "ripe for the picking." US "over the edge" sound artists have already succeeded in disrupting licensed programmes through phone-in participation as well as using illegal transmitters to "crash" on established frequencies. It would not be impossible for a group of subversive broadcasters to "swamp" an existing news phone-in programme with realistic reports of a catastrophic event tinged with political embarrassment. Back-up calls from apparent emergency services could easily convince the station's newsroom of the authenticity of the event. More highly staffed and experienced national newspapers have been duped by lone hoaxers such as "Rocky Ryan"[4] whose efforts have created front page embarrassment, and the newspapers had the advantage of hours to make a proper evaluation. In radio, presenters and producers have minutes and seconds.

So the spoof potential of radio lies in the willing desire to suspend disbelief. If this can be described as a human weakness then it is present in all of us. In radio, both listener and broadcaster can now find ways of exposing the medium's vulnerability.

---

[4]***Rocky Ryan:*** a hoaxer who made up believable stories and sold them to the British tabloids in the 1970s and 1980s

Tim Crook has written textbooks on radio journalism and radio drama. He is head of Radio in the department of Media and Communications at Goldsmiths' College, University of London, England, and presents *Through the Night* and *Newsfile* on the British radio station, LBC.

1. ***Response***
   a. Who is Orson Welles? Who is H. G. Wells?
   b. Describe what happened on October 31, 1938.
   c. How did Orson Welles and the producers of the radio program, *War of the Worlds*, convince the audience that New Jersey had been invaded by aliens from Mars? Would an audience today be fooled by such a broadcast? Explain.
   d. Do you think Tim Crook proved his thesis? Explain.

2. ***Media*** *Radio Productions* Locate a recording of the radio program *War of the Worlds* at your local library, or on the Internet. As you listen to it, make notes about how the show was produced and introduced. Discuss the effectiveness of the production.

In this radio script by humorist Paul Moth, no cultural icons or popular ideas are spared his cutting humour. As you are reading, keep a list of all the things that Paul and Kath spoof as they discuss the books anxious gift-givers can choose from.

Christmas Consumer Frenzy

Script by Paul Moth

from The Great Eastern: Newfoundland's Cultural Magazine

PAUL: The Xmas consumer frenzy is upon us, and that means the last hope for many bookstores. Here to discuss the Yuletide crop of bound scribbles, doodles and snaps is Ms. Wordworks herself, Kathleen Hanrahan.

KATH: Hello, Paul.

PAUL: Now, the gift book is truly the life blood of retailers isn't it?

KATH: Yes it is. People don't read so much anymore, but a book is … well it's readily available, usually in the price range for a Christmas book and hey, it's easy to wrap.

PAUL: Backing up a bit, why aren't people reading?

KATH: First I think there's a lifestyle question—more onerous work, greater demands at home—people can't find the time or are simply too tired to read. And secondly they've grown stupid.

PAUL: You know I'd thought that but I'm glad you said it. On to the Christmas goodies. You promised us only books 100% guaranteed to satisfy. Whaddaya got, whaddaya got?

KATH: First, *Places You Will Never Go*, a sumptuous marriage of glossy photographs and fluffy text, by Harriet Burton.

PAUL: Owww very sumptuous. The paper is … I don't know how to put it … so soft.

KATH: It's infused with hand lotion.

PAUL: Nice. This book is about?

KATH: The homes and extravagant lifestyles of our filthy rich.

PAUL: Ouch! Look at this bathroom! I'd dine there any day.

KATH: If you were ever invited.

PAUL: I don't have a hope, do I?

KATH: No.

PAUL: Not all fluff, Kathleen. The photographs are accompanied by handy and informative discussions about the architectural and design principles of the grand estates.

Kath: And some of the history of these great old families.

Paul: I see the Woolrights made their money through child labour.

Kath: Several generations ago. They now keep the industrial engine running with a canny mix of banking and offshore athletic footwear manufacturing.

Paul: Maintaining that tradition of child labour through the ages, that's great. Oh, and here's a photo essay about the local debutante ball.

Kath: Young, beautiful and so incredibly wealthy.

Paul: A winning combination.

Kath: Still this photographic essay shows the well-heeled lifestyle, warts and all.

Paul: Ah yes ... here's a debutante being sick ... all that *Veuve Cliquot.*[1]

Kath: There's one humiliating a busboy.

Paul: Those wacky super rich. We just can't get enough of them, can we.

Kath: Prestige Press, and just about affordable at 47.50.

Paul: Next?

Kath: *The Absolution Vodka Book.*

Paul: The booze people who do those fabulous ads?

Kath: The same. This is a book of those advertisements.

Paul: What? I pay to look at their ads!

Kath: They're quite exceptional and creative.

Paul: Where is this going to end? You can't buy clothes that don't have company logos plastered all over them; you try to phase out in front of the tube and you're subjected to infomercials; you ... ahhhhh look at this one, the little mouse, he's trapped in the vodka bottle, I think he's drunk. That's adorable. My Mom might like this, what's the asking price?

Kath: Thirty-two dollars.

Paul: Oh no, that's too much. Next.

Kath: For the kids there is yet another *Goofoids* book.

Paul: I hate those cartoons, the noise, the graphic violence, the supply-side economics—but you know my brother's kids can't get enough of them.

Kath: And I'll bet they love the *Goofoids* breakfast cereal.

Paul: My brother is afraid not to give it to them; claims they get ill without it, nauseous, sweaty, irritable . . .

---

[1]***Veuve Cliquot:*** a type of champagne

KATH: That's because it's addictive.
PAUL: Wow.
KATH: Still it's a complete breakfast.
PAUL: I have a bad feeling about this stuff; again I can't see the line between entertainment and advertising.
KATH: That's standard fare though these days isn't it, and look the RCMP have a contract with Disney so I mean ... in a way, this kind of predatory children's entertainment has the state's sanction.
PAUL: But the *Goofoids* characters smoke!
KATH: Cigars though, Paul, they're just hip to the scene.
PAUL: Next?
KATH: *Edna Greeley's Christmas Homemakers Extravaganza.*
PAUL: Get-a-load of the centrepiece. So woodsy, it's a virtual pine forest!
KATH: It's all carved from cheese. There ... pretzel skiers, little caper toques.
PAUL: The skis are anchovy I'd guess.
KATH: It's so pretty I don't think I could eat it.
PAUL: With the anchovies I'd attempt it, what kind of cheese is it?
KATH: That's a dip pond by the walnut grove. The ducks are ...
PAUL: I love a good Muenster, a ripe non-pasteurized Muenster. Sorry Kathleen, this looks like a lot of work.
KATH: Today's homemaker has to really put out lest they be accused of being a bad parent or spouse.
PAUL: Things are so different for kids these days hey? When I was growing up Catholics fasted through Advent so they would really appreciate their Christmas porridge.
KATH: Paul!
PAUL: Just kidding Kathleen. We always got a big feed of utility road-kill every Christmas.
KATH: That's comforting.
PAUL: At least you knew they weren't fed steroids. Thanks Kathleen and buy, buy, buy!
KATH: You too.
PAUL: God Bless.
KATH: Let's keep God out of it!

To perceive Christmas through its wrappings becomes more difficult every year.

E. B. White

Paulitorial by Paul Moth

Let's peel back the veil of personality that covers the media. Underneath that, what do you find?

You find me, Paul Moth. I am two people, I am Paul Moth, public radio host, and I am Paul Moth, the private individual. And you know nothing about the private individual. And I really mean nothing. That's the way I want it. Believe me, that's the way you want it, too.

Then there's the public Paul Moth, the radio presence.

It seems every time I become this public person, every time I pick up a microphone, the universe changes. The reality-modifying capabilities of the microphone have not been fully investigated.

Whatever, whenever the radio waves start rolling, weird things happen to me.

What is it about the emanation of radio pulses that disturbs the brains of some addled listeners?

And if those people are tuned in now, I have one message from both the public and private Paul Moth.

Who are you? And what are you doing in my head?

Paul Moth was born in 1949 in St. John's, Newfoundland and Labrador. He first worked in radio as a sports reporter with the Broadcasting Corporation of Newfoundland (BCN) in 1970, eventually hosting *In the Corners*, a weekly roundup of sport. Moth then entered the film industry and became well known in Mexican cinema, writing and directing 13 episodes of *Pepito el Grande* (Pepito the Great). After living in Los Angeles for a while he returned to Canada where he became host of the BCN's legendary *The Great Eastern.*

1. *Response*

a. Discuss the items on your list of all that Paul Moth pokes fun at or spoofs in this radio script. Do you think he was being fair? Do you appreciate Moth's sense of humour? Why or why not?

b. From the two examples here, describe the type of radio show that Moth hosts. Who do you think is his target audience? What is his purpose in producing this show? Would you enjoy listening to it? Explain your answer.
c. What explicit and implicit messages does "Christmas Consumer Frenzy" deliver?
d. Reread Moth's "Paulitorial." Discuss what he is saying about celebrity and media personalities. Do you agree or disagree? Explain.

2. ***Media*** *Radio Habits* List the reasons you have for listening to radio. What is it you expect to hear when you tune in to a radio station? What types of stations do you listen to? Question other students and family members about their radio listening habits. What conclusions can you draw about people's reasons for listening to radio?

Listen to at least five different radio stations over the next five days. Make sure you listen at different times during the day, for at least half an hour each time. Keep a list of everything you hear. Compare your lists to the lists of other students in the class. What types of programs do radio stations air? What is the most common type of programming? What do you think is the purpose of most radio programs? What different audiences are each of the stations you listened to trying to reach? What role does advertising play on each of these stations?

3. ***Writing*** *Various Formats* Choose a format to convey your response to one of Paul Moth's selections—an essay or editorial about your view of what it means to be a celebrity, a letter or anecdote about your experiences with Christmas shopping—or another format of your choice. Ask a peer editor to read your first and second drafts and suggest ways to improve your writing.

4. ***Oral Language*** *Group Discussion* Discuss your personal experiences and knowledge about the "Xmas consumer frenzy." What do you know about the practices of the media during the Christmas season? What happens to TV stations' broadcasting and advertising? What happens in stores? How does the Christmas season affect movie theatres? What relationship do entertainment media, advertising, and stores have with the consumer? How does all of this affect those who do not celebrate Christmas? Do you think the media are now showing more tolerance for those who do not celebrate it? Explain.

One Ocean

One-act radio play
by Betty Quan

Using the Chinese myth of the Jingwei bird, a daughter tries to bridge the physical and emotional gulf with her father in this memory play about the ideas of immigration and subsequent separation of families.

SCENE 1: *Narration. Inside memory.*
MUSIC: *Establish theme, continue under:*

DAUGHTER: *(older)* A long time ago. It was my favourite. A story. No, our story. Just a Chinese folktale. Yes. About the Jingwei bird and why she is always dropping sticks and stones in the ocean. When I was small, I used to pretend I was that little bird. I would soar through our communal courtyard with arms for wings. That was when we were still allowed to enjoy our stories, to tell our stories, before, before ... *Bah-bah.* Father. Do you remember like I do? Tell me about the Jingwei. Yes, like you used to do when I was small. You told me that story when I left Hong Kong for Canada. Do you remember? I was sad. We were both sad. Like a bird in your hand I was until you set me free across the sky, across the ocean. Such a long time ago, yet so close I can still see it unfolding before me. Father? Tell me a story. Like you used to do. *(as if repeating what she hears in memory)* "A long time ago." It seems like yesterday. A long time ago. But that is how we begin our stories, isn't it? We begin with "a long time ago."

SCENE 2: *Folktale remembered.*

FATHER: A long time ago there was an emperor who had a young daughter. They loved each other very much. But although his powers could touch all corners of the land, the emperor could see only as far as the shoreline that divided his kingdom with the sea.

DAUGHTER: Beyond that shoreline, his vision was limited, like a kite held high in a strong breeze—he could see the shape, but not the colours.

Music ends. Sound effects: birds, breeze, ocean, continue under:

DAUGHTER: Father, look at the waves, so tall they must be hiding something behind them. I will take my boat for a ride.

FATHER: *(as Emperor)* Not so far, not so far.

DAUGHTER: *(as Jingwei)* Don't worry, father. I'll be careful.

FATHER: *(as Emperor)* Why don't you wait a while? I'll join you. We can journey to the horizon together, where the sea meets the sun.

DAUGHTER: *(as Jingwei)* When? When can we do this? *(laughing)* You're always promising such things, father! You're too busy as Emperor. I'll go out on my own first. On my own adventure. Then, I'll show you what I've seen.

FATHER: *(as Emperor, laughing)* When?

DAUGHTER: *(as Jingwei)* What does that matter? We have all the time in the world.

DAUGHTER: *(older)* The sun was warm upon the little girl's face—

FATHER: —and the salty breeze off the water tempted her to travel farther and farther. To see what hid behind the tall waves of the sea.

DAUGHTER: *(older)* Far far far away she went, when suddenly—

Sound effects: thunder and rainstorm.

FATHER: *(as Sea God)* Who dares come this far upon the ocean of my reign?

DAUGHTER: *(older)* The Sea God's bad temper came upon the little girl.

Sound effects: Jingwei screams as the waves engulf her.

FATHER: The water became a blanket that covered her. And the little girl died.

Sound effects: all suddenly end.

Daughter: *(older)* Died? I don't remember her dying. Is that right? I thought the water changed her into a bird. Like magic.

Father: I would tell you that when you were small. When you didn't understand death.

Daughter: *(older)* Like I do now.

Father: It is only a story. *(continues)* The little girl's soul became a small bird called Jingwei.

Music begins.

Daughter: *(older)* Father, I died that day you sent me away.

Father: No, child, you were reborn. Now, continue the story.

Daughter: Angry was the spirit in that bird, angry at the sea it was for taking her away from her beloved father. And every day the Jingwei would carry in her beak stones and twigs from the mountains of the east and flying west ahead drop her small stones and twigs into the sea. And the Sea God finally noticed what Jingwei was trying to do.

Music ends. Sound effects: ocean. Close: the wings of a bird in motion.

Father: *(as Sea God, laughing)* Silly creature, my sea is wider and deeper than your limited imagination. You can never fill me up in a million years.

Daughter: *(as Jingwei)* But I can. Every day for a million years I will do this. Every day until one day. Until one day ... *(begin fade down)* Until one day ... Until one day ...

Father: And the small bird flew back to land—

Father & Daughter: *(older)* —only to return with another small stone or twig to drop into the sea.

Daughter: *(older)* And Jingwei said: "One day, there will be a bridge-between me and my father. One day, even if it takes a million years to build it." *(she no longer speaks as the Jingwei)* Soon, father. I will see you again. Soon.

Sound effects: fade down.

> Acting is just a way of making a living,
> the family is life.
>
> Denzel Washington

SCENE 3: *Airport.*

Sound effects: airplane's acceleration and ascent. Fades into airport interior: Chinese public address system, etc. Close: a swallow singing.

FATHER: Yes, yes, sing a goodbye song to my daughter. Here's a sunflower seed.

DAUGHTER: I don't think pets are allowed here.

FATHER: This is not just a pet, eh my little friend? Now keep your bag in full sight. Many pickpockets. There is more freedom here in Hong Kong but that doesn't mean there is less danger. Here's your ticket. Show it to that man over there. Where's your passport?

DAUGHTER: I don't want to go to Vancouver, father. Why me?

FATHER: Your big brother has a family now. You will go first, then settle down. Then we can join you.

DAUGHTER: When?

FATHER: Soon. Soon. Look at us now. We used to have a fine house and good food to eat. First the Japanese and the war, now Mao. Remember, just a few years ago, Mao decided China must have its Great Leap Forward? And the country went two steps forward and five steps back?

SCENE 4: *Narration. Inside memory. Music fades under:*

DAUGHTER: *(older)* Mosquitos, flies, rats, and sparrows: Mao called these the "four pests." 1958: It was the year I turned sixteen. *(bitter laugh)* Do you remember? Mao believed grain production was down because the sparrows were feeding on the backs of the people. Families were armed with pots and pans. We were to scare the sparrows out of the trees so they would eventually drop dead from exhaustion. 600 million of us, running under trees, in the countryside, in the cities, making enough noise to waken the dead. Yes, the sparrows ate the grain, but they also ate the insects. Without the sparrows, no one could control the insects. The sky would rain the corpses of little birds to join the corpses of 300 million people, dead of starvation.

SCENE 5: *Airport.*

Sound effects: airport interior. Close: the swallow singing.

FATHER: You know how lucky we were to get out of China?

DAUGHTER: I know.

FATHER: How can we Chinese have luck when we are killing birds!? This is why it is good we are here now. No more death. No more hunger. No more sacrificing our own symbols of fortune and happiness. Maybe my good luck has returned right here in this cage. Maybe now we will all have good luck.

DAUGHTER: Maybe's, nothing but maybe's.

FATHER: You have a chance now, can't you see? To start a new life in a new place.

DAUGHTER: Let me finish school first.

FATHER: *(joking)* Maybe you'll find a rich Canadian and marry him.

DAUGHTER: I'm 18 years old; I don't need a husband. I can try to find a job here, in Hong Kong.

FATHER: Just a temporary thing, you'll see. Your mother, your brother, me. We'll be a family again. We're relying on you. Work hard. Stay out of trouble. Be a citizen your new country can be proud of. When you're settled, you'll sponsor us to come. We'll join you later.

DAUGHTER: Please don't make me go, father.

FATHER: Who is the parent here? Who makes the decision?

DAUGHTER: Please, father, don't make me go all alone.

FATHER: Look, my Jingwei. Yes, you have always been like a little bird to me. If I could, I would always try to protect you, away from bad things. But this—this—is a good thing.

DAUGHTER: I don't want to go!

FATHER: Believe me, it's for the best. You'll like it in Canada.

DAUGHTER: Don't you want me to stay here, with you?

FATHER: It doesn't matter what I want. It's what I want for you.

FEMALE: *(over sound system, filtered)* Last boarding call for Flight 973 departing for Vancouver, Canada.

The announcer repeats this in Cantonese.

DAUGHTER: I've never been in a plane before, father. Have you?

FATHER: No. Not yet. But in time, no?

DAUGHTER: Yes, in time.

SCENE 6: *Airfield.*

Sound effects: airport exterior. Plane accelerating and ascending. Closer: the swallow's song.

FATHER: Goodbye! *(to himself)* Goodbye.

Sound effects: swallow singing.

FATHER: What's that? What are you singing about?

Sound effects: swallow singing. Metal clink of the cage being opened.

FATHER: Come on, there. No, it's not a trick. Out. Yes. Fly, go on, fly. Fly.

Sound effects: Close: the acceleration of a bird's wings, heard under:

FATHER: Build a bridge between me and my daughter. Make our ocean one.

SCENE 7: *Narration. Inside memory.*

Music: begins and continues under:

DAUGHTER: *(older)* You broke your promise. You never came. You let me leave you behind. I waited for you, father. For the family. A long time ago. Where are you? Are you here, with me? Did you follow on the shadow of the airplane's wings? *(voice begins to break)* Did I fly away like a kite in the breeze? So high up you can see the shape, but not the colours? Can you see me? I'm so far away but all you have to do is pull me home. Father. Father. When I finish building a bridge, will you cross it? Even if the stones are loose, and the twigs are breaking. Will you cross it? Father? *(beat) Bah-bah?* How big is the ocean?

Music ends. Sound effects: exterior: airfield. Plane's acceleration and ascent crosses into that of birds in flight, their wings in motion. Fade into ocean, water lapping on a beach. Up and out.

Betty Quan writes for radio, TV, and stage. She graduated from the University of British Columbia, and has served residences at The Canadian Film Centre Television Drama program and the Tarragon Theatre. In 1996 her play, *Mother Tongue*, was a finalist in the Governor General's Literary Award for Drama. She has written three plays, and her other work has appeared in the anthologies *Beyond the Pale* and *Taking the Stage*. This play aired on CBC's *Morningside* radio drama program.

1. ***Response***
   a. What is the message, spoken or unspoken, in this radio play? What makes you think so?
   b. How does Betty Quan use a folktale to tell her story?
   c. Use a graph or chart to show the changing emotion of the daughter. What clues to her emotions are there in the language she uses?

2. ***Making Connections*** Compare this play with "Christmas Consumer Frenzy" by Paul Moth. What is the purpose of each? Who is the audience? How are mood, theme, and message the same or different?

3. ***Drama*** *Perform a Radio Play* In a small group, prepare a presentation of this radio play, or one of Paul Moth's pieces. Consider how you will use your voice—volume, tone, pace, expression—to portray the emotion or humour of the piece you choose. Since no one sees the actors on radio, you don't have to memorize your lines, but can read them aloud. But you should be able to speak the lines smoothly and expressively. When you are ready, record your presentation on audio tape, using music and sound effects, as appropriate. Share your presentation with your class or a younger audience. Ask your audience for feedback on your performance and the production of the play.

4. ***Literature Studies*** *Mood* Discuss the mood of this piece, and how Quan achieves this mood. Compare her use of mood to other plays you have read or seen.

What is the most important aspect of mass media? What is their primary purpose? Read on to find out what one media critic thinks.

People as Products

Essay by Jean Kilbourne

MAKE NO MISTAKE: The primary purpose of the mass media is to sell audiences to advertisers. We are the product. Although people are much more sophisticated about advertising now than even a few years ago, most are still shocked to learn this.

Magazines, newspapers, and radio and television programs round us up, rather like cattle, and producers and publishers then sell us to advertisers, usually through ads placed in advertising and industry publications. "The people you want, we've got all wrapped up for you," declares the *Chicago Tribune* in an ad placed in *Advertising Age*, which pictures several people, all neatly boxed according to income level.

Although we like to think of advertising as unimportant, it is in fact the most important aspect of the mass media. It *is* the point. Advertising supports more than 60 percent of magazine and newspaper production and almost 100 percent of the electronic media. Over $40 billion a year in ad revenue is generated for television and radio, and over $30 billion for magazines and newspapers. As one *ABC* executive said, "The network is paying affiliates to carry network commercials, not programs. What we are is a distribution system for Procter & Gamble." And the CEO of *CBS* said, "We're here to serve advertisers. That's our *raison d'être*."

The media know that television and radio programs are simply fillers for the space between commercials. They know that the programs that succeed are the ones that deliver the highest number of people to the advertisers. But not just any people. Advertisers are interested in white people aged 18 to 49 who live in or near a city. *Dr. Quinn, Medicine Woman*, a program that was No. 1 in its time slot and immensely popular with older, more rural viewers, was canceled in 1998 because it couldn't command the higher advertising rates paid for younger, richer audiences.

This is not new: *The Daily Herald*, a British newspaper with 47 million readers, double the combined readership of the *Times*, *Financial Times*, *Guardian* and *Telegraph*, folded in the 1960s because its readers were mostly elderly and working class and had little appeal to advertisers.

The target audience that appeals to advertisers is becoming more narrow all the time. According to Dean Valentine, the head of Viacom's *UPN*, most networks have abandoned the middle class and want "very chic shows that talk to affluent, urban, unmarried, huge-disposable-income 18-to-34-year-olds because the theory is, from advertisers, that the earlier you get them, the sooner you imprint the brand name."

"Tripod Delivers Gen-X," proclaims a website/magazine's sinister ad, featuring a delivery man carrying a corpselike consumer wrapped from neck to toe in brown paper. Several other such "deliveries" are propped up in the truck. An ad for the newspaper *USA Today* offers the consumer's eye between a knife and a fork and says, "12 Million Served Daily." The ad explains, "Nearly six million influential readers with both eyes ingesting your message. Every day." There is no humanity, no individuality in this ad or others like it—people are simply products sold to advertisers, of value only as potential consumers.

Newspapers are more in the business of selling audiences than in the business of giving people news, especially as more and more newspapers are owned by fewer and fewer chains. They exist primarily to support local advertisers, such as car dealers, realtors and department store owners.

Once we begin to count, we see that magazines are essentially catalogs of goods, with less than half of their pages devoted to editorial content (and much of that in the service of the advertisers). An ad for a custom publishing company in *Advertising Age* promises, "The next hot magazine could be the one we create exclusively for your product."

> Millions of dollars' worth of advertising shows such little respect for the reader's intelligence that it amounts almost to outright insult.
>
> James Adams

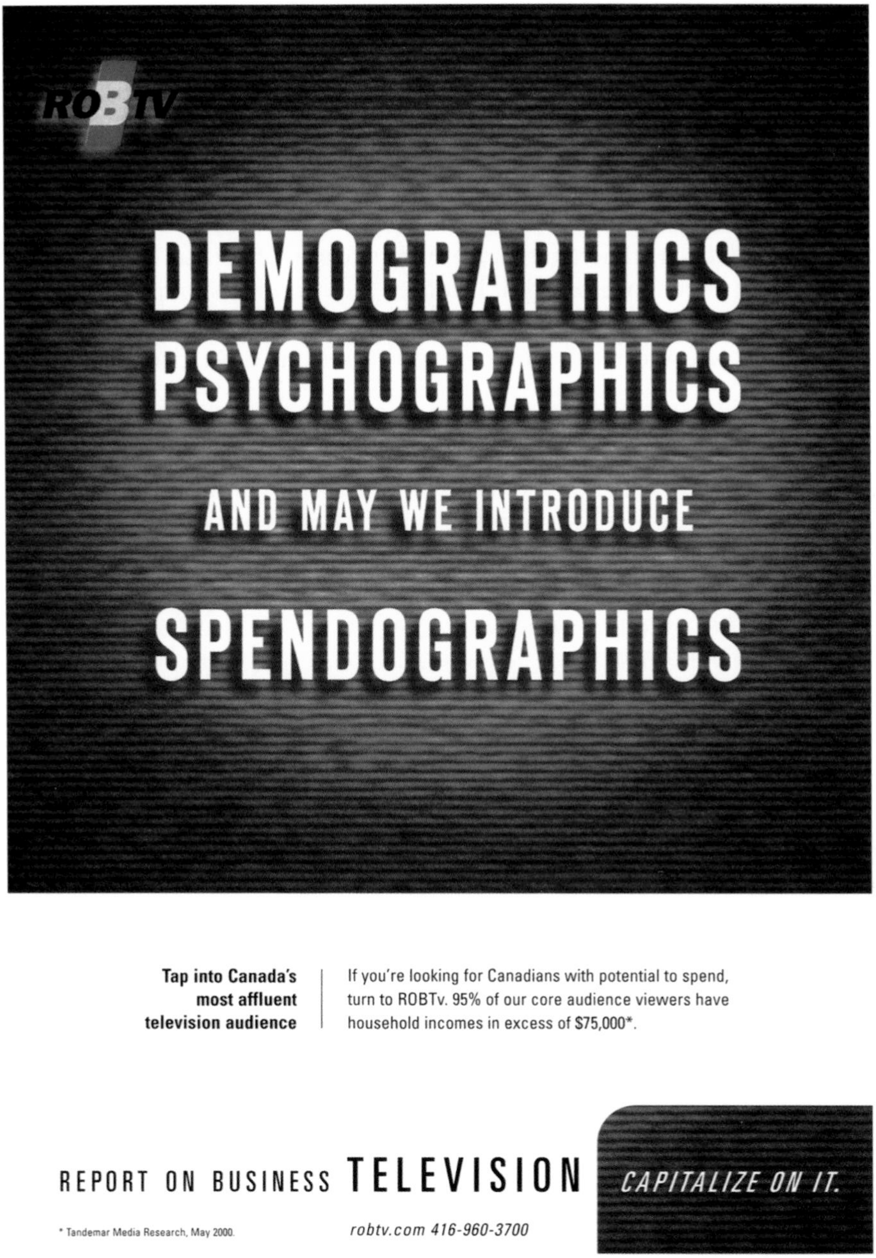

ROBTV

DEMOGRAPHICS
PSYCHOGRAPHICS

AND MAY WE INTRODUCE

SPENDOGRAPHICS

Tap into Canada's most affluent television audience

If you're looking for Canadians with potential to spend, turn to ROBTv. 95% of our core audience viewers have household incomes in excess of $75,000*.

REPORT ON BUSINESS **TELEVISION**

* Tandemar Media Research, May 2000.

robtv.com 416-960-3700

Examine this advertisement that appeared in an issue of *Marketing Magazine*, a magazine aimed at advertisers and marketers. Discuss the target market, purpose, and features of this ad, as well as its effectiveness.

And, in fact, there are magazines for everyone from dirt-bike riders to knitters to mercenary soldiers, from *Beer Connoisseur* to *Cigar Aficionado*. There are plenty of magazines for the wealthy, such as *Coastal Living*, "for people who live or vacation on the coast." *Barron's* advertises itself as a way to "reach faster cars, bigger houses and longer prenuptial agreements" and promises a readership with an average household net worth of over a million.

The Internet advertisers target the wealthy too, of course. Not surprisingly, there are no magazines or Internet sites or television programs for the poor. They might not be able to afford the magazines or computers, but, more importantly, they are of little use to advertisers.

Jean Kilbourne is a media critic, writer, lecturer, and expert on addictions, gender issues, and the media. She is internationally recognized for her pioneering work on the effects of alcohol and tobacco advertising, and for raising public awareness of how advertising encourages addictive behaviour. Kilbourne has made several documentaries based on her lectures, including *Killing Us Softly: Advertising's Image of Women*, and its sequel, *Still Killing Us Softly*. This selection is taken from her book *Deadly Persuasion: Why Women and Girls Must Fight the Addictive Power of Advertising*.

1. *Response*

a. Revisit the questions in the introductory paragraph of this article. How does Jean Kilbourne answer these questions? Do you agree with her? Why or why not?

b. Reread the second paragraph and identify the simile Kilbourne uses. Do you think it is an appropriate or effective comparison? Explain your answer.

c. What is the target audience for most advertisers identified in the article? Would you agree with the author that most advertisers are not interested in the poor or elderly? Explain.

d. Explain, in your own words, how the mass media "sell" us—the people who watch and listen to the media—to advertisers.

e. According to Kilbourne, advertisers only support TV and radio programs that attract a young, middle-class or upper middle-class audience. Do you think that this attitude affects the content of programs? Can you think of a TV show that depicts the lives of the poor or elderly?
f. How do you think someone in the advertising business would respond to the following assertion: "People are simply products sold to advertisers, of value only as potential consumers."

2. ***Media*** *Analysing Audiences* Choose one of the media mentioned in the article and examine several examples of it. Can you identify the audience that is targeted in the ads in each example? Do these examples support Kilbourne's argument? Explain.

   Kilbourne says that magazines are "essentially catalogs of goods" increasingly aimed at narrow audiences with highly specialized interests. Is this a bad thing? Visit a large magazine stand and note which interests and hobbies seem to have the most magazines. Note how many general interest magazines that would appeal to a very wide audience are still on the market.

3. ***Language Conventions*** *Comparatives and Superlatives* Advertising copy often uses comparatives or superlatives to make a product appear better than others. A cereal is not just good, it is great. A car is not just fast, it is the fastest. Look through a number of newspapers and magazines and consider the use of comparatives and superlatives in ads. What effect does this use have on the reader? Discuss how words sometimes seem to lose their meaning when you see them too often in ads or other media.

Advertise, or go under.
—Dorothy L Sayers

Consider the following statement from a magazine in the 1950s: "In very few instances do people really know what they want, even when they say they do."

—Advertising Age

Have things changed?

The *Trouble* With People

Essay by Vance Packard

Marketers always encountered difficulties in trying to persuade people to buy all the products their companies could fabricate.

One particularly disturbing difficulty was the apparent perversity and unpredictability of the prospective customers. Marketers repeatedly suffered grievous losses in campaigns that by all the rules of logic should have succeeded. The marketers felt increasing dissatisfaction with their conventional methods for sizing up a market. These methods were known in the trade most commonly as "nose-counting." Under nose-counting, statistic-minded interviewers would determine the percentage of married women, ages twenty-one to thirty-five, in Omaha, Nebraska, who said they wanted, and would buy a three-legged stove if it cost no more than $249.

The trouble with this approach, they found, was that what people might tell interviewers had only a remote bearing on how the people would actually behave in a buying situation when confronted with a three-legged stove or almost anything else.

Gradually, many perceptive marketers began becoming suspicious of three basic assumptions they had made, in their efforts to be logical, concerning the predictable behavior of human beings, especially customers.

First, they decided, you can't assume that people know what they want.

A major ketchup maker kept getting complaints about its bottle, so it made a survey. Most of the people interviewed said they would prefer another type the company was considering. When the company went to the expense of bringing out this other bottle in test markets, it was overwhelmingly rejected in favor of the old bottle, even by people who had favored it in interviews.

Second, some marketers concluded, you can't assume people will tell you the truth about their wants and dislikes even if they know them. What you are more likely to get, they decided, are answers that will protect the informants in their steadfast endeavor to appear to the world as really sensible, intelligent, rational beings. One management consulting firm has concluded that accepting the word of a customer as to what he wants is "the least reliable index the manufacturer can have on what he ought to do to win customers."

The Advertising Research Foundation took magazines to task for asking people what magazines they read frequently, and naïvely accepting the answers given as valid. The people, it contended, are likely to admit reading only magazines of high prestige value. One investigator suggests that if you seriously accepted people's answers you might assume that *Atlantic Monthly* is America's most-read magazine and some of the confession magazines the least read; whereas actually the confession magazines in question may have twenty times the readership of *Atlantic Monthly*.

A brewery making two kinds of beer made a survey to find what kind of people drank each beer, as a guide to its merchandisers. It asked people known to favor its general brand name: "Do you drink the light or the regular?" To its astonishment it found people reporting they drank light over the regular by better than three to one. The truth of the matter was that for years the company, to meet consumer demand, had been brewing nine times as much regular beer as light beer. It decided that in asking people that question it was in effect asking: Do you drink the kind preferred by people of refinement and discriminating taste, or do you just drink the regular stuff?

In another case the Color Research Institute asked a group of people if they borrowed money from personal-loan companies. Every person said no. Some of them virtually shouted their answer. The truth was that all those selected for interviewing were people who were listed in the records of a local loan company as borrowers.

Finally, the marketers decided it is dangerous to assume that people can be trusted to behave in a rational way.

A department store that had become skeptical of the rationality of its customers tried an experiment. One of its slowest-moving items was priced at fourteen cents. It changed the price to two for twenty-nine cents. Sales promptly increased 30 per cent when the item was offered at this "bargain" price.

Our toothbrushing habits offer a prime example of behavior that is at least seemingly irrational. If you ask people why they brush their teeth, most of them will tell you that their main purpose in doing so is to get particles of food out of the crevices of their teeth and thus combat decay germs. Toothpaste producers accepted this explanation for many years and based their sales campaigns on it. Advertising men who made a study of our toothbrushing habits, however, came upon a puzzle. They found that most people brushed their teeth once a day, and at the most pointless moment possible in the entire twenty-four-hour day, from the dental hygiene standpoint. That was in the morning just before breakfast, after decay germs had had a whole night to work on their teeth from particles left from supper—and just before the consumption of breakfast would bring in a new host of bacteria.

One advertising agency puzzling over this seemingly irrational behavior made a more thorough study of the reasons why we brush our teeth. It concluded that we are motivated by differing reasons, based on our personality. Some people, particularly hypochondriacs, are really concerned about those germs and are swayed by a "decay" appeal. (The hammering in recent years on all the wondrous anti-decay pastes has swollen the size of this group.) Another group, mostly extroverts, brush their teeth in the hope they will be bright and shiny. The majority of people, however, brush their teeth primarily for a reason that has little to do with dental hygiene or even their teeth. They put the brush and paste into their mouth in order to give their mouth a thorough purging, to get rid of the bad taste that has accumulated overnight. In short, they are looking for a taste sensation, as a part of their ritual of starting the day afresh. At least two of the major paste merchandisers began hitting hard at this appeal in 1955 and 1956. One promised a "clean mouth taste" and the other proclaimed that its paste "cleans your breath while it guards your teeth." (More recently one of these products got itself a new ad agency, as often happens, and the new mentor began appealing to the extrovert in us through the slogan, "You'll wonder where the yellow went—." Good results are reported, which simply proves there is always more than one way to catch a customer.)

Business Week, in commenting on the often seemingly irrational behavior of consumers, said: "People don't seem to be reasonable." However, it made this further point: "But people do act with purpose. Their behavior makes sense if you think about it in terms of its goals, of people's needs and their motives. That seems to be the secret of understanding or manipulating people."

Another aspect of people's behavior that has troubled marketers is that they are too easily satisfied with what they already have. Most of the marketers' factories have ever-larger warehouses full of goods to move.

By the mid-fifties American goods producers were achieving a fabulous output, and the output with automation promised to keep getting more fabulous. Since 1940, gross national product had soared more than 400 per cent; and man-hour productivity was doubling about every quarter century.

One way of viewing this rich, full life the people were achieving was the glowing one that everyone could enjoy an ever-higher standard of living. That view was thoroughly publicized. But there was another way of viewing it: that we must consume more and more, whether we want to or not, for the good of our economy.

In late 1955 the church publication *Christianity and Crisis* commented grimly on America's "ever-expanding economy." It observed that the pressure was on Americans to "consume, consume and consume, whether we need or even desire the products almost forced upon us." It added that the dynamics of an ever-expanding system require that we be "persuaded to consume to meet the needs of the productive process."

With growing productivity and prosperity the average American had five times as many discretionary dollars as he had in 1940. (These are dollars we have after we take care of our basic, immediate needs.) But discretionary dollars are also deferrable dollars—we can defer spending them if we are satisfied with what we already have. This hazard posed by so many optional dollars in our pockets was summed up quite eloquently in the October 24, 1955, issue of *Advertising Age* by an executive of the publishing firm of McGraw-Hill. He stated:

> As a nation we are already so rich that consumers are under no pressure of immediate necessity to buy a very large share—perhaps as much as 40%—of what is produced, and the pressure will get progressively less in the years ahead. But if consumers exercise their option not to buy a large share of what is produced, a great depression is not far behind.

In the early fifties, with overproduction threatening on many fronts, a fundamental shift occurred in the preoccupation of people in executive suites. Production now became a relatively secondary concern.

Executive planners changed from being maker-minded to market-minded. The president of the National Sales Executives in fact exclaimed: "Capitalism is dead—consumerism is king!"

There was talk at management conventions of "the marketing revolution" and considerable pondering on how best to "stimulate" consumer buying, by creating wants in people that they still didn't realize existed. An auto maker talked of increasing his car sales by selling to "those who do not yet know what they need."

This urgently felt need to "stimulate" people brought new power, glory, and prosperity to the professional stimulators or persuaders of American industry, particularly the skilled gray-flanneled suiters of New York's Madison Avenue, known as "ad alley." In 1955, $9,000,000,000 was poured into United States advertising, up a billion from 1954 and up three billion from 1950. For each man, woman, and child in America in 1955 roughly $53 was spent to persuade him or her to buy products of industry. Some cosmetics firms began spending a fourth of all their income from sales on advertising and promotion. A cosmetics tycoon, probably mythical, was quoted as saying: "We don't sell lipstick, we buy customers."

One big and intimidating obstacle confronting the stimulators was the fact that most Americans already possessed perfectly usable stoves, cars, TV sets, clothes, etc. Waiting for those products to wear out or become physically obsolete before urging replacements upon the owner was intolerable. More and more, ad men began talking of the desirability of creating "psychological obsolescence."

At a conference of gas-range people the conferees were exhorted to emulate the more up-to-date car makers in this business of creating psychological obsolescence. They were reminded that auto merchandisers strive to make everyone ashamed to drive a car more than two or three years. The gas-range people were told bluntly by the director of American Color Trends: "Ladies and gentlemen, you know and I know that too many housekeepers have the attitude that 'any old piece of equipment will do so long as it works at all.'" He described the recent trend to change the color of many products and explained: "All of these trends have a definite bearing on what you can do to step up the obsolescence of gas appliances."

By the mid-fifties merchandisers of many different products were being urged by psychological counselors to become "merchants of discontent." One ad executive exclaimed with fervor: "What makes this country great is the creation of wants and desires, the creation of dissatisfaction with the old and outmoded."

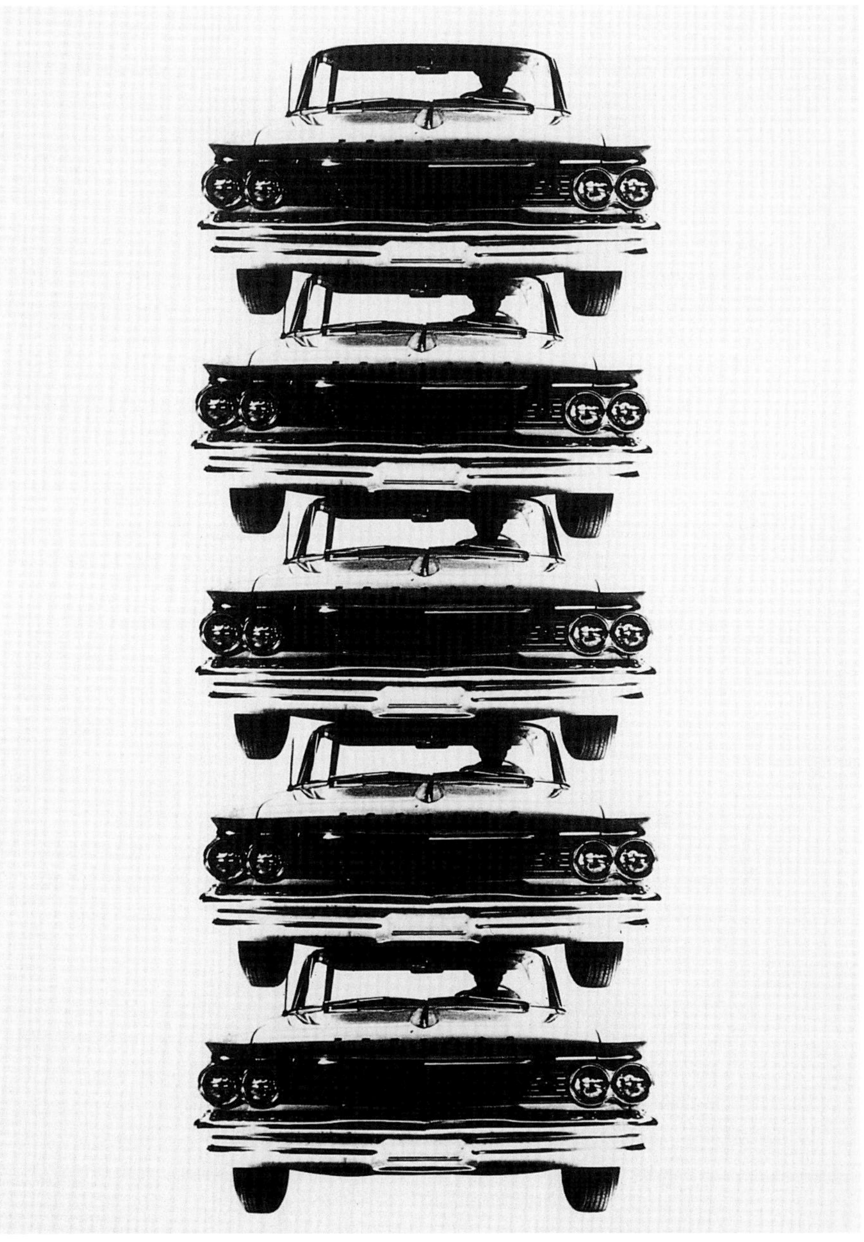

5 Autos Stacked on Top of Each Other. Photo by Alfred Gescheidt.

Write a short essay explaining how the above photo represents the society or marketing attitudes described in this essay. Alternatively, search for another photo that you think represents this society, or your own society.

Vance Oakley Packard was born in Granville Summit, Pennsylvania, in 1914. He was a U.S. non-fiction writer of popular sociological tracts, including *The Hidden Persuaders* and *The Status Seekers*. He died in 1996.

1. ***Response***
   a. List the three basic assumptions marketers were making about people, according to this essay. For each assumption, list one piece of evidence that proved to marketers that these assumptions were false.
   b. Explain the phrases *merchants of discontent* and *psychological obsolescence*. List any other marketing or media terms found in the essay. Include a definition for each term.
   c. This essay was first published in 1957. Discuss how it represents that era. Is this essay still relevant? Do you think media literacy courses in school have created wiser consumers? Explain your answer.
   d. Discuss some of the techniques that advertisers used, or still use, to reach their customers.
   e. What effect does the gender-biassed language in this essay have on the reader? Why are words like *ad men* no longer appropriate?

2. ***Making Connections*** Discuss the argument that both Kilbourne and Packard present in their essays. What stance does each writer take toward the advertising media? What would they have to say to one another about consumers or consumerism?

3. ***Media*** *Reaching Consumers* Find examples of ads—in print, or on TV, radio, or the Internet—that use any of the methods for reaching consumers discussed in this essay. Choose one ad to present to your class, commenting on the techniques it uses, the messages it sends, and its effectiveness.

   Is there a product that you think consumers are eagerly awaiting? Develop an ad for this new product. Choose one of the techniques mentioned in any of the advertising or marketing articles you have read so far.

Advertising is the key to world prosperity;
without it today modern business would be paralysed.
—*Julius Klein*

In the following selection, two young boys discuss the difference in their lives now that they are Canadian; it is 1949, and their province, Newfoundland and Labrador, has just joined Confederation.

All Part of Becoming Canadian

Autobiographical anecdote by Al Pittman from the essay "The Day I Became a Canadian"

"Listen Johnny," I said as soon as I got the chance, "you know what this means, now that we're living in Canada?"

"Of course I do," replied Johnny. But he didn't so I told him.

"It means all kinds of things. It means maybe now we'll be able to wear those U.S. Keds sneakers that they wear in the comics, instead of these old gum boots."

"How come?"

"Because Canada is a big place, my son. Bigger than the States even. My father said so."

"So?"

"So, if Canada is as big as the States, then it must have all that stuff in it."

"What stuff?"

"You know. The stuff in comics. Like where you can join a club and get all kinds of free prizes like spy glasses and roller skates and model airplanes and Double Bubble Gum."

"So what? My mother won't let me chew bubblegum. She says it's rude to blow bubbles, and it causes germs."

"Still, I bet you'd sneak a chew if it could make you fly."

"What do you mean, fly?"

"You know, like the kid in the comics. The one who blows big bubbles and flies all over the place. If you could blow a bubble big enough you could go right over your house, over the school even. If it was Double Bubble Gum you could."

"Go on! That's just comic book stuff."

"No. It's real. Cross my heart and hope to die. They really have things like that in places like the States and Canada. And now that we live in Canada, we'll have them too. Just imagine, being able to fly!"

Johnny was a real skeptic and refused to believe a word of it. But back then, when it all began, when I was nine, I, for one, firmly believed in Double Bubble Gum ads. The comic books had convinced me that if we could get Double Bubble Gum, then I could fly like the boy in the advertisements and float, borne up by the biggest bubble imaginable, over buildings and hills. And I could catch bank robbers if there were any around to catch, and I'd be a hero then to everyone who knew me. As far as I was concerned, it was all part of becoming Canadian.

Al Pittman was born in Placentia Bay, Newfoundland and Labrador, in 1940. He is a publisher, teacher, and editor and has written short stories, essays, plays, poetry, and children's stories. Some of his books include *Once When I Was Drowning* and *One Wonderful Fine Day for a Sculpin Named Sam.*

1. ***Response***
   a. How would you describe the tone of this article? Explain your reasoning.
   b. In your opinion, is the narrator unusually naïve for a boy his age? Explain.
   c. Have you, or anyone you know, ever had a similar experience to young Al Pittman's? Describe what happened and how you (or the other person) felt.

2. ***Media*** *Selling to Children* Investigate the rules that control various media and advertisements that are directed toward children. Do you think the existing rules are sufficient to protect children from being fooled by advertisers? Explain.
   Watch a children's program on TV, or examine a magazine designed for children, and analyse any ads you see. What conclusions can you draw about these ads?

3. ***Making Connections*** Choose one of the following activities:
   With a small group, improvise a discussion between the two boys in this selection, and the two adults in "The Sea-Monkey Lady" interview, which follows.
   Write another paragraph for the Vance Packard essay, "The Trouble with People," that uses this selection as an example to expand on, support, or disprove one of his points.

Be careful what you order from the back of comic books—your whole life could be affected, as Susan Barclay reveals in this radio interview with Arthur Black. Barclay is the author of the book The Ultimate Guide to Sea-Monkeys.

The Sea-Monkey Lady: Susan Barclay

Radio interview
by Arthur Black

ARTHUR: Susan Barclay of Chilliwack, British Columbia, is known as the Sea-Monkey Lady. She happens to be with me right now. Hi Susan.

SUSAN: Hi.

ARTHUR: Sea-monkeys, now these are the things that were on the back of the comic books, along with the X-ray spectacles and the Charles Atlas body-building programs.

SUSAN: Yep. Those are the same ones.

ARTHUR: I didn't know they were still even around.

SUSAN: They've been around for forty years now. Most people don't know they're still around.

ARTHUR: How did they start out? Do you know?

SUSAN: Back in the fifties, Harold Von Braunhut, who created these little guys, decided to tinker around with the genetics of different crustaceans, and came up with these ones.

ARTHUR: So, these are kind of a manipulated breed. You don't find these out in the ocean, right?

SUSAN: No. The actual name is *Artemia Salina*. That's the name for a regular brine shrimp.

ARTHUR: Brine shrimp. OK ...

Susan: … Yes. And these are called, because they're a genetically modified hybrid, they call these *Artemia Nyos,* N-Y-O-S, for New York Oceanic, I can't remember the S … *(laughs)*

Arthur: That's OK. *(laughs)* You could have faked it. I wouldn't know.

Susan: I *should* have made something up.

Arthur: So, uh, how do they go with pasta? No that's not funny, that's not funny, eh?

Susan: Oh, that's mean. *(laughs)*

Arthur: No, they're tiny. But you know, there's something missing here, Susan. 'Cause the ones that I saw on the back of the comic books, they all had little tiaras, and they carried a sceptre. These guys seem to be quite naked.

Susan: Well, if you look *real* close. No, I'm kidding. Unfortunately, if you look at the box it does say, "illustration is fanciful." Because I'm sure, I remember when I was six, I was convinced I was going to have a kingdom of my own. *(Arthur's voice over hers: Yeah, Yeah!)* But unfortunately, no, they look like … brine shrimp.

Arthur: Are these guys full grown? 'Cause these aren't even as big as the tip of my finger.

Susan: Um. Most of them are. Most of them in this tank are full grown. They get to about three quarters of an inch at the very most. And that's partially to do with the genetic modification, and that's also because they're brine shrimp and they're small.

Arthur: Yeah, they're small all right. Space is not a problem here. *(Susan laughs)* I've got, I guess you could call it a tank, and there's at least thirty of the guys in there. And the tank isn't much bigger than a … sort of like half a beer stein.

Susan: *(laughs)* It's twelve ounces, about the same as a Coke can. *(Arthur speaking over Susan: Yeah?)* It's not a lot. But if you look *very, very* closely you can see some of the *little* babies around there. It looks like, as you said, about thirty, but if you look *very* closely there's probably another twenty babies, and there's a few pregnant in there, so we're looking at …

Arthur: You can tell they're pregnant?

Susan: Yeah …

Arthur: … Wow! …

Susan: … You can actually tell male from female, you can tell when they're pregnant, and when they're not. They're … *(Arthur, over Susan:*

Holy smokes) … they're actually quite complicated little creatures for being such a … a small crustacean …

Arthur: *(speaking over Susan's last words)* A tiny thing. Yeah. They just look like a little eyelash. There's not much to them. Do you consider yourself the Jane Goodall of sea-monkeys?

Susan: *(Susan laughs)* That's an excellent question. Actually, I do know a man who's an expert who's called Jacques Goodall. So, I would have to say I'm more of the … the woman who used to … *Gorillas in the Mist*, Diane Fossey. *(Arthur over Susan: Yeah. Yeah, OK.)* Whereas Jane Goodall kept a hands-off approach, I prefer to get right in the sea-monkey …

Arthur: … You're real folksy with it. *(Susan over Arthur: Yeah. Yeah.)* I can see that. In fact, you have carrying arrangements I seem to see here. *(Susan over Arthur: Yes!)* In fact, you've got sea-monkeys on your wrist! What's that about?

Susan: I do! It's the sea-monkey watch! And it's an aquarium that not only tells the time, which is useful for getting to appointments, but you can pop the top off and pop a few of your favourite sea-monkeys in and take them around with you.

Arthur: Well, don't they get shaken up a lot?

Susan: They do, but sea-monkeys can handle it. Same concept as, they say you could drop an *ant* from the Empire State Building, *(Arthur over Susan: Uhn-hunh.)* and it wouldn't get hurt. Same thing with sea-monkeys, with their exoskeleton they're very strong, they haven't got, you know, the flesh to get hurt.

Arthur: So maybe it's like a roller coaster for them, I guess.

Susan: They really like the ride. *(Arthur over Susan: Yeah.)* So when I'm bringing the sea-monkeys down for a hundred kilometre drive today they quite enjoyed … I actually heard them going "Wheeee!" at one point. *(Susan laughs)*

Arthur: I was going to say … I thought I heard a little singing …

Susan: Well, they do sing. You know one of the things …

Arthur: They don't really, do they?

Susan: *(Susan laughs)* No! *(Arthur laughs)* One of the things I warn people … I have a list of do's and don't's with sea-monkeys, and sometimes people write to me and say "Is this true?" 'cause one of them is don't let them mow your lawn as they're allergic to freshly cut grass. *(Arthur over Susan: Oh?)* And people are always saying "Is this true?" They're three quarters of an inch long. I don't think they should be cutting grass in the first place; that's just animal cruelty. *(Arthur laughs)* And I say, don't lie to them, because they don't like being lied to any more than people do.

ARTHUR: Susan, do you spend a lot of time alone?

SUSAN: Yeah. A little too much. *(Both laugh)* With tanks and tanks of sea-monkeys around the room.

ARTHUR: I've been looking at these guys closely, trying to figure out how they *breathe.*

SUSAN: They breathe through their legs.

ARTHUR: Ah. I should have guessed.

SUSAN: I told you they were *fascinating.* They have little tubes that go through their legs.

ARTHUR: Yeah.

SUSAN: And they breathe in that fashion. Which is why they don't wear shoes. So, it's …

ARTHUR: Well, I can't even see legs, never mind … shoes.

SUSAN: They're *little* tiny legs. If you look very closely …

ARTHUR: Now how the heck would you know that?

SUSAN: That they breathe through their legs?

ARTHUR: Yeah.

SUSAN: 'Cause someone told me.

ARTHUR: *(laughs)* That's the best way to learn.

SUSAN: I'm not a marine biologist, although I do play one on TV.

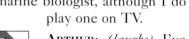

ARTHUR: *(laughs)* I've always regretted that I never—I guess I didn't believe that there were kings and queens brine shrimp—but if I was going to get into this, what, I get a starter sea-monkey kit? What happens then?

An ad circa 1957

Compare these images with current packages or ads for similar products.

A package circa 1962

Susan: Yeah. There's a number of different kits. But the basic sea-monkey kit is about $10. It's not a lot of money, I mean, in it you get three packages, you get the water purifier, where, just like goldfish, you have to prepare the water, you get the package of eggs, and you get yourself a package of food. And the tank. And that's all you need to start with. And then there are accessories that go with it, but …

Arthur: Yeah.

Susan: And you put the water in, put the water purifier in, and 24 to 36 hours, put the eggs in, and you have instant life.

Arthur: This is beginning to sound like the shopping channel.

Susan: *(laughs)* You know … well I have to admit, having explained this before, I've learned to make it quick for people.

Arthur: So. Can I use dog kibble? What do you feed them?

Susan: *(laughs)* Please don't. People have asked if they can put bananas in too. Don't put … anything you wouldn't stick in your ear, don't put in the tank. Basically, they live on algae and diatoms …

Arthur: Those are the little tiny tiny things …

Susan: Yes. You get the sea-monkey package food, which, everyone says, "Well, what if I run out?" It's so little the amount you use, I mean they're just little tiny creatures.

Arthur: Yeah.

Susan: You put a little scoop in and they'll feed themselves for weeks with it.

Arthur: Can you teach them to do tricks?

Susan: You can!

Arthur: No?!

Susan: You can, honestly. One of the things that sea-monkeys have is they're photo-reactive. So, just in the same way that a plant will turn to the light, sea-monkeys will react to light as well. So, if you turn the lights off, in your room, or wherever you have them, get your flashlight out, say you take the flashlight from one side of the tank to the other, they'll follow it.

Arthur: Really?

Susan: So if you do it in spirals, they look like they're spiralling …

Arthur: … No kidding?

Susan: And one of the tanks I've brought with me has a lighted cover on the top and what you can do is put that on. And if you leave that light on you'll see them all … gravitate to it … if it's in a dark room, they'll all gravitate eventually. And the ghostly galleon, which is another one of the tanks, comes with a glow-in-the-dark little ship. And if you put that in, eventually you'll see just that they're spending a little bit more time around this glow-in-the-dark …

Arthur: This already sounds like way more fun than the Internet.

Susan: Yeah. *(laughs)* I *enjoy* them. It's funny, 'cause people can't understand how brine shrimp could be so much fun, but in the same way that having goldfish is fun, these are great, *and* they have a lot of *kitsch* value to them, because everyone remembers them from when we were kids. So …

Arthur: *(speaking over Susan's last word)* Yeah, yeah, of course. Now listen, Susan, if I get attached to these guys, how long is it going to be before they leave me?

Susan: They say two years now. *(Arthur speaking over Susan: Yeah?)* And the only reason I haven't been able to prove that is because this new formulation has only been out for a little over a year. But this tank that's before you right now was started last February. And they're all doing great, they're doing fine, and they keep having … there's eggs and babies.

Arthur: Well, that's a problem. I can see an overpopulation, if I didn't want a whole bunch could I get them neutered?

Susan: OH! Please no! But you could in *theory*, you know, just take all the females out, and you wouldn't have any more babies. But that would be boring. And they tend to … once you see a couple of sea-monkeys mating, odds are they will stay like that … for … the rest of their natural lifetimes. They like to mate.

Arthur: They'll stay mating?

Susan: Yes. Well, they'll at least stay attached. The male has whiskers that come out of his chin, *(Arthur: AH!)* and what he does is he clings on to the woman, the female, and doesn't let go. And so they will stay …

Arthur: Is this like a really bad date?

Susan: *(laughs)* Yes. I always say, you know that's the one thing with sea-monkeys: you should set up a singles tank for them, and serve banana daiquiris, and keep them away, because they will mate like *silly!*

Arthur: Listen, there's something else unusual on the table here. This looks like one of those snow globes. What's that? There's a *castle* in the middle of it.

Susan: It's the sea-monkey magic castle and it's brand new. They've decided to soup some of the things up, instead of having the boring old little tank. And this thing rocks. It's the magic castle …

ARTHUR: The globe itself is maybe four or five inches high, and the castle is maybe two and a half inches high in the middle and it's got little crenellations around the top and spires and towers.

SUSAN: And there's little sea life on it. That has got to be the coolest tank they have. It's like a snow globe, and you can shake it up, not obviously too vigorously, but you can shake it up. And I actually had a friend at work, Wanda, who has the tank in her office. And she can't count how many times people have come in and said "Cool!" and started shaking … and you know there's water everywhere. So you have to be careful with them. But this is one of the new tanks that they've come up with. They're just fantastic.

ARTHUR: The other problem that occurs to me, is what if these accidentally get flushed down the toilet? Are we going to have killer brine shrimp …

SUSAN: Mutant sea-monkeys? *(laughing)*

ARTHUR: Yeah, running around in the sewers?

SUSAN: You must have read the weekly World News report from a few years ago. *(Arthur laughs)* There was an article in the weekly *World News* and it said "Killer Mutant Sea-monkeys Attack Swimmers off Florida Coast."

ARTHUR: I knew it. I knew it. You know, Susan, I don't think we have to interview anyone else. *(Susan laughs)* We'll just call you in once a week. You are like every *Basic Black* guest I've ever had, all in one.

SUSAN: I'm in here. Just tell me when to come and I'll be here. And the sea-monkeys love the ride so they enjoyed themselves. Although it seems like a very *strange* hobby to have—sea-monkeys—people get such a laugh out of it …

ARTHUR: Well, they're totally unthreatening. You couldn't possibly find anything sinister about them, could you?

SUSAN: But you'd be surprised, some people, I mean I get people asking me all the time, horrible, horrible ways to eat them. "My Granpa drank them. Are they poisonous?" And …

ARTHUR: … Somebody drank them?

SUSAN: Yeah. You know, I was asking my mom about this. "How would you accidentally drink sea-monkeys?" Mom said, "Well, if they put them in a cup." I said, "But don't you look at what you're about to drink? If you saw something moving …"

Arthur: So you never drank a sea-monkey?

Susan: No, well … OK, I have to confess.

Arthur: *(laughs)* You had a guilty look about you.

Susan: This is such an embarrassing story, because I'm encouraging people not to drink them. When I was in England, I had them in a Coke-type bottle with a cap on it so I could carry them around. 'Cause the tank does have two holes in the side for air, so I was scared they would tip out. And on the second-to-last day, I'd been doing so much travelling and having so much fun I wasn't sleeping much. And I woke up to take a swig of water, popped the top open and took this giant swig of sea-monkey water and I was about to drink it and I went "Whooooh" and I spat it everywhere. And then I just felt, after washing my mouth out, oh my … And I drank probably a good inch of the water before I'd realised it.

Arthur: So Susan, how were they?

Susan: Horrible! *(both laugh)* You know, it's not just the sea-monkeys, it's the *algae*. It's a lot of things people should *not* be eating.

Arthur: Do not put this in your mouth.

Susan: No, no!

Arthur: Good advice. Thanks for coming in, Susan, with your friends. Your dozens and dozens of friends.

Susan: Thank you very much.

Arthur: OK.

Susan: It's been a real pleasure.

Arthur: For me too. Susan Barclay of Chilliwack, B.C. She is the Sea-Monkey Lady. If anybody could possibly doubt that.

Music: "Under the Sea" instrumental music.

Arthur Black was born in Toronto in 1943. He has hosted the weekly national radio show, *Basic Black*, since 1983, and has written a series of books including *Black in the Saddle Again* and *Black by Popular Demand*. He has won many awards, including a 1977 George Cadogan Award for best weekly columnist; the 1986 National Radio Award for Best Opinion/Commentary; and the Stephen Leacock Medal for Humour in both 1997 and 1999.

1. ***Response***
   a. Have you ever ordered anything from the back of a comic book or magazine? If so, describe your experience, and how you felt.
   b. List the idioms and slang used in this interview, for example, *soup* or *rocks*. Define each item on your list, according to the context in which it is used. Why is this usage appropriate or effective in this context?

2. ***Oral Language*** *Discussion* Arthur Black and Susan Barclay raise several interesting media topics or issues—for example, the "souping" up of the tank as a snow globe or the false advertising of sea-monkeys with accessories like the tiaras or sceptre. Discuss these issues.

3. ***Media*** *Promotions* Susan Barclay appeared on *Basic Black* partly to promote her book *The Ultimate Guide to Sea-Monkeys*. Discuss what you know about the process of generating publicity for a book or other product or service. What else will authors or publishers do to raise public interest in a book? Who might be involved in a publicity campaign?

4. ***Language Conventions*** *Revising* As you read this script you probably noticed a lot of dashes, commas, and ellipses were used throughout. These often indicated a faltering or pause in the speech as the speakers responded spontaneously to each other in a live broadcast. Compare this to the two previous radio scripts in this unit—which were scripted and delivered smoothly—"Christmas Consumer Frenzy" and "One Ocean." Which of these scripts is the most realistic, representing everyday speech? How does the dialogue in "Sea-Monkey Lady" compare to dialogue you hear on other media—for example, TV shows, TV news, or movies?
   Choose one of the following tasks:
   Revise one of the scripts, removing any faltering speech, to make it read smoothly.
   Revise one of the scripts to make it seem more natural, like a conversation you might have at school or home.

The marketing department of any company needs to know how to use the media to generate publicity. The following article is a practical guide to publicity.

NO NEWS IS BAD NEWS

Using Publicity to Your Advantage

How-to article by Alexander Hiam
from *Marketing for Dummies®*

Publicity is coverage of your product or business in the editorial portion of any news medium. If, for example, *Consumer Reports* runs an article praising your product as best in a category, that's publicity. Good publicity. If, in contrast, the evening television news programs run a story saying that your product is suspected of causing numerous accidents, that's publicity, too. Bad publicity.

These two examples illustrate common reasons for journalists to cover a product as a story—either because the product is better or worse than expected. In both cases, *product quality is the key to publicity*. Keep this fact in mind.

The best way to initiate positive publicity is to design and make a truly superior product. The best way to generate negative publicity is to make something bad. So the quality of your product development and production/delivery processes is an important factor in your use of publicity. Good publicity starts with a pursuit of quality throughout your firm's management processes!

Here's a simple rule: When your organization and products are not getting covered at all, that's your fault as a marketer.

Marketers need to be proactive and generate some positive publicity. But when your product is getting bad coverage in the press, that's generally management's fault. Of course, you still have to take the rap and cope with the negative exposure, but because the problem most likely originates with management errors, you should involve senior management right away.

Public relations (PR) is the active pursuit of publicity for marketing purposes. PR is what you do to generate good publicity and try to minimize bad publicity. Generally, marketers are responsible for generating good publicity. If they create good stories and communicate them to the media effectively, the stories will be picked up and turned into news or entertainment content. Good publicity.

Marketers or general managers also wear the PR hat in smaller organizations, but large companies generally have a PR person or department whose sole job is to generate positive publicity. Also, many businesses hire *publicists* or *PR firms*—experts who do PR on a freelance or consulting basis.

There is also such a thing as *bad publicity*. Any negative news needs to be countered and the root causes eliminated if at all possible. Handling bad publicity is also an important marketing issue.

Marketers don't go looking for bad publicity. Bad publicity is usually the result of poor overall management (which produces bad financial results or poor quality products), or it is the result of specific management errors (like approving an unsafe design in order to get a product out quickly). And sometimes bad publicity is the result of plain bad luck—in which case, you'll need to present an honest, concerned face to the media until the storm blows over.

When something goes really wrong and the media are having a field day reporting it, then you have a *PR crisis*. The first step in solving a PR crisis is to get a top executive alone in a room and force him or her to tell you what really happened; once the media starts digging, the truth will eventually come out anyway. The next step is to try to get the executive to agree to come clean with the media by making a truthful statement about what went wrong and how the company plans to try and fix the problem. If you can't get management to do so, forget it. You won't be able to stem the tide of negative PR. The crisis will keep growing. In that case, your best fallback is to polish your resume and find a better job. (Only kidding!)

Crisis management is a gloomy topic, and hopefully you won't ever have to do it. In contrast, generating positive PR should be a daily or at least weekly marketing activity. The following sections show you how to do so.

How do I sniff out good stories?

To a journalist, a *good story* is anything that has enough public interest to attract readers, viewers, or listeners and hold their attention. More specifically, a good story for a journalist covering the plastics industry must be sufficient to hold the interest of people in that industry. And I'm sorry to say that most of what you want to communicate to your market is pretty far from a good story.

Journalists and editors do *not* want stories about

- Your new product or service and how it differs from competitors or your previous models (unless that's their coverage specialty)
- Why you or your company's senior executive think your products are really great
- Your version of an *old story*—one that they've covered in the same way before
- Anything that seems boring or self-serving to anyone who doesn't work for your firm

Yet those are the kinds of stories reporters often get, because the people handling PR generally aren't skilled journalists, and aren't even trying to *think like* skilled journalists. That's what you must do. You have to sniff out a story, put together sufficient information to back up the story, and script a version that is virtually ready to be run in your target media. To be good at generating positive publicity, all you have to do is ...

... think like a journalist!

What's the hook?

If you don't know how to think like a journalist, here's a simple exercise to help you get the idea. Scan today's newspaper (whichever one you like to read) and rank the top five stories based on their interest to you. Now analyze each one in turn to identify the one thing that made that story interesting enough to hold your attention. The *hooks*, the things that made each story interesting to you, will differ. But each story will have hooks. And even though they differ, these hooks have certain elements in common:

> A good ad should be like a good sermon: It must not only comfort the afflicted—it must also afflict the comfortable.
>
> Bernice Fitz-Gibbon

- Hooks are often based on new information (information you didn't know or weren't sure of).
- Hooks make that new information relevant to your activities or interests.
- Hooks catch your attention, often by surprising you with some thing you hadn't expected.
- Hooks promise some benefit to you—although the benefit may be indirect—by helping you understand your world better, avoid something undesirable, or simply enjoy yourself as you read the paper.

If you performed the preceding exercise, I think you could write the next paragraph as well as I can:

The logical conclusion is that you need to design hooks to make your marketing message into appealing stories for journalists to use. And your hooks need to be just like the ones that attracted your attention to those newspaper stories, with one exception: They must, somehow, be tied to your marketing information. At least a thin line has to exist from the hook to your brand identity, the news that you've just introduced a new product, or whatever else you want the public to know. That way, when journalists use your hook in their own work, they will end up including some of your marketing information in their stories as an almost accidental side effect.

Journalists don't want to help you communicate with your target market. They couldn't care less about your target market. But journalists are happy to use any good stories that you're willing to write for them, and if your product gets mentioned or your marketing manager gets quoted as a result, that's not a problem. So the secret, the key, the essence, of good publicity is to develop stories with effective hooks and give them away to overworked journalists who are eager for a little help from volunteers like you.

How do I communicate a story to the media?

When teaching PR most people start here—with the form, not the content. In my experience, content is 90 percent of the battle, form 10 percent, so I've reversed the traditional emphasis. But form does matter, too. You need to put your story into an appropriate and professional format so that journalists know what the story is and find it easy to work with.

The most important and basic format for communicating a story is the *press release* or *news release*, a short, written document with a clear headline at the top, sufficient facts and quotes to support a short news story, brief supporting background on the company/product involved, a date, and contact information for journalists who want to follow up with a phone call to get more information or to arrange an interview.

Yes, I know that's a lengthy definition, much longer than the ones in the textbooks on public relations. But when I define press release that way, I don't have to tell you much more about it for you to be able to write one yourself. Just make sure that you include all the elements that are in the definition—and that you have good content, a hook, to start with—and you will write an effective press release.

Figure 1 includes all the essential elements of format and style. You can use the release shown in the figure as a template for your own press releases.

March 31, 1997

FOR IMMEDIATE RELEASE

For more information, contact:
Alexander Hiam (413) 253-3658

CRAZY AUTHOR WRITES BOOK FOR DUMMIES

FIRST MARKETING TITLE TO ADDRESS REAL-WORLD NEEDS

AMHERST, Mass. — He's nearly done now. Just a section on public relations. Then the manuscript is off to production and — perhaps — history will be made. This title isn't just another book about business. This book is a redefinition of the marketing field that finally brings it up to speed with the harsh realities of business. And the book is, appropriately, by an author who straddles the boundaries between the ivory tower of business schools and the trenches of marketing management.

"What we teach about marketing on campus is pure fiction," complains Alexander Hiam, author of *Marketing For Dummies* (IDG Books Worldwide, Inc., 1997). "It's based on academic research, not on real-world practices and problems." Hiam threw out all his textbooks and visited past clients and other marketing practitioners before designing his new book. As a result, it . . .

Figure 1: Writing a killer press release

The odds of your release getting picked up by the media and receiving any coverage at all are terribly low. Sorry to disappoint you. Journalists and editors throw away more than 90 percent of the releases they receive. So your goal is to beat the odds by writing a release that stands out from the junk in a journalist's in-box.

To beat the odds, pay attention to content (to make sure you have a good story—see preceding). And avoid these errors that journalists complain about in press releases:

Don't send inappropriate or late releases. Target the right media and contacts. The food critic doesn't need a release about a new robotics manufacturing facility. And the business correspondent doesn't either, if the facility opened two months ago.

You need to build up an accurate database of media contacts, and to mail your press release first class on occasion to validate it (with first class mail, you get envelopes back if addresses don't work). Faxing or e-mailing your release is often sensible because journalists work on tight deadlines, so include fields for fax and e-mail numbers in your database. But I recommend developing a list by identifying authors of stories you like and think are similar to your own stories. That way you get a smaller list, but one that is a much tighter match with your content and target audience. Commercial lists and directories of journalists are readily available from mailing list vendors.

Don't make any errors. At all. Typos throw the facts into question. And don't include any inaccurate facts. You want the journalist to trust you to do his or her research, which is a big leap of faith. Prove that you are worthy.

Don't give incomplete contact information. Be sure that you include names, addresses, and phone numbers that work. Brief the contacts as to when to be available and what to say so they will be cooperative. Also, brief the switchboard or give journalists instructions for how to navigate through the computerized voice mail system. You don't want gatekeeping to prevent a reporter from making that interview!

Don't ignore the journalists' research needs. The more support you give them, the easier they can cover your story. You can include photos of the expert you've quoted in a mailed release (date, name of person, and information about the supplier of the photo to be included on the back or in the margin). Also consider offering plant tours, interview times, sample products, or whatever else may help journalists cover your story.

Don't bug the reporters. Journalists don't want to send you clippings of the articles they write, so don't bother asking. Nor do they care to discuss with you why they didn't run a story, or why they cut off part of that quote when they did run a story. They are busy with the next story. Forget about it. You should focus on the next story, too.

Don't forget that journalists work on a faster clock than you do. When a journalist calls about your release, return the call (or make sure that somebody returns it) in hours, not days. If you handle their requests slowly, they will have found another source or written another story by the time you get back to them.

Should I consider video and electronic releases?

You can get a story out to the media in other ways, too. You can generate a video release, with useful footage that a television producer may decide to run as is or as part of a news story. You can also put a written press release on the PR newswire or other such services that distribute hard copy or electronic releases to their media clients—for a fee to the source of the release, of course. You can also pitch your stories to the Associated Press and other newswires. I'm not going to cover these options, because they are not that important to many marketers, and because if you want to pursue them you will most likely need to hire a publicist or PR firm anyway. Just know that the options exist, and ask your publicist for details if these options seem appropriate to your story.

Alexander Hiam has worked in marketing for many years. He obtained degrees from Harvard, and from U.C. Berkeley, where he obtained an MBA in marketing and strategy. He taught marketing and advertising at the School of Management of the University of Massachusetts at Amherst, and has written many marketing books including *The Portable MBA in Marketing* and *The Entrepreneur's Complete Sourcebook.*

1. *Response*

a. List the steps a marketing manager will take to develop a good publicity campaign.

b. In your own words define the following: *good publicity, bad publicity, hook,* and *news release.*

c. This selection was picked up from the reference book, *Marketing for Dummies: A Reference for the Rest of Us!*® This book is intended to help instruct people just learning about marketing, or those who are in the business. How would you describe the style and tone of this selection? Do you think it is suitable to the author's purpose and intended audience? Explain.

d. How does publicity differ from advertising?

2. ***Media*** *Relationships* Discuss the relationship between the news media, publicity and marketing departments, and the audience of the news media. Why is it important for consumers to know about this relationship?

3. ***Drama*** *Role Play* Choose one of the following scenarios and role-play the possible conversation with a partner or small group:
   - The marketing manager of a large fast-food chain is called by a newspaper that wants to speak to him/her about mistreatment of union representatives.
   - The marketing department of a movie studio tries to generate media interest in the studio's remake of a 1950s classic.
   - The president of a large company that manufactures wheelchairs inadvertently reveals a major malfunction of the company's biggest seller while appearing on a hard-hitting news show.
   - The president of a toy company announces a new scholarship program at a press conference attended by local and national press.

   Take turns playing a variety of roles within your chosen scenario. Add as many details as you like to make your role play more realistic and interesting.

4. ***Language Conventions*** *Relative Pronouns* A *relative pronoun* is a pronoun that can introduce a subordinate clause. The relative pronouns are *who, whom, whose, which,* and *that.* When a subordinate clause is introduced by a relative pronoun, that clause serves as an adjective, modifying a word or antecedent in the main clause. For example:

   > Margaret Atwood, who recently won the Booker, has written over twenty books.

   Find one example in this article of a relative pronoun. How do relative pronouns increase clarity? How can you use relative pronouns in your writing?

"I cheered with each stinging tag and swinging blow delivered by this bunch of big-bat-swinging bullies."

Sports Logos an Insult

Opinion piece by Noah Augustine

Last Thursday evening, I watched rather helplessly as nine Indians were thrashed and battered about by just as many men in blue and white uniforms. Normally, I would have done something about it—called for backup, at least. Instead, I cheered with each stinging tag and swinging blow delivered by this bunch of big-bat-swinging bullies.

They were the Toronto Blue Jays, of course, beating up on the celebrated Cleveland Indians. And, although I am an Indian (Mi'kmaq, I prefer) hailing from the Maritimes, I remain a big fan of the Indian-swatting Jays. One might assume that because Cleveland proudly displays an image of some misshapen Indian that all people of Indian descent must be Cleveland fans. Not true. In fact, the use of this imagery is insulting to most aboriginal people.

A **logo** is an identifying symbol used as a trademark, in advertising, et cetera.

The issue of professional sports teams using Indian symbols is one that may not concern most Canadians, although it can be argued that Canadians have less tolerance for racism—and are less blatant in its exercise—than our neighbours in the U.S. We are, as they say, politically correct, at most times.

Nonetheless, for me, as an aboriginal person, the use of these religious symbols and caricatures of Indian chiefs or spiritual leaders as sports logos is as offensive to my cultural heritage as it would be for an African Canadian to observe the "Boston Blacks"—or for religious people to see the image of a rabbi, an archbishop or the Dalai Lama stitched into the shoulder patches of professional sports teams.

If a television image of thousands of baseball fans screaming "war chants" and waving fake tomahawks in support of the Atlanta

Braves is baffling me and my understanding of society, I can only wonder how such acceptance of less-than-subtle racism is affecting our younger generations. Who said it was okay for professional sports teams—and their millions of adoring fans—to adopt our cultural icons and images for mass ridicule?

One American youth, in a 1997 Grade 8 writing assignment on his school's use of an Indian symbol, explained it this way: "We simply chose an Indian as the emblem. We could have just as easily chosen any uncivilized animal." Is the education system the most effective tool we have in our fight against racism? I sometimes wonder.

With baseball's Atlanta Braves and Cleveland Indians, football's Kansas City Chiefs and Washington Redskins, and hockey's Chicago Blackhawks, professional sports organizations are turning a blind eye to racism in professional sports.

Professional athletes within these organizations serve as role models for all youth, including aboriginal youth. With this comes a certain responsibility.

Like so many Canadian kids, it is the dream of many aboriginal youth to someday lace up a pair of skates and face off against hockey's best. When Everett Sanipass, a Mi'kmaq from Big Cove First Nation, was drafted by the Chicago Blackhawks in the 1986 NHL draft, almost every aboriginal youth in Atlantic Canada proudly displayed the team logo—an Indian face with war paint—on everything from jerseys to lunch pails. Sanipass was the Wayne Gretzky of aboriginal hockey. It didn't matter which team he played for; what mattered was that he played in the big league. And if Sanipass said it was good, then it was great. The logo he wore could have just as easily been any "uncivilized animal." Kids do not recognize such symbols of racism but do become victims of the assault.

With dreams and aspirations comes sacrifice. It is admirable for sacrifice to be recognized as hard work and dedication, but let it not be admirable to accept tolerance of racism as just one more sacrifice.

Many feel that aboriginal people should be honoured that Indian imagery is the logo of some sports communities. But what honour lies in ridicule and mockery? Take, for example, a 1998 *Washington Post* sports headline, referring to a Dallas football victory over Washington, which read: "Cowboys finish off Redskins."

At the root of this issue is the trademark business. It's a multimillion-dollar industry. However, change is in the air. Last year, the Washington Redskins had seven trademarks, including their logo, cancelled for federal registration based on a complaint from several tribes. The Trademark Trial and Appeal Board found "Redskins" to be "disparaging" to native Americans. The ruling is under appeal.

Even though, as it is said, money makes the world go 'round, court actions can change that. Perhaps, someday, respect will have a greater value than the almighty dollar.

Noah Augustine is a newspaper columnist who has written articles for *The Toronto Star*.

1. ***Response***
   a. Do you agree with Noah Augustine? Give reasons for your opinion.
   b. How does Noah Augustine feel about the statement "We could have just as easily chosen any uncivilized animal"?
   c. What do you think would be a fair solution to the problem of Aboriginal sports logos?
   d. What do you think players could or should do if they found their team's logo offensive?

2. ***Media*** *Logos* Discuss other logos, how they developed, and what they represent. Consider other sports teams' logos, the logos used for TV stations, and those used for large corporations. What purpose do logos serve? What makes a logo good? Compare at least five logos, their meaning, their effectiveness, and their appropriateness.

   Obtain copies of team logos that use representations of Native people, such as the ones mentioned in the article. Design new logos for these teams that are non-offensive, yet are still interesting and eye-catching.

3. ***Writing*** *Letter* Assume you work in the public relations department of one of the sports teams that has an offensive logo. Write a reply to Augustine acknowledging his position, presenting your own, and suggesting a solution or compromise.

4. ***Critical Thinking*** With a small group, discuss the phrase *big-bat-swinging-bullies*. Is violence in sports a problem, in your opinion? Explain.

When you watch TV, is your brain or your body responding to the stimulus?

TELEVISION
The Collective Imagination

ARTICLE BY DERRICK DE KERCKHOVE

The New Media Context

Stephen Kline is the Director of the Media Analysis Lab at Simon Fraser University in Vancouver. He and his brother Rob have invented a sophisticated system to analyze people's physiological responses to anything they are being shown. Anything, everything and, especially, television. Kline's work on the impact of television advertising and programming is well-known. Recently, Stephen and his brother invited me to be one of their guinea pigs. They wired me to a computer with various skin-response devices. They attached one to my left middle finger for skin conductivity, another to my forehead—presumably to probe my brain activity—a third to my left wrist to take my pulse and the last over my heart area to monitor circulation. Another device, a rather crude joystick, was placed in my right hand. By pushing it forwards or backwards, I could indicate whether I liked or disliked what I was watching. Then Rob and Stephen left the lab and the show began.

I watched a fast paced jumble of typical viewing fare: sex, advertising, news, talk shows, sentimentality and tedium. The cuts seemed to average around fifteen seconds each. By normal TV standards, that speed does not appear to be excessive, though in my new role as a knee-jerk critic, I found it very difficult to keep up the pace with the joystick. By the end of the twenty-minute experiment, I was thoroughly frustrated, having failed to express much more than limp-wristed approvals or disapprovals. For many cuts, I hadn't had enough time to express anything at all.

When Rob and Stephen came back to rewind the tape and check the graphs on the computer, I told them my feeling of helplessness. They laughed and invited me to watch the screen while they replayed the tape in sync with the data. To my absolute amazement, I saw that every cut, every jolt, every change of image had been recorded by one sensor or another and fed into the computer. I could see the busy outlines of the graphs corresponding to my skin conductivity, pulse, heartbeat and to whatever mysterious response my forehead had been giving. I was flabbergasted. As I was labouring to express an opinion, my whole body had been listening and watching and reacting instantaneously.

TV Talks to the Body, Not the Mind

I drew two important conclusions from that experience. The first is that television talks primarily to the body, not to the mind. This is something I'd suspected for several years. The second conclusion was that, if the video screen has such a direct impact on my nervous system and my emotions, and so little effect on my mind, then most of the information-processing was actually being performed by the screen. These are hypotheses I want to explore in this study of our ubiquitous, intimate and yet so little-known relationships to our screens: our videominds.

Why is it so difficult, if not impossible, to concentrate when the TV is on? Because television is hypnotically involving: any movement on the screen attracts our attention as automatically as if someone had just touched us. Our eyes are dragged towards the screen like iron to a magnet.

Orienting and Defensive Responses

Understanding our television culture depends upon understanding how and why television fascinates us beyond our conscious control. As I've proved to myself with the Kline brothers' experiment, my neuromuscular system constantly follows images on video, even if my mind occasionally wanders. This is involuntary because of our antediluvian biological programming: the autonomic nervous systems of higher

> [TV] is our latest medium—we call it a medium because nothing's well done … It has already revolutionized social grace by cutting down parlour conversation to two sentences: 'What's on television?' and 'Good night.'
>
> Goodman Ace

mammals are trained to respond to any perceptible change in the environment that might be relevant to survival. We are conditioned to respond involuntarily to any kind of stimulation, internal or external, with what in clinical psychophysiology is called the Orienting Response (OR). This will either draw our attention towards the stimulus or alert the Defensive Response, which makes us recoil from it.

Now, you may well ask, in what way is TV relevant to our survival? In terms of content, not much. But television's principal action, as McLuhan never tired of repeating, happens not at the level of content but at the level of the medium itself, with the flickering light of the electron beam scanner. The changes and cuts in the shows provoke continuous OR's, drawing attention without necessarily satisfying it. In life, we accommodate stimuli as we get to know them: either we recognize them immediately or we quickly develop a strategy to deal with them. A completed response to a stimulus is called a closure. So in life, most stimuli awake an OR, call for a closure and receive it. With television, though, we are never done with the initial stimulus: TV provokes rapid successions of OR's without allowing time for closure.

The "Collapse of the Interval" Between Stimulus and Response

In a paper on cognitive responses to television, German media theorist Hertha Sturm made an important observation. When we watch television, we are denied enough time to integrate the information on a fully conscious basis.

> Rapidly changing presentations impair verbalization. Among these are uninterpreted changes in viewing angle, unpredictable flip-flops from picture to text or from text to picture. When confronted with rapidly changing presentations and speeded-up action, the viewer is literally driven from image to image. This demands constantly new and unexpected adaptation to perceptual stimulation. As a result the viewer is no longer able to keep up and ceases to internally label. When this occurs, we found, the individual acts and reacts with heightened physiological arousal which in turn results in a reduction of comprehension. The viewer becomes, so to speak, a victim of an external force, of rapid audio-visual sequencing.[1]

Picking up on this theme, Edward Renouf Slopek, a McGill University communications researcher and McLuhan Program Associate, coined the expression "collapsing the interval" to indicate that TV eliminates the distancing effect—the interval between stimulus and response—and the time to process the information in our conscious mind.[2] The suggestion is that television leaves us little if any time to reflect on what we are watching.

Jolts-Per-Minute (JPM's) and the "Missing Half-Second"

Orienting responses elicited by television are quite different from those elicited by the cinema. The light from the video screen does not bounce back into our eyes, it comes right at us through the screen, challenging us to respond, like the spotlight of the police interrogator in a movie. Hertha Sturm claims that it takes the mind at least half a second to provide proper closure to complex stimuli. She claims that TV denies this to the viewer, in what she terms "the missing half-second syndrome." It certainly took my mind several seconds to deal, albeit inadequately, with the material compiled by Stephen Kline. Sturm is probably correct in implying that television programming is deliberately geared to preventing verbalized responses, so as to make us easy victims of advertising messages.

Recently, Toronto media critic Morris Wolfe created the concept of "jolts-per-minute"—or JPM's—to describe how TV shows hit us.[3] The notion behind JPM's is that it takes a critical number of cuts to prevent the viewer from falling asleep or switching channels. TV must zap the zapper before he or she zaps the channel. JPM's that keep the attention alive may also prevent cognitive closure.

Sub-Muscularization and "Felt-Meaning"

However much people moralize, this is not necessarily a bad thing. One effect of the collapse of the interval is that in order to make sense of the rapid images we must somehow emulate the action with our bodies. Just as children faced with a new concept often find it helpful to act it out, we follow TV action with our bodies and even imitate the odd expression to better interpret it. This is what I call the "sub-muscularization effect"—analogous to the "sub-vocalization" strategy adopted by slow readers. Sub-muscularization is the interpretation of motion and action by a sort of sensorimotor mimicry involving the whole body. I suggest that we interpret gestures, postures and expressions on TV with a kind of sub-muscular response, expressed in muscle tone and stress factors. (The need for this kind of patterning can be observed in people's behaviour on the telephone where we usually accompany our sentences with many gestures and movements that we use in face-to-face conversation; perhaps this is because such physical involvement helps us to make sense of what we are saying.) Thus, "television sense" is not the same as "book sense." It is closer to what the American psychologist and philosopher, Eugene T. Gendlin, calls "felt-meaning."

Gendlin defines felt-meaning as "the equivalent of hundreds of thousands of cognitive operations" done in a split second by the body in response to stimuli.[4] Felt-meaning could be said to be a product of sub-muscularization. Indeed, as we experience events in our immediate surroundings, we store their relevant effects in various ways within our neuromuscular system. That is precisely what Hans Selye called stress. The Montreal-based clinical psychologist developed the theory of General Adaptive Syndrome (GAS) to account for the way we absorb the pressures of daily life, and how our body helps us to manage stress by sorting and storing stress's energy.

Although we know that we stop breathing when we are anxious or that we blush when we are put to shame, we are not usually aware of physical events happening within our bodies when we respond to people and situations. Felt-meaning is rarely conscious. But, in the background, it regulates and conditions our overall response to everyday matters. Felt-meaning precedes logic and may be more comprehensive than thought. Thus, the deeper effect of television might occur at the level of felt-meaning, offering little chance of response. Television evokes Orienting Responses that are woven into the fabric of our neuromuscular system.

"Grazing and Zapping Is the Way We Attend to Everything"

With this comment, social critic Michael Ignatieff condemned television. It probably reflects the opinion of many Canadians when he claims that "TV is turning us into a clever but shallow culture." It is easy to heap blame upon television. Often, without more than a hunch to go on, people attribute to television the instigation of social evils, everything from rape and murder to cynical apathy. Recently, a group of committed citizens in Vancouver felt so strongly about the dangers of television that they commissioned a series of TV ads to discourage people from watching. ("This sight is bad for you: stop looking right now.")

> I'm always amazed that people will actually choose to sit in front of the television and just be savaged by stuff that belittles their intelligence.
>
> Alice Walker

There are arguments about programming, ethics, aesthetics and invasions of privacy. But only a handful of critics, people like Jerry Mander, George Gerbner, Joshua Meyrowitz, Neil Postman and, certainly, McLuhan, have begun to understand the deeper message of the medium. TV is challenging our previously dominant, literate mindset by substituting its own tactile, collective orality. It threatens the sacrosanct autonomy we have acquired through reading and writing.

You Don't Watch TV, TV Watches You

There is not much that is "innocent" about the way we use our eyes. The following observation is by Jean-Marie Pradier, a professor of drama at the University of Paris and founder of an international association on Organized Human Performing Behaviours (OHPB).

> Social life, sexuality, and aggression are mainly ruled by visual components. This is perhaps why gazing is so severely controlled by precise codes and display rules. It is also why most of the human cultures have created freely viewed objects (paintings, sculptures, photographs, films) and freely viewed individuals (sportsmen and women, dancers, actors, and actresses, but also priests and public figures) along with free viewing spaces and events (theatre, carnival, hot urban districts) where it is possible to be a voyeur.[5]

Is television a free-viewing area? The relevance of this question was brought home to me at a clever video art installation by Mit Mitropoulos, a Greek communication artist from MIT. In *Face to Face,* two live participants sit back to back and converse with each other's images in real time on closed-circuit TV. Deceptively simple, the experience was unforgettable when I participated as one of the conversational partners. Irrespective of whether I did or didn't know my partner beforehand, I felt as if there were none of the usual barriers to staring someone right in the face. You could almost pick your nose in the context of this new electronic intimacy. True, I measured for the first time the extent to which we are terrified of faces in live contact, but what struck me more was that for the last thirty years we have unwittingly been watching our TV personalities without a trace of shyness. TV voyeurism is the "uncensored gaze." Perhaps television does provide a free-viewing area.

Or so it seems. The deep involvement required by viewing and the fact that most of our responses are involuntary bear witness to the changing power relationship between consumer and producer. When we read, we scan the books, we are in control. But when we watch TV, it is the TV scanner that "reads" us. Our retinas are the direct object of the electron beam. When scanning meets glancing, and makes eye contact between human and machine, the machine's glance is the more powerful. In front of the television set, our defences are down; we are vulnerable and susceptible to multi-sensory seduction. Thus, the real meaning of Prime Time could be "priming time," that is, the best time to prime the mind of the television viewer. As Tony Schwartz, New York advertising executive and TV critic, suggested, "TV is not a window on the world, it's a window on the consumer."[6]

Notes

1. Hertha Sturm, "*Perception and Television: The Missing Half Second,*" *The Work of Hertha Sturm*, edited and translated from German by Gertrude J. Robinson (Montréal: McGill University, Working Papers in Communications, 1988), 39.
2. Edward R. Slopek, "Collapsing the Interval," *Impulse* (n.d.): 29–34.
3. Morris Wolfe, *Jolts: The TV Wasteland and the Canadian Oasis* (Toronto: James Lorimer and Co., 1985).
4. Eugene T. Gendlin, *Experience and the Creation of Meaning* (New York: Free Press, 1964), 27.
5. Jean-Marie Pradier, "Toward a Biological Theory of the Body in Performance," *New Theatre Quarterly* (February 1990): 89.
6. Tony Schwartz, *Media: The Second God* (Garden City, NY: Anchor Books, 1983).

Derrick de Kerckhove is Professor in the Department of French and Director of the McLuhan Program in Culture and Technology at the University of Toronto. He worked with Marshall McLuhan in the seventies, acting as translator, assistant, and co-author. *The Skin of Culture* is his first major Canadian publication.

1. ***Response***
   a. Is Derrick de Kerckhove's attitude toward TV positive or negative in this article? How did you reach that conclusion?
   b. Are you "in control" when you watch TV, or is the TV in control, as de Kerckhove suggests? Explain.
   c. What is the most interesting point this article makes, in your opinion? Why is this point interesting?

2. ***Vocabulary*** Reread the selection and list any words you are unfamiliar with. Can you figure these words out from their context? Can you use clues in how the words are constructed—their prefixes, roots, suffixes, et cetera? List a definition for each word and then check a dictionary. How does working out the meaning of unfamiliar words in context help you understand the selection?

3. ***Making Connections*** Note the people and studies de Kerckhove quotes or refers to in this article. Choose one of these to investigate further. Read the original article, or at least part of the book, or read other works by that person. Are the author's arguments sound? Explain. What stance does that person take toward media? Did de Kerckhove faithfully represent that stance in his use of the work?

4. ***Media*** *Anti-TV Ads* In this selection, de Kerckhove describes a TV ad that tries to persuade viewers to shut off the TV. Why is this advertising campaign ironic? Why might a TV network refuse to run such ads? How effective do you think these ads would be? What might make these ads more effective? What might be a better medium for this campaign?

The quiz show has been around for a very long time, and the quiz show format described in this article will seem strangely familiar.

The Quiz Show Format

Article by David Halberstam

THE RADIO QUIZ SHOWS WERE, IN RETROSPECT, SMALL POTATOES, with prizes to match. On *Take It Or Leave It,* the ultimate challenge was the "$64 question"—a phrase that even worked itself into the American vernacular by 1945. In the new age of television, though, everything had to be bigger and better. Americans were not going to sit home, glued to their television sets, wondering whether some electronic stranger, who had briefly entered their living rooms, was going to be able to double his winnings from $32 to $64. In the postwar era that was pocket money.

Such was the dilemma facing Lou Cowan in early 1955. Cowan, one of the most inventive figures in the early days of television, needed a gimmick for a game show worthy of television, one so compelling that millions of Americans would faithfully tune in. He needed high drama, and what better way to achieve that than a *very* large prize? Six hundred and forty dollars? Not so terribly exciting. Nor, for that matter, was $6,400. "But $64,000 gets into the realm of the almost impossible," he thought. Cowan liked the double-or-nothing format—so he envisioned a contestant who had answered a series of questions correctly and won the dizzying sum of $32,000. At that point it would be time to play double or nothing, for $64,000. With one answer to one question, an ordinary American could be wealthy beyond his or her wildest dreams.

The concept depended on the belief that seemingly unexceptional Americans did indeed have secret talents and secret knowledge. That appealed greatly to Cowan, who, with his Eastern European Jewish background, had a highly idealized view of his fellow citizens' potential to reach beyond the apparent limits life had dealt them. His was an idealistic, almost innocent belief in the ordinary people of the country. Cowan's wife, Polly, daughter of a successful Chicago businessman and a graduate of Sarah Lawrence College, most decidedly did not like the idea for the show. She thought it essentially a corruption of the real uses of learning—glorifying trivial memorization rather than true thought and analysis. She believed that the rewards for knowledge should not be huge amounts of cash, doled out in front of millions of cheering strangers, ultimately to benefit commercial hucksters; instead, it should be the joy of knowledge itself. She did not hesitate to make her feelings known to her husband and in a way the debate in the Cowan household reflected the schizophrenic nature of the program itself—a compelling mix of achievement, purity and, of course, avarice.

Polly's doubts did not deter her husband. With his generous and optimistic nature, he saw the show as emblematic of the American dream; it offered everyone not only a chance to become rich overnight but to win the esteem of his fellow citizens. It proved every American had the potential to be extraordinary. It reflected, one of his sons said years later, a "White Christmas" vision of America, in which the immediate descendants of the immigrants, caught up in their optimism about the new world and the nobility of the American experiment, romanticized America and saw it as they wanted it to be.

Cowan was an independent television packager, a familiar figure in the early days of television; he and others like him came up with ideas, found sponsors, and then sold the entire package to the then rather passive networks. He sold this idea to Revlon, which was so enthusiastic that Walter Craig, an executive of the advertising agency that worked for Revlon, locked the door at Cowan's initial presentation and said, "Nobody leaves this room until we have a signed contract."

The name of the program was *The $64,000 Question*. It aired for the first time from 10:00 to 10:30 P.M. in June 1955, on CBS. It was an immediate hit. Millions of people identified with the contestants—who were very much like neighbors. The program showed a CBS psychologist named Gerhart Wiebe who said, "We're all pretty much alike, and we're all smart." The show contained all kinds of dramatic touches attesting to its integrity. The questions sat all week in a locked vault at a bank, and when they finally arrived on the set, they were transported by an executive from Manufacturers Trust, who was accompanied by two armed guards. An IBM machine shuffled the questions on the set.

Eight thousand dollars was the maximum a contestant could win on one show; then he or she had to come back next week. Suspense would start building. At the eight thousand-dollar level, the contestant had to enter an isolation booth; presumably so no one in the studio audience could whisper an answer. The speed with which the program enthralled the entire country was breathtaking. Its success surprised even Lou Cowan. The show offered hope of an overnight fortune, and it proved that ordinary people were not in fact necessarily ordinary. As such there was a powerful chord of populism to it. But more than anything else, it appealed to the viewers' sense of greed. Five weeks after its premiere, *The $64,000 Question* was the top-rated show on television. Studies showed that approximately 47.5 million people were watching. The sales of Revlon ("the greatest name in cosmetics") skyrocketed. Some Revlon products sold out overnight, and the show's master of ceremonies had to beg the public to be more patient until more Revlon Living Lipstick was available. The head of Hazel Bishop, a rival cosmetics company, subsequently blamed his company's disappointing year on the fact that "a new television program sponsored by your company's principal competitor captured the imagination of the public." It was the most primal lesson yet on the commercial power of television.

The contestants became the forerunners of Andy Warhol's idea of instant fame: people plucked out of total anonymity and beamed into the homes of millions of their fellow Americans. Between ten and twenty thousand people a week wrote letters, volunteering themselves or their friends to be contestants. After only a few appearances on the show, audiences began to regard the contestants as old and familiar friends. Perhaps, in retrospect, the most important thing illuminated by the show was how easily television conferred fame and established an image. Virtual strangers could become familiar to millions of their fellow citizens.

One of the first contestants, Redmond O'Hanlon, a New York City policeman, whose category was Shakespeare, reached the $16,000 plateau. At that point he decided to stop and, in his words, put "the conservatism of a father of five children" over "the egotism of the scholar." Soon Catherine Kreitzer, a fifty-four-year-old grandmother whose category was the Bible, reached $32,000. She was confident, Mrs. Kreitzer said, that she could win the full amount, but she stopped, quoting from the Bible: "Let your moderation be known unto all men." Perhaps the most engaging of all the early contestants was Gino Prato, a New York shoe repairman, whose category was opera. He easily reached the $32,000 plateau, whereupon his ninety-two-year-old father in Italy cabled him to stop at once. Prato, in time, became roving ambassador for a rubber-heel company, was given season tickets to the Metropolitan Opera, and went on to other television shows as well.

If the producers faced a dilemma in the beginning, it was the hesitance of the top contestants to go for the ultimate question. Some of it was the fear of losing everything and some was the nation's then extremely harsh income tax schedules. As Kent Anderson pointed out in his book *Television Fraud*, a contestant who went for the whole thing was risking almost $20,000 in order to win only $12,000 more.

A Marine captain named Richard McCutcheon became the first contestant to go all the way. Bookies kept odds on whether or not he could get the right answer. His field was cooking, not military history. With an audience estimated at 55 million watching, on September 13, 1955, he became the first contestant to climb the television Mt. Everest. For $64,000 he was asked to name the five dishes and two wines from the menu served by King George VI of England for French president Albert Lebrun in 1939. He did: consommé quenelles, filet de truite saumonée, petits pois à la françaises, sauce maltaise, and corbeille. The wines were Château d'Yquem and Madeira Sercial. The nation was ecstatic—it had a winner. "If you're symbolic of the Marine Corps, Dick," said Hal March, the emcee, "I don't see how we'll ever lose any battles."

Everyone involved seemed to profit from the show: Lou Cowan soon became president of CBS; the bank official who was in charge of the questions became a vice-president at Manufacturers Trust. But no one profited more than Revlon. The impact of the show upon its revenues was a startling reflection of changes that were taking place every day in more subtle ways because of the ferocious commercial drive of television and its effect upon both consumers and industry.

Revlon, at the time, was the leading cosmetics company in the nation, but Coty, Max Factor, and Helena Rubinstein were relatively close behind in net sales. In 1953, for example, Revlon had net sales of $28.4 million; Helena Rubinstein had $20.4 million; Coty had $19.6; Max Factor, $19 million; and Hazel Bishop, $9.9. All in all, it was a fairly evenly divided pie, and Revlon's sales increased on average about 15 percent annually in the years just before 1955. But sponsoring the quiz show changed all that. In the first six-month season, Revlon increased its sales from $33.6 million to $51.6—a stunning 54 percent increase. The stock jumped from 12 to 20. The following year saw sales increase to $85.7 million. By 1958 Revlon completely dominated its field. (Asked later by a staff member of a House subcommittee whether sponsoring *The $64,000 Question* had anything to do with Revlon's amazing surge to the top, a somewhat disingenuous Martin Revson answered, "It helped. It helped.")

Not surprisingly, *The $64,000 Question* produced a Pavlovian response to its success. Suddenly the networks were flooded with imitations, all of them for big prize money. The people in Cowan's old organization came up with *The $64,000 Challenge*. Others produced *Tic Tac Dough*, *Twenty-One*, *The Big Moment*, *Beat the Jackpot*, and *The Big Board*. There was even talk of *Twenty Steps to a Million*.

By 1956, the appeal of these shows appeared to be limitless; then subtly, and soon not so subtly, there was the inevitable pressure that television especially seemed to inspire: to improve the show by manipulation, to *cast* it—that is, to ensure each contestant would find some special resonance with the millions of people watching at home. The process began naturally enough at first, with the preference to choose a contestant possessed of considerable charm over a contestant without it. Soon the producers, by pretesting, were able to tell where a candidate's strengths lay and what his [or her] weaknesses were, without the contestants themselves even knowing what was happening: Prato knew Italian opera but little about the German opera; McCutcheon knew French cuisine rather than Italian or British. "We wrote the questions into the matrices of their existence," Mert Koplin, one of the men who worked on *The $64,000 Question*, later said. As the pressure built for ratings, the manipulations grew more serious. Some guests would be put through dry runs only to find that when they appeared on the live shows, the questions were remarkably similar to the ones they had answered correctly in the rehearsal. (McCutcheon, it turned out, was deeply bothered by this and thought seriously of getting out; he was encouraged to remain a contestant by his family. Later he told Joe Stone, the prosecutor from the New York District Attorney's office, that he thought the shows were fraudulent and immoral, and he disagreed violently with the claim of the various producers that the rigging had hurt no one.)

The Revlon executives from the start were extremely outspoken about the guests on the two shows they sponsored, *The $64,000 Question* and *The $64,000 Challenge*. Starting in the fall of 1955, there was a weekly meeting in Martin Revson's (Charles Revson's brother) office, where he and his top advertising people critiqued the previous week's shows and contestants. Revson was not shy about telling what he wanted to happen and who he wanted to win. He posted a chart in the meeting room with the ratings on it; if the ratings were down, it was the fault of the contestants. Were the contestants too old? Too young? Were they attractive enough? The criticism was often brutal. (The Revsons apparently did not like a young psychologist named Joyce Brothers, who appeared as an expert on boxing. Thus the questions given her were exceptionally hard—they even asked her the names of referees—

in the desire to get her off the show; their strategy had no effect: She became the second person to win $64,000.)

More and more, with so many different shows vying for public approval, the producers found it was the quality of the contestants themselves—and the degree to which the nation identified with them—that made the difference. When the Barry and Enright company, one of the big hitters in the world of game shows, introduced its new game in March 1956, called *Twenty-One*, loosely based on the card game of the same name, Dan Enright was confident it would be an immediate success. Two contestants would answer questions for points, without knowing how many points their opponent had. Enright thought it was a sure bet for unbearable dramatic excitement, especially since the audience would know more about the competition than the contestants themselves. He was dead wrong. The premiere was, he said later, a dismal failure, "just plain dull." The day after, Marty Rosenhouse, the sponsor, made an irate call to say he did not intend to own a turkey. "Do whatever you have to do," he told Enright, "and you know what I'm talking about." Those were the marching orders for Enright and his staff.

Fixing the show did not particularly bother Enright; the quiz shows had never been about intelligence or integrity as far as he was concerned; they were about drama and entertainment. "You cannot ask random questions of people and have a show," one game-show producer later said. "You simply have failure, failure, failure, and that does not make entertainment." That made it a predatory world, and Enright excelled in it. He was not, Dan Enright reflected years later, a very nice man in those days. He was totally compelled by work, wildly ambitious, and utterly self-involved. "I was determined to be successful no matter what it cost," he said, "and I was greedy, greedy, not for money, but for authority, power, prestige and respect." The end, he believed at the time, always justified the means. People were to be used; if you did not use them, he believed, they in turn would use you. Soon—with considerable fixing—*Twenty-One* became a huge success; at a relatively young age, Enright had already exceeded his own expectations, and he was wealthy and powerful. People coveted his attention and gave him respect. Thus he was able to rationalize everything he was doing.

David Halberstam is the author of many books, including *The Best and the Brightest,* and *The Powers That Be.* His book *Summer of '49* was a number one *New York Times* hardcover bestseller. Halberstam has won many major journalism awards, including the Pulitzer Prize. This excerpt was taken from his book, *The Fifties.*

1. ***Response***
   a. Why did Polly Cowan object to her husband's ideas for a quiz show? Do you agree or disagree with her? Explain.
   b. How are the quiz shows described in this selection similar to or different from the quiz shows of today?
   c. Was it inevitable that the quiz shows became crooked, as the article suggests? Explain.
   d. Discuss the relationship between the quiz shows, their sponsors, and the audience.
   e. Speculate on why quiz shows are so appealing.

2. ***Making Connections*** To find out the full story behind the quiz show *Twenty-One*, watch the 1994 movie *Quiz Show* directed by Robert Redford. Discuss the issues of integrity and honesty in TV shows that this movie raises.

3. ***Media*** *Quiz Shows* With a small group, develop 20 questions for a quiz show about quiz shows. You may need to do some research to help you with the questions. Once you have the questions and answers, produce a quiz show—with the help of volunteer contestants. Use current quiz show formats as a model or develop your own format.

The box sanctified, conferred identity.
The more familiar the face, the more
to be trusted.

—*P. D. James*

What do the movies *The Perfect Storm, Shakespeare in Love,* and *Fatal Attraction* all have in common? Test screenings.

What Would You Change?

Article by Claudia Puig

In *The Perfect Storm*, moviegoers are spared a litany of the fishermen's final maudlin thoughts. In *The Patriot,* Mel Gibson shares a kiss with his sister-in-law, but their passion stops there. And in *Scary Movie*, potshots are aimed at a previous summer hit, *Big Momma's House.*

These changes were made because Hollywood listened to people like Peter Larkey, a veteran of test screenings, one of the most important and secretive processes shaping today's movies.

"I get to say, 'This movie is awful,' 'This character has to go,'" says Larkey, a 27-year-old computer graphics designer who lives in Northridge, Calif. "It's kind of changed the way I look at films. I'm always thinking, 'What could they have cut out?'"

Filmmakers may bristle at the presumptuousness of these armchair critics, but test-screening feedback—be it visceral, written or conversational—now holds lots of clout in Hollywood. And studios, especially with big-budget summer fare, demand the insurance. "We all have to go through it because there's so much riding on the movie," *The Perfect Storm* director Wolfgang Petersen says.

Months before a movie's opening, studios hire market researchers to see how a film plays. Researchers recruit an audience, usually at malls or multiplexes. The screening usually takes place a few days later, and those who make it in sign a statement promising not to disclose anything about the film.

During the movie, researchers (and often filmmakers and studio execs, sitting anonymously in the darkened theatre) scrutinize the audience members, watching to see whether they laugh, tense up or, God forbid, snooze. After the movie, audience members fill out questionnaires, answering queries such as "What would you tell your friends about this movie?" Or "What are your feelings about the way the movie ended?" Afterward, 12 to 20 audience members often are asked to stay for additional discussions.

The typical film is test-screened three times, but for some, the process is repeated as many as 10 times. Testing is considered especially useful for comedies, action flicks and thrillers.

"Test screenings help the artist and studio fine-tune the material and refine their intentions," says Marc Shmuger, president of marketing at Universal Pictures. "The research process rests squarely in that awkward intersection between art and commerce."

The belief that test screenings can predict commercial success became widespread with 1987's *Fatal Attraction*. Test audiences balked at the original version, in which Glenn Close's character committed suicide to a *Madame Butterfly* aria. So the ending was made more sensational, with a slasher-movie-style battle between Close and the family she has been terrorizing. The movie was a hit, grossing US$156.6 million, and test screening was credited with the victory.

But no accurate formula has surfaced. "It certainly does not work that you can ever say, 'If X movie passes at Y level, then you can put an equal sign and come up with a box-office figure on the other side of the equation,'" Shmuger says.

For filmmakers, the process can be excruciating. "It's pretty nerve-racking to go out there with a film that's not finished and take it before an audience," Petersen says. "But if you want to check if a joke works or if a movie is too long, to find out the broad strokes, it's good. Even though it's painful to present your child that's not really born yet or ready for an audience, you do always learn something."

Audiences can point out lapses in logic, major holes or confusing things, says Robert Zemeckis (director of *What Lies Beneath*). "Sometimes it's a timing thing. I'll think, 'I anticipated a bump there in the audience, and I didn't get it. What is it?' Maybe the lead-up to it was too long or too short."

Sometimes, tests confirm filmmakers' highest expectations. That was the case with the raunchy comedy *Scary Movie*, one of summer 2000's surprise hits. "Moviegoers have been scared by teen movies for a while, and we were thinking to ourselves, 'We bet the audience wants to consider themselves ahead of the curve, and they're ready to laugh at this stuff,'" producer Bo Zenga says. "The screenings were a validation of what we were doing."

Because screenings went so well, the filmmakers moved the opening from spring to mid-July to capitalize on summer moviegoing crowds. That gave them time to shoot extra scenes with more timely jokes, including jabs at the comedy *Big Momma's House*.

Often, the information does not spell out a clear course of action, as was the case with *Shakespeare in Love*. The audience seemed to like the movie, even applauded at the end, says co-screenwriter Marc Norman. "The next day we were told there was a strange anomaly on the Q-and-A cards. They were asked, 'Would you recommend it to a friend?' And that number was somewhat less than the figure for 'Did you enjoy the movie?'"

Eventually, Norman says, "The consensus arrived at was that the movie was satisfying people all the way through until the last five minutes, and then it was kind of letting them down."

So Tom Stoppard rewrote the scene in which Shakespeare (Joseph Fiennes) says goodbye to Viola (Gwyneth Paltrow) with more passion, and the scene was reshot, even though both actors had moved on to other projects and had to be flown back to England, sets had to be rebuilt, costumes dusted off and a film crew put together. "We had no idea if this was the answer to the testing problem, and it cost Miramax quite a lot of money," Norman says.

But when the movie was put to the screening test again, the two figures were in sync, and the movie not only was a box-office success, but also won seven Oscars, including best picture.

The Blair Witch Project, *Wag the Dog*, *Seven* and *Austin Powers: International Man of Mystery* were hits that tested poorly. Among movies that have scored high but underperformed: *Titan A.E.*, *Happy, Texas* and *Iron Giant*.

If *Blair Witch* taught Hollywood anything, says Amir Malin, president of Artisan Entertainment, which released the film, "it's that formulas really can't capture whether a movie will click. In the end, you go with your gut."

Claudia Puig is a newspaper columnist who has written articles for the *National Post*.

1. ***Response***
   a. What do you think is the author's opinion about test screenings? Big-budget movies? How did you reach that conclusion?
   b. What benefits do the filmmakers derive from test screening, according to this article? Do you think it is worth the expense? Explain.
   c. Does the idea of test screening mean that we, as audiences, are getting the kind of movies we want? Is the most popular movie always the best movie? Why or why not?
   d. Consumer products, such as food, beverages, cosmetics, and cars, have long been tested on focus groups before being put into final production. Do you feel that filmmakers should respond to the feelings of the public in this way, as if they were introducing a new chocolate bar? Should novelists ever do this kind of testing too? Explain.

2. ***Media*** *Movies* Discuss movies you have seen where you left feeling completely satisfied or unsatisfied. What elements of the movie contributed to that feeling?

   Consider five box-office hits that you have seen in the past year. For each movie, list at least two recommendations that you would have made to improve them if you had been part of a test-screening audience. Discuss the movies, and your ideas with others. Explain the key change you would like to see, and give reasons why you think your change would be an improvement.

3. ***Language Conventions*** *Quotes Within Quotations* Notice in the following quotation how an internal quotation is treated:

   > "They were asked, 'Would you recommend it to a friend?' And that number was somewhat less than the figure for 'Did you enjoy the movie?'"

   Examine the article for other quotes within quotations. List the rules to follow for using punctuation and capital letters when using a quote within another quotation. Check that you have punctuated quotes correctly within your own writing.

The following selections present popular scenes from classic movies that have stood the test of time.

Screen Scenes

Scripts by various authors

The following scene comes from the movie *The Grapes of Wrath*, which is about a poor farming family during the 1930s Depression. In this scene, Tom Joad tells his mother he can no longer meekly accept the status quo of rich and poor; he plans to protest, wherever and whenever he can.

"I'll Be There"

written by Nunnally Johnson,
from *The Grapes of Wrath* by John Steinbeck

Exterior tent camp, night. Medium shot shows Ma and Tom sitting down, facing each other. Cut to close shot of Tom.

Tom Joad: I been thinking about us, too, about our people living like pigs and good rich land layin' fallow. Or maybe one guy with a million acres and a hundred thousand farmers starvin'. And I been wonderin' if all our folks got together and yelled—

Cut to close shot of Ma.

Ma Joad: Tommy, they'd drag you out and cut you down just like they done to Casey.

Cut to Tom.

Tom: They'd drag me anyways. Sooner or later they'll get me one way or another. Till then—

Cut to Ma.

MA: Tommy, you're not aimin' to kill nobody?

Cut to Tom.

TOM: No, Ma, not that. That ain't it. Just, as long as I'm an outlaw anyways, maybe I can do something, just find out somethin', just scrounge around and maybe find out what it is that's wrong *(Cut to medium shot of both.)* and see if they ain't somethin' that can be done about it. I ain't thought it out that clear, Ma. I can't. I don't know enough.

Cut to Ma.

MA: How am I gonna know about ya, Tommy? They could kill ya and I'd never know. They could hurt ya. How am I gonna know?

Cut to Tom.

TOM: Maybe it's like Casey says. A fellow ain't got a soul of his own, just a little piece of a big soul, the one big soul that belongs to everybody, then—
MA: Then what, Tom?
TOM: Then it don't matter. I'll be all around in the dark. I'll be everywhere, wherever you can look. Wherever there's a fight so hungry people can eat, I'll be there. Wherever there's a cop beatin' up a guy, I'll be there. I'll be in the way guys yell when they're mad. *(Cut to Ma.)* I'll be in the way kids laugh when they're hungry and they know supper's ready *(Cut to Tom.)* and where people are eatin' the stuff they raise and livin' in the houses they build. I'll be there, too.

Cut to Ma.

MA: I don't understand it, Tom.

Cut to medium shot both.

TOM: Me neither, Ma. But it's just somethin' I bin thinkin' about. Give me your hand Ma. *(Both stand. Camera pulls back.)* Goodbye.
MA: Later, when this is blowed over, you'll come back?
TOM: Sure, Ma.
MA: Tom, we ain't the kissin' kind, but … *(Kisses his cheek, he kisses hers.)*
TOM: Goodbye, Ma. *(He walks away, her back is to camera also.)*
MA: Goodbye, Tommy.

Long shot of Tom Joad, Ma in foreground as he disappears.

MA: Tommy.

Cut to long shot of Ma, as she collapses back onto platform. Music up, Red River Valley. Fade to long, long shot of man walking up hill, silhouetted against rising sun.

Henry Fonda and Jane Darwell in *The Grapes of Wrath*; Tom Joad's (played by Fonda) farewell scene.

Grapes of Wrath, The (1940) 129m. ★★★★ D: John Ford. Henry Fonda, Jane Darwell, John Carradine, Charley Grapewin, Dorris Bowden, Russell Simpson, John Qualen, O. Z. Whitehead, Eddie Quillan, Zeffie Tilbury, Darryl Hickman, Ward Bond, Charles Middleton, Tom Tyler, Mae Marsh, Jack Pennick. Classic Americana of Okie moving from dust bowl to California during Depression, lovingly brought to screen. Fonda, as ex-con, is unforgettable in role of his life. Darwell, as determined family matriarch, and Ford won well-deserved Oscars. Written for the screen (from John Steinbeck's classic) and produced by Nunnally Johnson. Don't miss this one.

From *Movie and Video Guide* by Leonard Maltin

In this scene from the Christmas classic, *It's a Wonderful Life*, honest, earnest George confronts his long-time enemy, Potter.

"Scurvy Little Spider"

from *It's a Wonderful Life* by Frances Goodrich, Albert Hackett, Frank Capra, and Jo Swerling

Interior scene, Potter's office; George, Potter, and his manservant are present. See all three, Potter lighting George's cigar as George leans over his desk. Cut to close up of George as he sits down in an extremely low chair, intended to place the tall George at physical disadvantage. His face is level with desk. Pull back, see George, and Potter back view.

George: *(nervously)* Well, I … I suppose I'll find out sooner or later, but just what exactly did you want to see me about?

Cut to Potter medium shot, can see George in profile still. Manservant stands to right of Potter, silent and motionless throughout.

Potter: *(laughs)* Oh, George, now that's just what I like so much about you. *(pleasantly and smoothly—like a snake)* George, I'm an old man, and most people hate me. But I don't like them either, so that makes it all even. *(Cut to George, looking surprised by this insight.)* You know just as well as I do that I run practically everything in this town but the Bailey Building and Loan. You know, also, that for a number of years I've been trying to get control of it … *(Cut to Potter.)* … or kill it. But I haven't been able to do it. You have been stopping me. In fact, you have beaten me, George, and as anyone in this county can tell you, that takes some doing. Now, take during the depression, for instance. You and I were the only ones that kept our heads. You saved the Building and Loan; I saved all the rest.
George: Yes. Well, most people say you stole all the rest.

Cut to George.

Potter: The envious ones say that, George, the suckers. *(Cut to Potter.)* Now, I have stated my side very frankly. Now, let's look at your side. *(Cut to George.)* Young man, twenty-seven, twenty-eight … married, making, say … forty a week.
George: *(indignantly)* Forty-five!

James Stewart in *It's a Wonderful Life.* This scene shows George, played by Stewart, during his conversation with Potter.

POTTER: Forty-five. Forty-five. Out of which, after supporting your mother, and paying your bills, you're able to keep, say, ten, if you skimp. A child or two comes along, and you won't even be able to save the ten. Now, if this young man of twenty-eight was a common, ordinary yokel, I'd say he was doing fine. *(Cut to Potter.)* But George Bailey is not a common, ordinary yokel. He's an intelligent, smart, ambitious young man—who hates his job—who hates the Building and Loan almost as much as I do. *(Cut to George.)* A young man who's been dying to get out on his own ever since he was born. A young man … the smartest one of the crowd, mind you, a young man who has to sit by and watch his friends go places, because he's trapped. Yes, sir, trapped into frittering his life away playing nursemaid to a lot of garlic-eaters. *(Cut to Potter.)* Do I paint a correct picture, or do I exaggerate?

Cut to George.

GEORGE: *(taken aback)* Now what's your point, Mr. Potter?
POTTER: My point? My point is, I want to hire you.
GEORGE: *(dumbfounded)* Hire me?

POTTER: I want you to manage my affairs, run my properties. George, I'll start you out at twenty thousand dollars a year.

George drops his cigar on his lap. He nervously brushes off the sparks from his clothes. Stands.

GEORGE: *(flabbergasted)* Twenty thou—twenty thousand dollars a year?

Cut to Potter; George in profile in shot.

POTTER: You wouldn't mind living in the nicest house in town, buying your wife a lot of fine clothes, a couple of business trips to New York a year, maybe once in a while Europe. You wouldn't mind that, would you, George?

Cut to George.

GEORGE: Would I? *(looking around skeptically)* You're not talking to somebody else around here, are you? You know, this is me, you remember me? George Bailey.

Cut to Potter.

POTTER: Oh, yes, George Bailey. Whose ship has just come in—*(Cut to George—see back of Potter's head.)* providing he has brains enough to climb aboard. (*Cut to Potter smiling. Cut to George grinning. He sits in low chair.)*

GEORGE: Hah! Holy Mackerel. Well, how about the Building and Loan?

Cut to Potter—gesturing angrily.

POTTER: Oh, confound it, man, are you afraid of success? I'm offering you a three-year contract at twenty thousand dollars a year, starting today. *(Cut to George.)* Is it a deal or isn't it?
GEORGE: *(stands)* Well, Mr. Potter, I … I … I know I ought to jump at the chance, but I … I just … I wonder if it would be possible for you to give me twenty-four hours to think it over?

In my films I always wanted to make people see deeply. I don't want to show things, but to give people the desire to see.

Agnès Varda

Cut to Potter, smoothly understanding.

POTTER: Sure, sure, sure. You go on home and talk about it to your wife.
GEORGE: I'd like to do that.
POTTER: Yeah. In the meantime, I'll draw up the papers.
GEORGE: *(still seemingly hypnotized by the sum)* All right, sir.
POTTER: *(offers hand)* Okay, George?

Cut to George, leaning over, offering hand.

GEORGE: *(taking his hand)* Okay, Mr. Potter.

As they shake hands, George feels a physical revulsion, frowns. In that moment of physical contact he knows he could never be associated with this man. George drops his hand with a shudder, wipes hand on suit. He peers intently into Potter's face.

GEORGE: *(vehemently, shaking off his earlier daze)* No … no … no … no, now wait a minute, here! *(Cut to Potter.)* Wait a minute! *(Cut to George.)* I don't need twenty-four hours. I don't have to talk to anybody! I know right now, and the answer is no! NO! Doggone it! *(getting madder all the time)* You sit around here and you spin your little webs and you think the whole world revolves around you and your money. Well, it doesn't, Mr. Potter! In the … in the whole vast configuration of things, I'd say you were nothing but a scurvy little spider. You … *(He turns and shouts at the manservant, impassive as ever beside Potter's wheelchair.)* And that goes for you, too! *(sticks cigar in mouth, heads to door, saying to the secretary in the outer office as he leaves)* And it goes for you, too!

It's a Wonderful Life (1946) 129m. ★★★★ D: Frank Capra. James Stewart, Donna Reed, Lionel Barrymore, Thomas Mitchell, Henry Travers, Beulah Bondi, Frank Faylen, Ward Bond, Gloria Grahame, H.B. Warner, Frank Albertson, Todd Karns, Samuel S. Hinds, Mary Treen, Sheldon Leonard, Ellen Corby. Sentimental tale of Stewart, who works all his life to make good in small town, thinking he's failed and trying to end his life. Guardian angel Travers comes to show him his mistake. Only Capra and this cast could pull it off so well; this film seems to improve with age. Capra, Frances Goodrich, Albert Hackett, and Jo Swerling expanded Philip Van Doren Stern's short story "The Greatest Gift" (which had originally been written by Stern as a Christmas card!) Remade for TV as *It Happened One Christmas*. Also shown in computer-colored version.

From *Movie and Video Guide* by Leonard Maltin

In this scene from the movie *A Raisin in the Sun*, Asagai visits a friend, Beneatha, on her moving day. What was supposed to be a day of triumph for Beneatha—moving into a bigger place—turns into a day of despair when she discovers her brother has been conned out of the insurance money that was to pay for a new home.

"I'M TIRED OF LISTENING"

from *A Raisin in the Sun* by Lorraine Hansberry

Interior apartment. Beneatha sitting, knock on door. Beneatha opens door to Asagai. He comes in, talking, rolling up sleeves, moving around room.

ASAGAI: I had some free time so I came over. I thought I might help with the packing. Oh-ho, I love the look of packing crates! The sight of a household in preparation. Movement, progress—It makes me think of Africa.
BENEATHA: Africa!
ASAGAI: Well, what kind of mood is this? I thought I'd find you full of sunlight today? Have I told you how deeply you move me? *(approaches her to hold her face. She puts her own hands up to face, breaking down—he begins to realize she is upset.)* Something wrong?
BENEATHA: Asagai, he gave away the money.
ASAGAI: Who gave away what money?
BENEATHA: The insurance money. My brother, he just gave it away. *(she moves away, agitated)*
ASAGAI: Gave it away?
BENEATHA: He made an investment! With a man even Travis [her nephew] wouldn't have trusted with his most worn-out marbles!
ASAGAI: And it's gone?
BENEATHA: Gone!
ASAGAI: I see. I'm very sorry.
BENEATHA: But you know, my brother's not the one who's to blame. Oh no, by *his* lights he did what made sense to him. My mama's the crazy one. My mama's the one who just handed him the money. She just got up one fine day and just gave away my future.
ASAGAI: *(approaching her)* Perhaps you don't see things as well as your mother does?
BENEATHA: Oh this is the end for me. You know, it takes money to go to school ...Well what difference does it make anyway? I mean, why would anybody want to be a doctor in this nutty world?

From left to right: Diana Sands, Sidney Poitier, and Ruby Dee in *A Raisin in the Sun.* Diana Sands plays Beneatha, the sister of Sidney Poitier's character.

Asagai: My, aren't we full of despair? ... Look here, was it your money? *(takes her shoulders, turns him to face her)* I said, was it your money that was lost?
Beneatha: It belonged to all of us.
Asagai: Can't this make you see that there is something *wrong* *(gestures with both hands)* if all the dreams in this house—good or bad—

had to depend on something that might never have happened—if a man had not died? We used to say, back home, accident was at the first and will be at the last—but a poor tree from which the fruits of life may bloom.

Beneatha: Asagai, what is the matter with you? Listen, my family has been wiped out! *(moves away)* What's the matter—don't they use money where you come from?

Asagai: *(following her)* I see only that you, with all of your keen mind, cannot understand the greatness of the thing that your mother tried to do. You're not too young to understand. For all of her backwardness she still acts. She still believes that she can change things. And to that extent she is more of the future than you are at this moment.

Beneatha: Well, all I know is that when somebody can get up in the morning and, without consulting you, *(she moves away, back to Asagai)* just blithely hand away your future then life is impossible, it's futile. It's despair!

Asagai: Listen …

Beneatha: No! I'm tired of listenin'. *(moves towards door)*

Raisin in the Sun, A (1961) 128m. ★★★★ D: Daniel Petrie. Sidney Poitier, Claudia McNeil, Ruby Dee, Diana Sands, Ivan Dixon, John Fiedler, Louis Gossett. Lorraine Hansberry play receives perceptive handling by outstanding cast in drama of black Chicago family's attempts to find sense in their constrained existence. Remade for TV in 1991.

From *Movie and Video Guide* by Leonard Maltin

1. *Response*

a. What emotions do the characters portray during each of the scenes in this selection? What clues to their emotions are there in the words they use?

b. What is the message—implicit or explicit—of each scene?

c. Considering the year in which each movie was released and the scene included here, what do you think was the audience's reaction to each movie at the time it was released?

d. Read the capsule reviews that appear after each scene. Discuss the features of these capsule reviews. Compare them to full-length movie reviews from newspapers or magazines.

2. ***Language Conventions*** *Non-Standard English* Discuss the language in these three scenes and why most of the scriptwriters have used non-standard English. What else do you notice about the dialogue? What does the language reveal about the characters? Is the language of each scene appropriate? Effective? Explain.

   Examine a piece of your own writing and the dialogue your characters use. How can you make your characters seem more real by using non-standard or informal English?

3. ***Drama*** *Presenting the Scene* With a partner, plan a presentation of one of these scenes. Think about the gestures you will use, and the position of your bodies. As well, experiment with volume, pace, and tone, as you rehearse. When you are ready, present this scene to your class.

4. ***Media*** *Directing Movies* Like novelists, movie directors develop scenes to create tension, move the action along, and establish character. With a small group, discuss the stage direction included with each of these scenes. Are there any terms you do not understand? Focus on one scene, and consider the effectiveness of its direction. If possible, view this scene, and make notes on how effectively the director creates tension, moves the action along, or establishes character. How would you change this scene or its direction?

5. ***Writing*** *Personal Response* Consider your personal response to one of these scenes. Choose a suitable writing format—a letter, poem, story, script, essay, et cetera—to convey your response to an audience of your peers.

If there wasn't something called
acting, they would probably hospitalize
people like me.

—*Whoopi Goldberg*

This selection takes you behind the scenes at *CTV News* with a news researcher. Are there any aspects of the job that surprise you?

JUST *the* FACTS

Diary by Sue Kanhai

How best can I describe my fabulous job? No two days are ever the same. There's no telling who you'll bump into in the hallway. And there's only one way to know what sort of day you're about to have—by jumping in. Each day I see some of Canada's most famous and respected news anchors and I talk to national reporters about the stories they're working on.

Our department works together in a fairly small, bustling room. We each have workspaces that include a desk, computer, filing cabinet, TV, and tape cueing machine. We screen footage daily, and so make good use of our gadgets. It's quite normal to hear phones ringing, producers or editors chatting about a request, newscasters burbling away on various TV sets, and the sounds from different video segments being cued and viewed nearby all at the same time. Depending on your mood, it can be a mild, pleasant hum or a maddening cacophony! Shelves of dictionaries, encyclopedias, government publications, directories, almanacs, newspapers, magazines, and videotapes surround us. These are very well-thumbed resources, and are kept close at hand. Our more traditional-looking, proper library—with floor-to-ceiling shelves of more news magazines, cross-Canada newspapers, political policy books, microfiche, a full tape vault, and newspaper clippings files—is just a flight of stairs away.

The chatter and buzz can be amusing. There's the bored, "How many seats did the Liberals have at dissolution again?", the frantic, "Who took the mayor's press conference from yesterday?", and the exasperated, "How ON EARTH do you spell deoxyribonucleic acid?" My co-workers are amazing; I can pick up so much sometimes from just sitting back and surveying the activity. As in any workplace, each person has his or her own area(s) of interest; here, particularly, the benefits multiply. It's incredible the amount of specific, detailed information our group has at its fingertips.

Now that you know a little about our environment, let me take you through a day-in-the-life of a news researcher.

9 – 10 a.m.

Ah, the morning, such a rare opportunity for peace and quiet! After settling in and checking my e-mail, I begin perusing one of our four daily newspapers; I also scan the news wires to see what's lined up for today. Soon I'm called into action. One of the producers from *CTV Newsnet* is looking for an expert who can speak on camera early this afternoon about a recent court ruling. We happen to have an excellent in-house resource, a co-worker at *Canada AM* who has many contacts; I consult her for any leads. While she's looking, I decide to try *The Blue Book*, University of Toronto's resource for journalists that lists over 1600 academic experts. I also scan recent articles on the subject from our clippings file for people who've commented in the past. Together, we forward the producer three names, with job titles and phone numbers.

10 – 11 a.m.

Yesterday it was reported that one of the major political parties had a carefully worded but contentious proposal buried in its election platform. The leader of the party tried to play it down when questioned about it, and we ran his response on last night's broadcast. Today, an assignment editor at the national news desk would like to know the stances of the other four parties on this same issue. To begin, I visit each party's Web site and do a keyword search of each platform. This turns up little, for several reasons. First, the exact wording used by each party can and does vary. Second, as turned out to be the case here, perhaps not all parties chose to include the information in their platforms. After discussing it with a fellow researcher, we decide that calling party headquarters is next. We leave detailed messages, and hope our calls will be returned before the end of the day.

11 – 12 p.m.

An active case of tuberculosis has been detected in a Toronto neighbourhood, and we are called with both video and research requests. Needed: footage of doctors examining chest X-rays and adults getting vaccinations against TB, as well as general information about TB. A co-worker pitches in to find the footage, while I search for information. My first stop is Health Canada's Web site; I'm looking for any past warnings or advisories that have been issued. Next I search both the Internet and our own newspaper clippings files for the symptoms, causes, and treatments of the disease. Information from Health Canada and a good medical piece from one of our national newspapers will suffice. I e-mail the document to the reporter who requested the info, and my co-worker arranges to have the footage fed to their bureau.

12 – 1 p.m.

A piece of proposed legislation that was tabled months ago resurfaces for discussion. It's been a while since the topic's been in the news, and a reporter would like an update. She's looking for summary and analysis pieces specifically. We use several fee-for-service databases that allow us to search magazines, newspapers, and journals from all over the world. These articles are extremely useful in providing both context and an overview of complex situations. The costs for these services (mostly online) vary, but are generally pretty substantial. The one drawback is that only text is available. For charts, graphs, and statistics, we have to rely on our own clippings files. To help reduce search time, we've had training in search strategies by the companies that build these databases. I search by keyword (including combinations of keywords), publication, date, and word length, and, happily, find exactly what I need. A copy of the file is shared with our electronic news service, as we think they might appreciate the update.

1 – 2 p.m.

There's just enough time for a quick lunch before another request rolls in. The promotions department is cutting a promo for tonight's national news broadcast. They need stock shots of busy shoppers walking in a mall to indicate recent retailing statistics. They would also like yesterday's footage of the Russian president's visit to Cuba, as he is due to arrive in Ottawa shortly.

2 – 3 p.m.

A leading international political figure died on this day nearly thirty years ago. A memorial is to be held, which we will run footage of, but a head shot of the man is needed by graphics. Each of the news items we archive on tape has a record created for it that describes its contents. This is called the *shotlist.* We can search our records for this man, and by reading the codes in the shotlist, we can see whether or not a story contains the type of shot we're looking for—in this case a MCU (medium close-up), CU (close-up), or H&S (head & shoulders) shot.

A graphic artist will work with the video we've selected and create an over-the-shoulder graphic from it. (These typically sit on the upper right-hand corner of your screen, over the anchor's shoulder, as he or she reads the intro to a story.) While I seek this out, a co-worker does a quick encyclopedia and Internet search for background information on this man. He's looking for the exact spelling of a political sect and highlights of his major accomplishments.

3 – 4 p.m.

A lull in the afternoon. Downtime like this, while rare, is easy to fill in a place this busy. I can check the wires for the latest news, finish looking through the day's newspapers, and catch up on some outstanding archiving. Each day one of us is assigned to archive the previous night's national news broadcast. We analyse each story filed, looking for good visuals, memorable statements, and important events or meetings. The test we apply is: Is this newsworthy enough that it'll be valuable five or ten years from now? Certain significant events it's obvious we should keep for historical value: a peace treaty being signed, a space mission, election coverage, etc. But this is just the beginning. Someone (or some thing) may not *seem* terribly important, but if a search of our database shows we have no existing similar footage, it may well be worth keeping. We'll often ask each other's opinions.

4 – 5 p.m.

A producer from *W-Five* has requested the monthly national unemployment rate for each month of the current year. We must always provide the source of our research, and are always looking for up-to-date, reliable information. Good sites to rely on include those run by the government, universities, or professional associations. It's imperative that we analyse any possible bias in the figures we send on. By using good judgment first, and then providing our source, we can be reasonably sure the information is reliable. Ultimately, the decision rests with whoever requested the figures.

Writer, editor, and researcher **Sue Kanhai** studied French Language, Literature, and Translation at the University of Toronto. She reads widely and avidly and enjoys writing both fiction and non-fiction. She has worked in publishing, but is currently employed as a researcher for a national news program.

1. ***Response***
   a. Before reading this article, what did you think a modern newsroom was like?
   b. How did this article change your perceptions about a modern newsroom?
   c. How would you describe the tone of this piece and the diction the author uses? What contributes to the tone?
   d. What aspect of being a news researcher would you like most? Least?
   e. Discuss a news program you have watched recently, considering the questions listed under the headings About the text, About production, and About the audience in Cam MacPherson's article "Looking at the Media."

2. ***Research and Inquiry*** Use print or human resources, or the Internet, to find out about another behind-the-scenes job at a news station. What training, education, and background does the job require? What skills or talents are needed to do the job effectively? As a class, share your information about the different jobs people perform to bring you a newscast.

3. ***Media*** *Preparing the News* With a small group, plan and create a video newscast for a local or school event. Each person in the group can assume the role of a different person behind the scenes at a news station, from researcher to newscaster.

While news is important, news interpretation
is far more important.
—*H. V. Kaltenborn*

What drives an editorial cartoonist? Read on to find out.

Laughter Soothes His Soul

Profile
by Paul Melting Tallow

Everett Soop's body is frail and weak, but his heart and soul are as strong as the Rocky Mountains that watch over him and the land that he loves.

He's lived with the muscular dystrophy that has confined him to a wheelchair for 40 years, with diabetes further ravaging his body. Despite all the physical adversity he's faced in life, his great spiritual strength has allowed him to look back with few regrets and little bitterness.

Born on the Blood Reserve in southwestern Alberta in 1943, Everett was raised in an area of the reserve known as Bull Horn, near the town of Cardston. His childhood was typical for the children of the Blackfoot-speaking Bloods, or Ahkainah (Many Chiefs), as they call themselves, carefree with no concern for the world outside the reserve. Time was spent playing with his friends, riding horses and getting into mischief.

"For me it was a happy childhood because I didn't know what was going on. Ignorance is bliss, I guess."

Everett's hunger for knowledge gave him the driving force to continue on at the Cardston schools until he eventually graduated from Grade 12 in 1963, unlike many who had followed him into town. He was one of only three Ahkainah students to graduate.

"In Grade 7, there must have been about 40 or 50 of us but they all quit." Everett remembers the subtle and overt racism from students that made it difficult for him and his fellow Ahkainah students to attend school. He said he believed that, in order to deal with the racism and ostracism, the two other Ahkainah students who graduated had to convert to the church.

Undaunted, Everett's determination to succeed was as solid as the stone in the Mormon temple rising across the street from the school and he survived because, "I didn't give a damn. I just wanted to get an education and that was all."

In addition to his tenacity, he had his strong-willed mother, Josephine, to push him and support him through all the adversities. He said she began cracking her whip to drive him to work hard at achieving his goals when he was a child and, now that she's 85 years old, she's still cracking that whip over his head. But he knows the whip was wielded by a gentle, loving hand.

It was during his time at the Cardston schools that he first displayed his talent for cartooning; combining his acerbic wit and artistic talents to satirize his teachers, fellow students and family members.

After his high school graduation, Everett sought to enhance his artistic qualities by enrolling at art schools in Banff and Calgary. At the Alberta College of Art in Calgary, Everett once again encountered racism. An instructor told Everett that he didn't expect too much from him because he was Native and Natives were not known for their success.

"He said we've only had two and they didn't amount to anything. One of them was Gerald Tailfeathers and the other one was Alex Janvier. Those were really good examples to fail and I wanted to become a failure like them."

Tailfeathers received commissions for his work from the Canadian Pavilion at Expo 67, the Glenbow Museum in Calgary and Canada Post. Janvier was advisor at the Expo 67 Indians of Canada Pavilion, a member of the Professional Native Indian Artists Incorporated, represented Canada in a Canadian/Chinese cultural exchange in 1985 and was commissioned to create murals at the Canadian Museum of Civilization.

Unfortunately, since the provincial government sponsored his education, Soop had to abide by its rules. One rule was he could not miss more than 10 percent of total class time; Everett missed 14 percent so he was suspended for a year. Undeterred, he enrolled in the arts program at Brigham Young University in Utah. It was at the university that he discovered journalism could be the perfect medium to express his artistic abilities and his satirical wit.

"In the back of my mind I've always enjoyed editorial cartooning. It never occurred to me 'til I was down there ... that [editorial cartooning] was my real interest."

He returned to Calgary to enroll in the journalism program at the Mount Royal College and to be closer to home and family. Unfortunately, social conditions prevalent in Calgary's newsrooms and the rest of the country did not favor Native journalists.

At the end of his first year of studies in 1968, Everett got a summer job drawing cartoons for the Blood Reserve's *Kainai News*. The newspaper, one of Canada's first, albeit government-funded, Native newspapers, was just beginning its inaugural year of publication.

"My first day on the job they were having their editorial meeting and they were talking about the dog situation in Cardston. I started coming up with outrageous ideas like maybe the dogs were showing us the way. The Mormons in Cardston and the Bloods will not mix, but if the dogs can mix, maybe we can mix. The sarcasm went right to work and I felt right at home."

He didn't return to Mount Royal and the summer job turned into a career. *Kainai News* became his home for the next 13 years.

Everett's political cartoons soon gained him fame and notoriety in Native communities across Canada and the United States. With each issue his cartoons became more and more outrageous and satirical until the editorial staff had to rein him in. Everett denies full responsibility for his stinging observations but, humbly, shares the credit with everyone at the newspaper.

"It became a lot of fun because I wasn't alone. Maybe it looks like I got the credit all the time but everybody had their input, throwing their ideas."

Everett's cartoons became so popular in the community that the paper allowed him to express his views in his own column. He continued to tickle the funny bones of his friends and admirers while ruffling the feathers of his victims.

Scorn and even threats of bodily harm from those that he offended did little to discourage him; instead, he developed a thick skin. Although his favorite targets were the politicians he considered pompous and who considered themselves infallible, he addressed all social injustices and issues.

"Humor really has nothing to do with being funny. It's about being angry. Seeing all these things that are corrupt, that are destroying us, the injustices."

While most of his opinions were formed by his empathy for the victims of injustice, the underdogs as he calls them, he received encouragement from the more socially aware in the upper strata of reserve society.

The late Senator James Gladstone, Canada's first Aboriginal senator, saw the need for Everett's brand of humor and his criticism of politicians. The senator was there to give Everett emotional support when he felt like quitting.

These images are examples of Soop's work. The image at top left is the cover for his book called *I See My Tribe Is Still Behind Me!*, a collection of his editorials and cartoons. Soop's controversial cartoons and editorials angered many in his community.

"He talked to me for a while and I was all perked up and ready to go again. With that kind of encouragement I got meaner and it got more fun."

With his satirizing of politicians, it was ironic that he ran for and won a seat on the Blood Band council in 1982. He claims government cutbacks that resulted in his losing his position at *Kainai News* forced him into the political arena. He had ambitions of returning to art school but the nearest ones in California and Indiana were too far away.

His stay in Utah had proven that it was too expensive for him to attend art school in the United States, especially with Canadian currency on the short end of the exchange rate.

"So I thought, 'why not go into council?' That would be equal to a Ph.D. in cartooning. Besides that, I had been calling them jackasses for 15 years. I wanted to know what it's like being a jackass."

During his time in office, Everett continued to champion the underdog and the disadvantaged, in particular, the physically disabled. He was appointed to chair the council's health committee in 1985 and was instrumental in the opening of the reserve's health centre. Although many in his community give him the credit for the health centre, his humility will not allow him to accept it.

"It was started a good 20 years before then. A lot of people worked towards it and it didn't happen until they were long gone."

It helped him to understand that the rewards of hard work don't become immediately apparent, unlike most politicians who he says claim the results of years of hard work by their predecessors as their own accomplishments.

These days life is slower for Everett, diabetes and muscular dystrophy have all but consumed his body and put severe limitations on his activity.

Throughout the years of living with his disabilities, it was Everett's humor that gave him the courage to face life and it now gives him the strength to continue living. He's even able to find humor in the enormous difficulty performing simple functions that his disabilities have caused.

"I find every difficulty and every adversity in my life funny.... I think humor has been a gift given to me, not just to share with others, but for myself to survive, to be able to laugh at myself. Other than that, what else is there to do but cry?"

Paul Melting Tallow is a journalist and photographer. He has worked for *Alberta Sweetgrass*, the Aboriginal newspaper of Alberta, and has contributed articles to *Windspeaker*, Canada's national Aboriginal news source.

1. ***Response***
   a. Reread the first paragraph of this article again and decide whether you think the author's description of Soop is exaggerated. Develop your own simile to describe Soop.
   b. Discuss Soop's words: "I find every difficulty and every adversity in my life funny.... I think humor has been a gift given to me, not just to share with others, but for myself to survive, to be able to laugh at myself. Other than that, what else is there to do but cry?"
   c. Was there any part of Everett Soop's story that you found particularly striking? If so, what and why?
   d. What qualities, skills, and characteristics do you think make someone a good editorial cartoonist?

2. ***Visual Communication*** *Analyse Art* Examine the four cartoons in this selection. How does Soop create humour using both text and visuals? What words would you use to describe these cartoons? Everett Soop and Paul Melting Tallow speak of Soop's cartoons as being controversial, and raising the ire of both the Aboriginal and non-Aboriginal communities. Is there anything in these examples of his work that would account for their reactions? Explain.

3. ***Vocabulary*** Notice how this article spells *humour* (humor) using the American spelling, and uses the Canadian spelling for *centre*. Why might the author have used both American and Canadian spelling? What effect does it have on the reader? Do you think using Canadian spelling is important? Why or why not?

4. ***Media*** *Editorial Cartoons* Collect at least twelve editorial cartoons from more than one newspaper or source, and from several artists. Compare the content, subject matter, bias, and humour of each cartoon, and the artists' styles. Choose one cartoon and write a brief report outlining its purpose, audience, and effectiveness.

5. ***Research and Inquiry*** Find out more about the editorial-cartooning career of Everett Soop or another artist. Develop a short profile of the person, including examples of his or her work. Prepare a multi-media presentation for this cartoonist, for example, using slides, video, music, and words.

"What's a multi-hued collection of 300,000 data points to do?"

"CYBERANCHOR" Delivers All the E-News That's Fit to Click

Newspaper article by Ann Perry

Two days after her Internet debut, newscast phenom Ananova has invitations to Britain's top parties and two marriage proposals.

With all those options, what's a multi-hued collection of 300,000 data points to do?

"I think what we've got to make sure is that she doesn't get too big-headed," said Debbie Stephens, a press officer with Ananova Ltd. "We're keeping a careful eye on her social calendar."

Billed as the world's first virtual newscaster, the computer-generated cyberanchor, whose delicate features, big eyes, green neo-punk hair and sensitive delivery have already inspired outpourings of fan devotion, reads breaking news at the click of a mouse.

Judging from the traffic at Ananova's Web site, she's a huge hit, with millions of cyberviewers clicking in since her debut in April 2000.

"This is a day to remember just like man's first step on the moon," said an e-mail message from Eric Dufort of Quebec.

Another fan wrote: "The future is here at Ananova ... You're the best in the world."

But James Burns couldn't believe his eyes—or ears. "Very realistic," he wrote. "Are you sure she's not real?"

All this attention begs the question—who is Ananova?

The origin of her name has already sparked debate, but her creators claim they chose it simply because it's unique.

On her Web site, Ananova warns against making up nicknames such as "Ana" or "Nova" on pain of her "blowing a few circuits."

Younger than this millennium, Ananova's baby pictures consist of a series of drawings and computer models that document her rise from featureless *tabula rasa* to 28-year-old newsreading cyberbabe with a three-dimensional head that comprises 300,000 constantly changing data points.

Her creators at Ananova Ltd., formerly the new media division of Britain's Press Association news agency, sifted through hundreds of photographs to develop a composite drawing that was sent to Glasgow-based Digital Animations Group for the cybersurgery that would bring her to life.

What they came up with was a green-haired cross between Posh Spice and computer game action hero Lara Croft from *Tomb Raider.*

"We wanted someone who was going to be distinctive, someone who was going to be easily recognizable and we wanted to try to get away from the blonde and brunette stereotype," said Stephens.

But in a business that worships youth, Ananova isn't just another pretty face.

Her brain is a powerful Internet tool that continuously searches more than 10,000 Web sites around the world to gather breaking news and automatically index the information into subject areas.

A team of 30 journalists and editors sifts through the mass of information, choosing the top stories and deciding what Ananova is going to say.

After that, the techies input the text and code it with appropriate emotional tags that prompt Ananova to deliver her two-minute newscasts with appropriate feeling and flair with the press of a button by her techno-puppeteers.

From a sombre update on clashes between farmers and war veterans in Zimbabwe, Ananova can change her mood for a less-serious story with a raised eyebrow and a fetching smile while intoning: "How bizarre is this?"

When Ananova's creators found their own British English pronunciation too formal, they opted for a neutral "mid-Atlantic" accent that blends British, American and Canadian cadences.

While Ananova has not been in the news business long enough to become a diva, she's definitely high maintenance. She has a crack staff of 80 designers, information technology developers, producers and journalists working around the clock to put words in her mouth.

Still, the technology behind her isn't all that new.

Ananova is simply a marriage of a text-to-speech system to video animation, synchronizing the movement of her mouth and her voice—technologies that already operate on Saturday morning cartoons.

What is innovative about Ananova, say her creators, is the speed with which she can adapt to the pressure-cooker environment of breaking news.

"To actually get a system that can uphold that kind of traffic and to be able to change it on literally split-second notice so she can change her mannerisms, voice, and the information she's delivering, that's what's ground-breaking," said Stephens.

But the buzz among Web surfers isn't so much about Ananova's bits and bytes as her instant celebrity style.

After media hype began swirling around the mysterious green-haired waif in January, her corporate managers ran a competition that attracted tens of thousands of entries from around the world to decide on her first words.

The result? An edgy—if somewhat stilted— "Hello, world. Here is the news—and this time it's personal."

Ananova's personal life has already galvanized Internet entrepreneurs who are lining up to create the personality behind the pixels.

A European architectural firm has volunteered to design a tastefully decorated home for Ananova. The only problem is she'll need a body first.

But that shouldn't be hard for a popular gal like Ananova who's getting the kind of offers from fans usually reserved for living, breathing news anchors. Some leading British designers are already jockeying to build what, according to rumours, will be her slender 5-foot-7 frame.

Despite Ananova's instant fame—she has already done interviews on NBC and CNN—skeptics say that, like digitized icon Max Headroom of the 1980s, her cyberstar will soon fade.

"It's a cute technology that will execute what you tell it to do, but to suggest that it has real artificial intelligence and understanding of what it's reading is misleading," said Jordan Worth, an Internet analyst at International Data Corp. (Canada) Ltd.

But Worth worries certain advantages of cyberanchors like Ananova may put flesh-and-blood newscasters out of business.

"You can fire them on a whim, you can replace them and their demands are minimal," deadpanned Worth about cyberjournalists. "There are probably no digital prima donnas to deal with. But at the same time they don't provide much fodder for the tabloids and *Frank*,[1] so that's, in my mind, a bad thing."

Unlike her human counterparts, however, Ananova will commit no unseemly bloopers. Why? Because Ananova's nothing short of e-perfect.

[1] ***Frank:*** a satirical magazine

Ann Perry is a newspaper columnist who has written articles for *The Toronto Star.*

1. ***Response***
   a. Discuss how and why Ananova was created.
   b. Even though viewers know that Ananova is just an electronic fake, why do they like her? Why do you think Ananova has become an overnight sensation?
   c. Discuss the phrases *media hype, media sensations,* and *overnight success.* How are these concepts connected? Use other current examples in your discussion.

2. ***Media*** *Designing a Cyberanchor* What image has Ananova been created to project? If you were part of the design team creating another cyberanchor for a competing news site, what type of appearance and image would you want to achieve? Describe your design and image in detail. Consider gender, ethnic background, and age as three of your criteria.

3. ***Research and Inquiry*** Check out the Ananova site, if you are not already familiar with it. What is your reaction to Ananova and her skills as a newsreader? Is she "real" enough for you? Do you agree with the final decisions of her designers? What changes would you suggest making to her voice and appearance?

   Examine the Web site carefully and evaluate the style and substance of what it offers in comparison to other online news sites. To find the location of other sites, use the key words *online news sites.*

4. ***Critical Thinking*** When a newsreader can be digitized so effectively, why bother with a human? What are the advantages of creations like Ananova over human newsreaders? How would you feel about the elimination of human anchors on network TV newscasts, and their replacement by Ananova's cybercolleagues?

   What lies ahead for Ananova and other computer-generated "people" on the Internet? Do you see other areas where such artificial people could find work? Explain.

On the news two dozen events of fantastically different importance are announced in exactly the same tone of voice. The voice doesn't discriminate between a divorce, a horse race, a war in the Middle East.

—*Doris Lessing*

Brainstorm a list of new media or computer technologies that you think will affect your world. How will you fit into this world?

The Net Generation

Article by Don Tapscott

The baby boom was the biggest population wave ever—until it was eclipsed by the Net Generation. The N-Generation now represents 30 percent of the population, compared to the boomers' 29 percent. For the first time, there is another generation large enough to rival the cultural hegemony of the ubiquitous boomers. But what makes N-Geners unique is not just their large numbers, but that they are growing up during the dawn of a completely new interactive medium of communication. Just as the much more limited medium of television influenced the values and culture of the baby boomers, a new force is helping shape the N-Gen wave. They are spending their formative years in a context and environment fundamentally different from their parents.

Many people think the new media and television are analogous because they both involve screens. For example, the term *screenagers* has been used to describe today's youth. TV viewers and Net surfers alike have been called *couch potatoes*. Social critic Neil Postman has said that through the information highway, information is becoming a new form of garbage—and with computers and televisions we will all be "amusing ourselves to death," the title of his 1994 book.

Those who say that the Net is all about a bigger crop of couch potatoes not only have a cynical view of humanity, but they ignore the budding experience with interactive technologies. Unfortunately for these commentators and fortunately for kids, the similarities between the two technologies end with the screen. In fact, the shift is more like from couch potato to Nintendo jockey.

TV is controlled by adults. Kids are passive observers. In contrast, children control much of their world on the Net. It is something they do themselves; they are users, and they are active. They do not just observe, they participate. They inquire, discuss, argue, play, shop, critique, investigate, ridicule, fantasize, seek, and inform.

This makes the Internet fundamentally different from previous communications innovations, such as the development of the printing press or the introduction of radio and television broadcasting. These latter technologies are unidirectional and controlled by adults. They are very hierarchical, inflexible, and centralized. Not surprisingly, they reflect the values of their adult owners. By contrast, the new media is interactive, malleable, and distributed in control. As such it cherishes a much greater neutrality. The new media will do what we command of them. And at this moment, tens of millions of N-Geners around the world are taking over the steering wheel.

This distinction is at the heart of the new generation. For the first time ever, children are taking control of critical elements of a communications revolution.

On the Net, children must search for, rather than simply look at, information. This forces them to develop thinking and investigative skills, and much more. They must become critics. Which Web sites are good? How can I tell what is real and what is fictitious—whether it's a data source or the alleged teenage movie star in a chat session?

Further, children begin to question assumptions previously unchallenged. On the Net, there is a great diversity of opinion regarding all things and constant opportunities to present your views. This is leading to a generation which increasingly questions the implicit values contained in information. Information becomes knowledge through the application of human judgment. As children interact with each other and the exploding information resources on the Net, they are forced to exercise not only their critical thinking but their judgment. This process is contributing to the relentless breakdown of the notion of authority and experience-driven hierarchies. Increasingly, young people are the masters of the interactive environment and of their own fate in it.

Because the Net is the antithesis of TV, the N-Generation is in many ways the antithesis of the TV generation.

The Web That Ate TV

There are, of course, aspects to TV which have been positive. Not all content is vacuous: TV is a distribution channel for good movies, documentaries, sports events, music, comedy, interviews, and news. It's simple to use. Most of us have programs which we know and usually enjoy. The quality of TV in terms of production values is usually high, especially when compared to most current Web sites. TV and radio have also acquired a level of interactivity with talk shows and phone-in programs such as *Larry King Live*. TV is also somewhat a communal experience as you sit with others in front of the electronic hearth.

There is also a role for passivity. As Frank Biondi, former president and CEO of Viacom, says, "TV is, at bottom, a passive experience, which is its beauty." In other words, the great thing about television is that you can come home after a long day at school or work and veg out in front of the TV.

True, there is some couch potato in all of us, including kids. On Saturday night, your son and his girlfriend may want to sit on the couch and be entertained rather than to construct some elaborate Net experience. Sometimes we want the content to rule rather than ourselves. Indeed, opportunities for "veging" in the digital economy will be even greater than today.

In 1997, it became very fashionable to talk about so-called *push technology* or *Web-casting*. Simply put, content is pushed to your screen rather than you seeking it. Instead of surfing the Net for information, content providers send you new information from categories you have previously requested—such as sports scores for your favorite teams, stocks you care about, the weather, and eventually anything. *The Wall Street Journal* proclaimed that the Net had finally found a viable business model—television.[1] *Business Week* announced that Web-casting would cut through the clutter of the Net "using the same principle as broadcasting."[2] Screen saver software—using push technology to bring customized news and information to the screen when your computer is idle—took off.

In reality, push technology is not a return to broadcasting but simply another thread in the richly developing tapestry of the Net. Over time, such Web-casting, including the casting of live TV programs, will be assimilated into the Net.

But television is not dead, just television as we know it—a rigid, one-way medium delivered by networks that schedule programming according to their estimates of likely viewership. Those who view the Net as another TV channel have got it backward. Sometime early in the next century, television programs will become accessible through the Net. Rather than talking about TV versus the Net, we will talk about stored access of content versus real-time access. In *stored* (asynchronous) access, the user picks up previously sorted content (information, music video, a drama, sitcom, news program) when convenient. In *real-time* (synchronous) use, people access content (a sports game, election reporting) as it is occurring.

Your favorite TV shows will become a Web incident or site. First viewings of a sitcom, soap, or events like a football game or presidential address will be watched simultaneously by many. Such real-time simultaneous transmissions simply become part of the interactive world. TV schedules will be subordinated to the schedules that really count—those of our own lives and families and organizations. Interactivity enables us to program our lives better and to integrate the content we desire according to schedules that are important, not those arbitrarily determined by a TV network.

Rather than the Web becoming a push medium, TV is moving into the world of pull. If you want to sit back and watch the news, *Casablanca*, or an *I Love Lucy* rerun, go ahead and veg out. The difference is that prime time becomes any time. And if you would rather explore Mayan ruins, visit with your daughter at university, participate in a discussion about college basketball, analyze your personal finances, or find out why you have chest pains, you can do that, too. Ultimately, NBC television will become another Web site and the schedule will exist only for first-time viewings.

Just how strong is the N-Gen preference for the digital media over television? Very. Carla Bastida is a 9-year-old who lives in Barcelona, Spain. Last Christmas she was confronted with a choice: the family could replace its broken VCR or buy a color printer. She says that "there was no choice, really. I wanted the printer."

Hollywood and broadcasting executives should take note that she chose the printer because it was "more important" for her and the computer was "more fun" than watching TV and videos. Says Dad, "Carla gets bored just watching TV."

If you contrast N-Geners with their parents, it isn't difficult to see how this rejection of television came about. Baby boomers have witnessed the computer revolution, but they have viewed it through a couch potato mentality. That doesn't mean all baby boomers are getting fat, but that we've become accustomed to the broadcast delivery of information.

Keeping current is not widely seen as an interactive activity. To many boomers, keeping current means turning on the six o'clock news (although even that is declining in popularity).

In the midst of the massive social changes and the era of short-sighted but widely practiced corporate downsizing, boomers have embraced computer and information technology but they have done so under duress. Baby boomers are constantly being reminded that computer-facilitated networks are a personal and economic survival tool that will revolutionize everything—whether they are prepared for it or not. N-Geners, on the other hand, view it as a natural extension of themselves. It is, in fact, the specific medium that will follow and perpetuate the force of their youth, just as television has traced the lives of the boomers.

Notes

1. Bank, David. "Selling Pants on PointCast," *The Wall Street Journal*, 13 December 1996, p. A1.
2. *Business Week*, 24 February 1997, pp. 95–104.

Don Tapscott is the bestselling author of a number of books, including *The Digital Economy*, and co-author of *Paradigm Shift*. He is the president of New Paradigm Learning Corporation, and chairman of Digital 4Sight, both based in Toronto. Digital 4Sight is a research "think tank" funded by some of the world's leading financial, technology, retail, manufacturing, and government organizations.

1. *Response*

a. This article was taken from a book called *Growing Up Digital*. Given this title, and the content and language of this selection, who do you think is the target audience for such a book? What makes you think so?

b. What is Don Tapscott's main idea in this article? How does he support this idea?

c. Is there a statement in this article that you strongly agree or disagree with? Explain.

2. ***Media*** *Comparing Formats* Tapscott compares TV to the Internet in a general way. Make a more specific comparison of these two media by comparing one specific item on each —a news report, for example. Consider content, delivery, style, techniques, who sponsors the item, who produces it, and who the audience is. Does either item contain any bias? What is the medium's relationship with its audience? With its sponsors? Use a chart to share your conclusions with others.

3. ***Vocabulary*** Consider the following sentence:

    > For example, the term *screenagers* has been used to describe today's youth.

    How is the word *screenager* appropriate? Inappropriate? What other invented words connected with the Internet does this article use? How would you define these words? What other Internet-related words would you like to see added to the English language?

If one ox could not do the job they did not try to grow a bigger ox, but used two oxen. When we need greater computer power the answer is not to get a bigger computer, but ... to build systems of computers and operate them in parallel.

—*Grace Murray Hopper*

Do you think playing computer games can be addictive? Explain your answer.

If I Can't Have Beer, at Least Give Me a Playstation

Essay by Rob Blizzard

I had little homework after school the other day. As the class neared its end, I had already imagined what the remainder of the day would consist of. Without homework the possibilities were limitless. I could go for a jog, read a book, see some friends. Instead, I watched the television.

Why play a game of street hockey when you could watch a game from the comfort of your couch? And in the televised version there are professional athletes who are far better than I could ever be, so why should I even try to imitate them? The far better course of action would be to wallow in my own inactivity. This will allow my brain to shift into a mode most easily likened to a coma. Nothing short of sleep is more relaxing. This is how I spent my day.

Along the same lines, I had become addicted to a computer game a couple of weeks ago. Called *Sims,* it allows you to create an alter-ego and guide him/her through the daily toils of life. You must tell your character to eat, sleep, shower, play pool, or what have you.

When I had first heard of the game's concept I mocked it. After all, if you wanted to experience the daily routine of a life in minute detail, why not get off the computer and do so? I scared myself at one point when I had actually told my character to play on his computer. For a few minutes I was actually playing a game that involved a miniature me playing a game.

Why not lose the middle man and just live for yourself? For the exact same reason that people watch the television. It is a comfortable way of living life with all the illusions of reward without the risks. It is easier and more convenient to live life through the television or computer.

It is odd that in this era of unsurpassed technology and advancement, the area of quickest growth is the entertainment industry. Why, if life is better than it has ever been before, do we spend so much time attempting to escape from it? We build games that mirror our own world. The only difference is that time can be turned back and mistakes can be undone. It is a world better than ours and for that reason it is addictive.

Maybe Sony Playstations and five-hundred channel satellite accesses are the newest form of alcohol. Alcohol traditionally being the method of escape for past generations. Unfortunately for booze, a minimum age has been set to prevent those most susceptible to addiction from contact. It is here Nintendo has the edge, it can target the youngest and most vulnerable—legally.

Rob Blizzard is a high-school student who contributes to the teen column for the Moose Jaw *Times-Herald.*

1. *Response*

a. What is the author's tone in this essay? What words or phrases demonstrate this tone?

b. What is the thesis of this essay? What arguments support this thesis?

c. Do you agree with the author's thesis? Explain.

2. *Writing* *Essay* Choose a media issue that interests you and write an essay that examines it. Your purpose is to persuade an audience of your peers about your point of view. Use an organizational structure, such as cause-and-effect or comparison, to present your argument. As Blizzard has done, choose a title for your essay that grabs the readers' attention. Remember that your conclusion should offer a new insight into the argument.

3. ***Literature Studies*** *Comparing Essays* Compare this essay to "People as Products" by Jean Kilbourne. What structure has each author used? What literary devices does each author use? Which do you think is the more effective essay? Explain your reasoning.

4. ***Media*** *Advertising* Examine some ads for computer games; check the copy in catalogues, magazines, or on packaging. How is what the manufacturers say about their product like or unlike what Blizzard says? What implicit, as well as explicit, messages does the copy contain?

   Choose one of Blizzard's statements and develop a real ad, or a parody of a real ad, for a new computer game.

Computers are useless. They can only give you answers.

—Pablo Picasso

"Another field has become open for women to explore ..." proclaims Samantha Peters in this editorial.

Being a Woman in a Man's Game World

Editorial
by Samantha Peters

BEING A WOMAN IN A MALE-dominated industry is always a difficult task, but from personal experience, it seems to be exceptionally hard in the fields of technology and computer information. For decades, women have been fighting for equal rights and the ability to do jobs that men commonly do. Now, it isn't uncommon to see women in warehouses, driving heavy machinery, working in an office, or even in operating rooms. With the advent of the dawning technological era, however, another field has become open for women to explore.

Being a part of a game development team myself, I work with a male-dominated team on a daily basis. There is only one other woman on our staff, an exceptionally talented 2D artist, aside from myself, making the female influence amongst the team rather minimal in comparison to everyone else. Thankfully, we work in an environment that is quite favorable for us; the men we work with have no qualms with working with us.

Unfortunately, this often doesn't extend beyond our own team. Much of my work exists in the realm of public relations, and on a daily basis I am confronted with at least one man that either a) doesn't believe me, or b) refuses to take me seriously. These men range from so-called professional contacts to potential fans to just people I happen to meet on a daily basis. This is just one facet of a custom that has been etched into society for hundreds of years, a custom that most women despise and fight to overcome: the subservience of the female gender and intellectual dominance of males.

I was skimming the Net the other day, reading my usual plethora of gaming sites that I keep track of, and I came across something that made me stop and almost do a double take. A banner ad for computer cases, of all things, with a rather anorexic-looking young lady draped across it wearing nothing but a skimpy little bikini. This really got me thinking about just how biased the computer and gaming world is when it comes to men.

This banner is obviously targeted at the males in the world, as I know very few women that would take one look at that scantily-clad girl and say "You know, I really need a new case for my computer" and click on that link. I do, however, know a few men that would follow through. This, combined with the sheer number of booth bunnies lead me to only one conclusion: this is a male industry.

Chances are, the person that made the ad was a man, and the people that put it up are probably men too. People hiring booth bunnies? I'd say mostly men. How many banner ads do you see with buff men in speedos trying to sell you a case fan? I'm not saying I want to see this, because honestly, I don't think seeing some sexy guy shakin' his tight li'l butt around is going to make me buy a Cyrix over a Pentium 3.

Another thing I've noticed in the gaming world (and more broadly, in the world in general), is a tendency for expectations to be placed on women, for how they should act, what they should do, etc. For example, it's not uncommon to see women in my position as a public relations representative, but how many female coders are there in the world? Sure, I bet there's a bunch of women that play *Ultima Online* or *Diablo 2* or *Icewind Dale*, but not nearly as many that play *Quake 3 Arena*. Of course, this is only a guess on my part from playing or witnessing all of the above, but I would say there is a much higher female ratio in *Diablo* than there is in *Q3A*. From the men that I've talked to, and the experiences I've had, it's expected that I would like role playing games, but action? Nah, that's a male thing. But, if I did happen to be one of the rare few that played an action game like *Half-Life* or *Quake*, then it would be assumed that I'm vicious, not all that feminine, loud, and extroverted. I'd say that at least some of the women that play *Quake* are like this, but I wouldn't go so far as to brand an entire gender in a game based on the actions of a few.

The fact is, in the gaming world, women are a minority, both in the fields of creating and playing games. Truthfully, female game developers and gamers are much more commonplace than they were years ago, but the common belief amongst most men in the

640K ought to be enough for anybody.

Bill Gates

community is that in this world, women are a rare commodity, a precious few that brave a male-dominated realm, and special measures should be taken to attract more women into developing and playing games. To be honest, choosing to play or even create games is a personal choice of taste, and if there are fewer women than men, so be it. It is harder on the women that do take part, but that doesn't mean we want special attention, good or bad.

Being a woman anywhere that's male-dominated is hard, but there's not much us ladies can do but persevere and keep on doing what we want to do, turning down the marriage proposals from the awe-struck guys that say "Wow! A female gamer? I'm in heaven! Will you marry me?!?!" Believe me, I've heard it myself, and for all you women that haven't heard it yet, hang on, because I'm sure you will eventually.

Samantha Peters is a game designer with Klache Entertainment and a full-time student in the School of Communications at Simon Fraser University in Vancouver, B.C. Views presented in this article are her own, based on personal experience and readings.

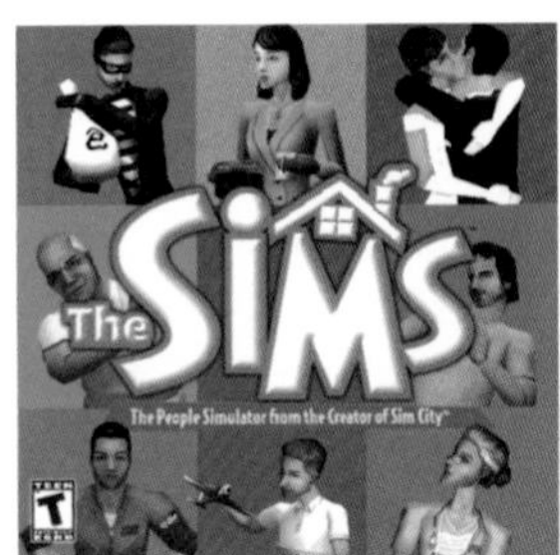

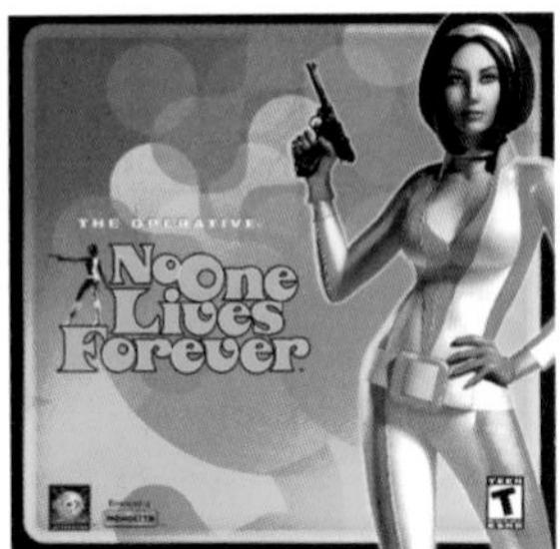

Examine these covers from popular computer games. Considering the cover design, describe each game. Which game do you think would be the most realistic? Explain your reasoning. How has each cover been designed to appeal to a certain audience?

1. ***Response***

   a. This editorial was taken from an Internet Web site that includes articles about computer games and the Internet. Who do you think is Samantha Peters' audience? What is her purpose? What viewpoint does the editorial express? How is her viewpoint supported?

b. Survey the students in your class to find out if they agree with Peters' viewpoint. Compare your own ideas about this issue with those of Peters, and others in your class.
c. How does this editorial resemble an essay? How does it differ? How do elements of the editorial form enhance the meaning of this selection?

2. ***Literature Studies*** *Interpretation* As a group, discuss your interpretations of this editorial. Do you all agree about the author's message? If not, explore how your interpretations differ. How is your interpretation of this editorial influenced by the values of your society? How does the language and syntax of the editorial affect readers and their interpretations?

3. ***Writing*** *Responding to the Editorial* Respond to this editorial by writing your own editorial or by writing a letter to an editor. Clearly present your opinion, and support it with arguments and facts.

4. ***Media*** *Gender Bias* One of the problems that can occur when mostly men (or women) create something media-related, like a computer game, is that overt or hidden gender bias can become part of that creation. Examine a number of games (or choose another media form—perhaps one that has been created by women rather than men) for gender bias. Who created this product? What was their purpose in creating it? Is there a gender bias? What effect does this have on their audience? Write a report on your findings.

5. ***Language Conventions*** *Reflexive Pronouns* The pronouns *myself, himself, herself, itself,* and so on, are used for two purposes; they are used for emphasis as in the line:

   He himself denied any involvement in the movie.

   When these pronouns are used to refer back to the subject of the sentence or phrase, they are known as reflexive pronouns, as in:

   She taped herself for the audition.

   Check this selection to see how these pronouns have been used. Which use is for emphasis? Which use is reflexive?

Glossary

In the **active voice**, the subject of a sentence does the action: *The dog ran into the street.* Use the active voice when possible. It uses fewer words and is more precise than the passive voice. See **Passive Voice.**

An **allegory** is a simple story, such as a fable or parable, whose major purpose is to teach a moral lesson. An allegory can always be read on two levels—one literal, the other symbolic. The underlying meaning can be parallel to, but different from, the surface meaning.

An **allusion**, in a literary work, is a reference to another literary work, or a person, place, event, or object from history, literature, or mythology.

An **analogy** is the illustration of one idea or concept by using a similar idea or concept. An analogy is sometimes phrased as a simile.

The **antagonist** of a narrative or dramatic work is the primary person in opposition to the hero or **protagonist**.

An **archetype** is a theme, symbol, character, or setting that can be found throughout literature, folklore, and media so often that it comes to reflect some universal human character or experience. For example, Robin Hood is an archetypal hero.

Assonance (also known as *vowel rhyme*) is the repetition of similar or identical vowel sounds within the words of a poem or other writing.

Beat writers were a group of American writers from the 1950s, whose loose writing style was a form of self-expression, often accompanied by jazz music. Poet Lawrence Ferlinghetti was a major beat poet who strongly influenced later generations.

Bias is an inclination or preference that makes it difficult or impossible to judge fairly in a particular situation.

A **cacophony** is a harsh or clashing sound, often caused deliberately for effect.

A **caesura** is a pause in a line of verse, generally agreeing with a pause required by the sense.

Climax See **Plot.**

Consonance is the repetition of similar or identical consonants in words whose vowels differ. For example, *gripe/grape/grope.*

Diction refers to the way an author expresses ideas in words. Good diction includes grammatical correctness, skill in the choice of effective words, and a wide vocabulary.

A **dynamic character** is one who undergoes a significant and permanent change in personality or beliefs.

A **eulogy** is a tribute to someone who has just died, and is often delivered as a speech at a funeral.

A **fact sheet** presents key information about a particular topic, issue, or organization. It provides concise answers to basic questions. Some fact sheets are written in point form, others in full sentences.

Figurative language uses words to paint a picture, draw an interesting comparison, or create a poetic effect. **Literal language** says what it means directly. Language can be figurative or literal.

Free-verse poetry is written without using regular rhyme or rhythm. Images, spacing, punctuation, and the rhythms of ordinary language are used to create a free-verse poem.

Foreshadowing is a plot technique in which a writer plants clues or subtle indications about events that will happen later in the narrative.

Hyperbole is a deliberately exaggerated statement made for effect.

Imagery is the pictures or impressions that writers create in the minds of their readers. To create these pictures, they use descriptive techniques such as figures of speech (simile, metaphor, personification, oxymoron), onomatopoeia, alliteration, and allusions.

Irony occurs when a statement or situation means something different from (or even the opposite of) what is expected. Another type of irony is **dramatic irony**. It occurs in plays when the audience knows something that the characters do not.

A **literary essay** presents an interpretation or explores some aspect of one or more works of literature.

A **loaded word** is a word intentionally chosen to evoke a strong response in a reader—usually an emotional response.

A **logo** is an identifying symbol used as a trademark in advertising.

Mass media is any method by which a message is communicated to a large audience at the same time—movies, radio, TV, books, magazines, or the Internet.

A **media text** is any media product—movie, radio show, CD, TV program, et cetera—that is selected for critical examination.

A **metaphor** is a comparison of two things that are not alike. The comparison suggests that they do share a common quality: *Her words were a knife to my heart.*

Parallelism is the intentional use of identical or similar grammatical structure within one sentence or in two or more sentences.

Parallel structure is the repeated use of the same phrase or sentence, or the repeated use of a similar sentence structure. Parallel structure can be used to create balance or place emphasis on certain lines.

In the **passive voice**, the subject of the verb receives the actions: *The fire was extinguished.*

Personification occurs when objects, ideas, or animals are given human qualities: *The sun smiled down on me.*

Plot refers to the events in a story. It usually has five elements: exposition, rising action, climax, falling action, and resolution.

- The **exposition** or introduction sets up the story by introducing the main characters, the setting, and the problem to be solved.
- The **rising action** is the main part of the story where the full problem develops. A number of events is involved that will lead to the climax.
- The **climax** is the highest point in the story where something decisive occurs.
- The **falling action** follows the climax. It contains the events that bring the story to its conclusion.
- The **resolution** or denouement is the end of the story and traces the final outcome of the central conflict.

A **point of view** is the vantage point from which the author tells a story. The four most common points of view are *first person* (I, me), *omniscient* (all-seeing), *limited omniscient* (all-seeing from the viewpoint of a group of characters), and *objective* (he, she, they, it).

A **précis** is a concise summary of a text. It is written in full sentences, but contains only the most important information.

Racist language is any language that refers to a particular cultural or ethnic group in insulting terms, but racism also exists in more subtle forms.

- Mention a person's race only if it is relevant to the context. If a person's race or ethnic origin is relevant, be specific:
  Irrelevant/Vague: *Dago is African.*
  Relevant/Less Vague: *Dago is proud of her Nigerian heritage.*
- Avoid making generalizations about any racial or cultural group:
  Stereotype: *The Welsh are great singers.*
  Better: *The Welsh have a long tradition of singing.*

Resolution See **Plot.**

A **rhetorical question** is one that is asked for effect, and that does not invite a reply. The purpose of a rhetorical question is to introduce a topic or to focus the reader on a concern.

Rhythm is the arrangement of beats in a line of poetry. The beat is created by the accented and unaccented syllables in the words used in each line.

A **satire** is a work that criticizes something—for example, a person, a characteristic, an institution, or a government—by depicting it in a humorous, sarcastic, or scornful way.

Sexist language is language that degrades or unnecessarily excludes either women or men. It is best to avoid generalizing about males and females unless the claims are based on scientific facts.

- Whenever possible, replace words such as *fireman*, *policeman*, and *man-made* with non-sexist alternatives such as *firefighter*, *police officer*, and *fabricated*.
- Avoid using the masculine pronouns *he, him,* or *his* to refer to both men and women.

A **stereotype** is an oversimplified picture, usually of a group of people, giving them all a set of characteristics, without consideration for individual differences.

Suspense is a feeling of tension, anxiety, or excitement resulting from uncertainty. An author creates suspense to keep readers interested.

Style is the overall texture of a piece of writing; the particular way in which the ideas are expressed. Style is made up of many elements including diction, figurative language, sentences, and tone.

A **symbol** is something that represents something else—for example, the lion can be a symbol of courage.

The **symbolic meaning** of a work is developed through the symbols that the author includes.

A **theme** is a central thesis or idea that is expressed directly or indirectly in a literary work.

The **thesis** of an essay is the main idea or argument that the author is attempting to prove.

Tone is the implied attitude of the writer toward the subject or the audience. Tone differs from mood, which describes the emotional feeling of the work more generally. The tone of a piece of work can be described, for example, as *angry*, *satiric*, *joyful*, or *serious*.

Transition words indicate relationships between ideas. Writers use them to suggest links between sentences or paragraphs.

Index of Titles and Authors

Acknowledgments

Every reasonable effort has been made to trace ownership of copyrighted material. Information that would enable the publisher to correct any reference or credit in future editions would be appreciated.

12 "Mirror Image" by Lena Coakley. Reprinted by permission of the author. **21** "The Prospector's Trail" by Cathy Jewison. Reprinted with permission of the author. **39** "Love Must Not Be Forgotten" by Zhang Jie, translated by Gladys Yang, Chinese Literature Press, 24 Baiwanzhuang Rd., Beijing 10037, People's Republic of China. **52** "Saturday Climbing" from *What Can't Be Changed Shouldn't Be Mourned* by W. D. Valgardson. © 1990 by W. D. Valgardson. Published in Canada by Douglas & McIntyre. Reprinted by permission of the publisher. **61** "The Maiden Wiser Than the Tsar" from *World Tales: The Extraordinary Coincidence of Stories Told in All Times, in All Places* by Idries Shah, © 1979 by Technographia, S. A., and Harcourt, Inc., reprinted by permission of Harcourt, Inc. **71** "Bluffing" by Gail Helgason, from the collection *Fracture Patterns*, published by Coteau Books. Reprinted with permission. **78** "The Labrador Fiasco" by Margaret Atwood. © 1996 O. W. Toad, Ltd., first published in the United Kingdom by Bloomsbury Publishing. **90** "Snow" by Ann Beattie. Reprinted with the permission of Simon & Schuster from *Where You'll Find Me and Other Stories* by Ann Beattie. © 1986 by Irony & Pity. **94** "A Secret Lost in the Water" from *The Hockey Sweater and Other Stories* by Roch Carrier, translated by Sheila Fischman. © 1979 by House of Anansi Press. Reprinted by permission of Stoddart Publishing Co. Limited. **98** "The Pose" by Anwer Khan, translated by Muhammad Umar Memon, from *Domains of Fear and Desire: Urdu Stories*. Reprinted with permission. **103** "The Elephant" from *The Elephant* by Slawomir Mrozek. © 1962 by McDonald and Co. (Publishers) Ltd. Used by permission of Grove/Atlantic, Inc. **117** "Brooms for Sale" by Thomas Raddall is reprinted with permission of Dalhousie University. **124** "The Liberation of Rome" by Robin Hemley from *Sudden Fiction (Continued)* edited by Robert Shapard and James Thomas. Reprinted by permission of Sterling Lord Literistic, Inc. © by Robin Hemley. **135** "Soul-Catcher" by Louis Owens. Reprinted by permission of the author. **145** "Wilhelm" by Gabrielle Roy, translated by Harry L. Binsse. © Fonds Gabrielle Roy. **152** "He-y, Come on Ou-t" by Shinichi Hoshi, translated by Stanleigh Jones, from *The Best Japanese Fiction Stories* by John L. Apossolou and Martin H. Greenberg. Reprinted with permission. **165** "A Poet's Advice to Students." © 1958, 1965 by the Trustees of the E. E. Cummings Trust. © 1958, 1965 by George J. Firmage, from *A Miscellany Revised* by E. E. Cummings, edited by George J. Firmage. Used by permission of Liveright Publishing Corporation. **167** "Poetry Is ..." by Betty Lies. Reprinted with permission of the author. **168** "What You Are Doing Now" by Gary Hyland. Reprinted by permission of the author. **169** "How Beautifully Useless" by Raymond Souster is reprinted from *Collected Souster* by permission of Oberon Press. **171** "After a Heated Argument" by Kaneto Tota from *Modern Japanese Haiku: An Anthology* translated by Makoto Ueda, © 1976. Reprinted by permission of University of Toronto Press. **172** "Calgary 2 am" from *Postcards Home: Poems New and Selected* by Christopher Wiseman. © 1988 Sono Nis Press, Victoria, BC. **173** "God's World" by Edna St. Vincent Millay. From *Collected Poems*, HarperCollins.© 1913, 1941 by Edna St. Vincent Millay. All rights reserved. Reprinted by permission of Elizabeth Barnett, literary executor. **175** "Canadian Sunrise" written by Joan Besen. © 1998 Published by *Retsyo Songs (Socan)*/ Administered by *Bug*. All Rights Reserved. Used By Permission. **178** "As in the Beginning" by Mary di Michele. Reprinted with permission of the author. **183** "Not only marble, but the plastic toys" from *Making Cocoa for Kingsley Amis* by Wendy Cope. London: Faber and Faber Limited. **186** "To Make a Prairie" by Emily Dickinson from *The Collected Poems of Emily Dickinson* edited by Thomas H. Johnson, Cambridge Mass.: The Belknap Press of Harvard University Press, © 1951, 1955 by the President and Fellows of Harvard College. Reprinted by permission of the publishers and the Trustees of Amherst College. **186** "World's Shortest Pessimistic Poem" by Robert Zend. Reprinted with permission of Janine Zend. **187** "Writer's Block in the Computer Age" by Peggy Smith Krachun. Reprinted by permission of the author. **188** "A Spider Danced a Cosy Jig" by Irving Layton from *The Collected Poems of Irving Layton*. Used by permission of McClelland & Stewart, Ltd. *The Canadian Publishers*.

189 "Crazy Times" from *Collected Poems* by Miriam Waddington. © Miriam Waddington 1986. Reprinted by permission of Oxford University Press Canada. **190** "Very Like a Whale" from *Verses From 1929 On* by Ogden Nash. © 1935 by Ogden Nash, renewed. Reprinted by permission of Curtis Brown, Ltd. **194** "St. George" by Nancy Senior. Reprinted by permission of the author. **196** "The Unknown Citizen" by W. H. Auden from *Collected Poems of W. H. Auden* edited by Edward Mendelson. Reprinted by permission of Faber and Faber Limited. **197** "#9" by Lawrence Ferlinghetti, from *A Far Rockaway of the Heart*, © 1997 by Lawrence Ferlinghetti. Reprinted by permission of New Directions Publishing Corp. **199** "The Sunlight" by Chief Dan George. Reprinted by permission of Hancock House Publishers. **200** "Universal Soldier" by Buffy Sainte-Marie. Reprinted with permission of the author. **201** "There Will Come Soft Rains" by Sara Teasdale. Reprinted with the permission of Scribner, a Division of Simon & Schuster, from *The Collected Poems of Sara Teasdale* (New York: Macmillan, 1937). **201** "I Believe" by Robert Fulghum from *It Was on Fire When I Lay Down on It* by Robert Fulghum. © 1988, 1989 by Robert Fulghum. Used by permission of Villard Books, a division of Random House, Inc. **202** "the laughing heart" by Charles Bukowski. © 1996 by Linda Lee Bukowski. Reprinted from *Betting on the Muse: Poems & Stories* with the permission of Black Sparrow Press. **203** "The Sun Witness" from *I See Cleopatra and Other Poems* translated by Nurunnessa Choudhury and Paul Joseph Thompson. London: Egmont Children's Books. **204** "Take Something Like a Star" from *The Poetry of Robert Frost* edited by Edward Connery Lathem. © 1949, 1969 by Henry Holt and Co., © 1977 by Lesley Frost Ballantine. Reprinted by permission of Henry Holt and Company, LLC. **208** "Hockey" by Scott Blaine from *Grab Me a Bus ... and Other Award Winning Poems* by Malcolm Glass and M. Joe Eaton. © 1971 by Scholastic Inc. Reprinted by permission of Scholastic Inc. **209** "The Rain Hammers" by Michael Wade from *Passages (Literature of Newfoundland and Labrador) Book 3*, Breakwater, St. John's, © 1980 Michael Wade. **211** "Prelude #1" from *Collected Poems 1909–1962* by T. S. Eliot. London: Faber and Faber Limited. **211** "The Spider Holds a Silver Ball" by Emily Dickinson from *The Collected Poems of Emily Dickinson* edited by Thomas H. Johnson, Cambridge, Mass.: The Belknap Press of Harvard University Press, © 1951, 1955 by the President and Fellows of Harvard College. Reprinted by permission of the publishers and the Trustees of Amherst College. **214** "Gaining Yardage" by Leo Dangel from *Home from the Field* (Spoon River Poetry Press, Granite Falls, Minnesota), © 1997 by Leo Dangel. **215** "Snake" by D. H. Lawrence from *The Complete Poems of D. H. Lawrence*. Reprinted with permission of Lawrence Pollinger Limited and the estate of Frieda Lawrence Ravagli. **219** "Legend" by Judith Wright from *A Human Pattern: Selected Poems* (ETT Imprint, Sydney © 1996). **220** "The Child Who Walks Backwards" by Lorna Crozier. Reprinted with permission of the author. **224** "This Morning I Sat" by Rosalie Fowler. Reproduced with permission of Breakwater, St. John's. © Rosalie Fowler. **226** "Nothing Is Like Nothing Else" by Elizabeth Brewster. Reprinted with permission of the author. **227** "The New House" by Maya Angelou from *I Shall Not Be Moved*. © 1990 by Maya Angelou. Reprinted by permission of Random House, Inc. **228** "Death of a Young Son by Drowning" by Margaret Atwood from *Selected Poems 1966-1984*. © 1990 Margaret Atwood. Reprinted by permission of Oxford University Press Canada. **229** "My Father Is a Simple Man" by Luis Omar Salinas from *The Sadness of Days: Selected and New Poems*. Reprinted with permission. **230** "Ethics" from *Waiting For My Life* by Linda Pastan. © 1981 by Linda Pastan. Used by permission of W. W. Norton & Company, Inc. **237** "A Bird Came Down" by Emily Dickinson from *The Collected Poems of Emily Dickinson* edited by Thomas H. Johnson, Cambridge, Mass.: The Belknap Press of Harvard University Press, © 1951, 1955 by the President and Fellows of Harvard College. Reprinted by permission of the publishers and the Trustees of Amherst College. **240** "Dulce Et Decorum Est" by Wilfred Owen from *The Collected Poems of Wilfred Owen*. © 1963 by Chatto & Windus, Ltd. Reprinted by permission of New Directions Publishing Corp. **241** "Harlem" by Langston Hughes from *The Collected Poems of Langston Hughes*. © 1994 by the estate of Langston Hughes. Used by permission of Alfred A. Knopf, a division of Random House, Inc. **248** "It's Time to Think About Visors" by Ken Dryden. © 2000 Time Inc. Reprinted by permission. **252** "The Importance of Being Earnest" by Lynn Coady. Originally published in the September 2000 issue of *Quill & Quire*. © 2000 by Lynn Coady. **256** "Whose Lathe?" From *Dancing at the Edge of the World* by Ursula K. Le Guin. © 1984 by Ursula K. Le Guin. Used by permission of Grove/Atlantic, Inc. **260** "Alarm Bells for Civilization" by Gwynne Dyer. Reprinted with permission.

272 "Progress" © 1996, by Alan Lightman, from the collection titled *Dance For Two* (Pantheon Books, New York.) Used by permission of the Author. First published in *Inc. Magazine*. **276** "The Time Factor " by Gloria Steinem. © Gloria Steinem. **281** "Joy" from *How to Read a Poem ... and Start a Poetry Circle* by Molly Peacock; "Filling Station" by Elizabeth Bishop from *The Complete Poems 1927–1979*. © 1979, 1983 by Alice Helen Methfessel. **290, 291** "In Support of Nick Bantock's 'Life Class'" by Kristal Fung. Reprinted with permission of the author. "Life Class" from *The Artful Dodger* by Nick Bantock. Reprinted with permission of Raincoast Books. **293** "A Comparison" by Sylvia Plath from *Johnny Panic and the Bible of Dreams*. Reprinted by permission of Faber and Faber Limited. **296** "The Short Story Defined" by Peter Hung from *Literary Cavalcade*, May, 1991 issue. © 1991 by Scholastic Inc. Reprinted by permission of Scholastic Inc. **301** "The Shack" by Margaret Laurence from *Heart of a Stranger*. © 1976 by Margaret Laurence. Used by permission of McClelland & Stewart, Ltd., *The Canadian Publishers*. **315** "Dis?Ability on the Internet" by Heather Proud from *Paralinks: The Electronic Magazine for People with Spinal Cord Injury*. Reprinted with permission. **319** "Chicken Hips" by Catherine Piggott from the *Globe and Mail*, March 20, 1990. Reprinted with permission. **323** "What Colour is a Rose?" from *Funny, You Don't Look Like One: Observations from a Blue-Eyed Ojibway* by Drew Hayden Taylor. Penticton, B.C.: Theytus Books Ltd., 1998. © 1998 Drew Hayden Taylor. **326** "Some Thoughts on the Common Toad" by George Orwell (© George Orwell, 1946). By permission of Bill Hamilton, Literary Executor of the Estate of the Late Sonia Brownell Orwell and Martin Secker & Warburg Ltd. **331** "Homage to Barcelona" by Marjorie Doyle from *A View of Her Own*. Reprinted with permission of the author. **338** "Lessons From a Walk in a Rain Forest" by David Suzuki From *Earth Time: Essays*. © 1998 by Dr. David Suzuki. Reprinted by permission of Stoddart Publishing Co. Limited. **345** "In Memory of W.O. Mitchell" by Fred Stenson. Reprinted with permission. **351** "Mann and Machine" from *Contemporary Canadian Biographies, June 1999: Steve Mann: Scientist, Inventor, and Artist,* Toronto Public Library CPLQ. Stamford, CT: Gale Research Publications, Thomson Information/Publishing Group. **358** Excerpt from *Long Walk to Freedom: The Autobiography of Nelson Mandela*. © 1994 by Nelson Rolihlahla Mandela. By permission of Little, Brown and Company (Inc.). **378** "The Psychological Power of Radio" by Tim Crook. Reprinted by permission of the author. **388** *One Ocean* by Betty Quan. © 1994 by Betty Quan. First broadcast on CBC-Radio. Reprinted with permission of The Pamela Paul Agency Inc. **395** "People as Products" by Jean Kilbourne. Reprinted with the permission of The Free Press, a Division of Simon & Schuster, Inc., from *Deadly Persuasion: Why Women and Girls Must Fight the Addictive Power of Advertising* by Jean Kilbourne. © 1999 by Jean Kilbourne. **400** "The Trouble with People" from *The Hidden Persuaders* by Vance Packard, © 1957 by Vance Packard. **407** "All Part of Becoming Canadian" from *The Day I Became a Canadian* by Al Pittman. St. John's, NF: Breakwater Books Ltd. Reprinted with permission. **418** "No News is Bad News: Using Publicity to Your Advantage" from *Marketing for Dummies*® by Alexander Hiam. Foster City, CA: IDG Books Worldwide Inc. **429** "Television: The Collective Imagination" from *The Skin of Culture: Investigating the New Electronic Reality* by Derrick de Kerckhove. Toronto: Somerville House Publishing, 1995. © 1995 Derrick de Kerckhove. Reprinted with permission. **437** "The Quiz Show Format" from *The Fifties* by David Halberstam, © 1993 by The Amateurs Limited. Used by permission of Villard Books, a division of Random House, Inc. **444** "What Would You Change?" by Claudia Puig. © 2000, *USA Today*. Reprinted with permission. **470** "'Cyberanchor' Delivers All the E-News That's Fit to Click" by Ann Perry, *Toronto Star*, April 21, 2000. Reprinted with permission – The Toronto Star Syndicate. **474** "The Net Generation" from *Growing Up Digital: The Rise of the Net Generation* by Don Tapscott. New York, NY: McGraw-Hill. © 1998 by the McGraw-Hill Companies, Inc.

Visual Credits

11 Dave Robertson/Masterfile. **44** Andrew Hunter and Gu Xiong. **89** *Travelers* by Judith Currelly/Diane Farris Gallery, Vancouver. **92** *Illinois Farm* by Richard Hamilton Smith/The Image Works. **114** ©Bettmann/CORBIS. **133** Chris Alan Wilton/Image Bank. **163** *Rock painting, Zimbabwe,* Holton Collection/SuperStock. **174** *Spring Wind—Apollo Coast* by Paul Grignon, visit his Web site at www.paulgrignonart.com. **191** *Winter's Blanket #1* by David McEown, courtesy of the artist. **195** *St. George and the Dragon,* c.1460 Paolo Uccello (1397-1475) (oil on canvas), National Gallery, London, UK/The Bridgeman Art Library International Ltd. **210** Harald Sund/Image Bank. **218** Marilyn Conway/

Image Bank. **229** Réunion des Musées Nationaux/Art Resource, NY. **247** Andrew Judd/Masterfile. **265** Abrams/Lacagnina/ Image Bank. **269** Image Select/Art Resource, NY. **277** *Allées Piétonnières* by Jean-Pierre Stora/Grand Design/SuperStock. **306-309** From *Down Home: A Journey into Rural Canada* by William DeKay, published by Stoddart Publishing Co. Limited. Copyright © 1997 William DeKay. **349** Charles Clarke. **356** Courtesy of Steve Mann. **369** Geoffrey Gove/Image Bank. **397** Report on Business Television. **405** Albert Gescheidt/Image Bank. **450, 452, & 456** Photofest. **467** Courtesy of Everett Soop. **485** Courtesy of developers Monolith Productions, Inc. and publishers Fox Interactive. s